THE METHODS OF STATISTICS

By the same Author

TECHNOLOGICAL APPLICATIONS OF STATISTICS

STATISTICS
Home University Library, Oxford University Press

THE
METHODS OF STATISTICS

by

L. H. C. TIPPETT

*British Cotton Industry
Research Association*

Fourth Revised Edition

Published in the U.S.A.
by
DOVER PUBLICATIONS, INC.
180 Varick Street
New York 14, New York

LONDON
WILLIAMS AND NORGATE LTD

NEW YORK
JOHN WILEY & SONS INC.

FIRST PUBLISHED . . 1931
SECOND EDITION, REVISED 1937
THIRD EDITION, REVISED 1941
REPRINTED . . 1945, 1948
FOURTH EDITION, REVISED 1952

PRINTED IN GREAT BRITAIN BY
THE GARDEN CITY PRESS LIMITED
LETCHWORTH, HERTFORDSHIRE

PREFACE

THE statistical scene has changed very much since 1930, when I first wrote this book, and most change has occurred since 1937, the date of the last substantial revision. Up to about 1930 Professor Karl Pearson's work still formed the chief basis of statistical theory and practice, and Professor R. A. Fisher's work and methods were only beginning to achieve recognition and adoption ; now, Pearson's work has become part of our unacknowledged heritage and Fisher's work is having its full influence. In 1930 there seemed to be room for a book that attempted to present the methods of both schools in perspective and to expound Fisher's methods in comparatively simple terms, for his *Statistical Methods for Research Workers*, important though it is, is not easy reading to everybody. Now the differences and controversies of 1930 are dead, and a simple exposition of Fisher's methods is no novelty. In 1930 one book could adequately cover almost the whole field, and even after the first pride of literary parenthood had passed I did not see many important omissions from THE METHODS OF STATISTICS for several years. Now the subject has so ramified that one book cannot cover the field ; special monographs have been or could be written about sampling for industrial inspection ; sampling for surveys ; biological assay and probit analysis ; experimentation in various fields ; the analysis of time series ; multi-variate and discriminant analysis ; short-cut methods of statistical analysis; and the theory of mathematical statistics. Finally, there is one change that is exceedingly small in the total statistical scene but significant from the point of view of this book —I have added twenty years to my experience.

After the end of the war it became clear that the current edition of this book was out of date—what should be done ? I did not long entertain the idea of allowing it to die : my *amour propre* and the publishers' interest (I did not consult them on this) forbid that as long as the book finds acceptance ; and there is evidence to support a belief that the book has a place. I decided to retain the main features and characteristics of the old editions and to improve the exposition and fill in gaps as far as I could. In doing this I often came early to a point for some branch of the subject, beyond which I did not feel competent to lead the reader ; I was content to lead him so far and give some guidance for further reading.

The book is thus a general introduction to the methods of statistics, but it is doubtful if any other statistician would regard it as balanced. (Whether there is such a thing as balance in these things in any absolute or objective sense is a moot point.) Broadly, I have gone as far in each branch of the subject as my own knowledge and experience permit. The various applications of the analysis of variance, for example, are much more fully dealt with than anything else ; and I regret that lack of understanding (which I have not time at the present to try to correct) prevents even a mention of factor analysis.

The book covers its field systematically, and knowledge of the earlier chapters is assumed for the understanding of the later ones. I have tried to explain the logical basis of all the methods described, and have also given mathematical proofs where they are easy and likely to help understanding, but it is not essential to follow these. The mathematics required is just about what a natural scientist or engineer is likely to learn in the course of his studies. Readers are strongly advised to work through the examples. Statistics is not difficult, but some of its ideas are new to some people ; and comprehension of an elusive point often comes while working through the arithmetic of an example.

All tables, figures and equations are given the number of the section in which they appear ; and if there are more than two of either in any section the second, third and so on respectively have the letters a, b, etc., added.

I have not developed a system of notation that is entirely consistent and in which one symbol has only one meaning throughout. To do this would probably involve the use of unfamiliar alphabets and departures from well-established conventions ; it would be wasteful as well as presumptuous for an individual author to attempt the task, for his proposals would be unlikely to find general acceptance. A list of references is given at the end of the book and each is indicated in the text by the name of the author and the date.

Tables and charts are given at the end of the book so that with their aid most of the methods can be applied with an accuracy sufficient for many practical purposes. I am very grateful to Professor R. A. Fisher and Messrs. Oliver & Boyd ; to Professor

E. S. Pearson and the Biometrika Trust ; and to Professor L. M. Milne-Thomson and Messrs. Macmillan & Company for permission to use copyright material for these tables and charts.

For examples I have drawn on the literature, to which references are given, and on data supplied by my colleagues at the Shirley Institute, for all of which I am grateful.

Finally I thank Mr. G. A. R. Foster, Mr. C. Mack, and Mr. T. Vickers, who have helped in discussions and in reading the manuscript and proofs. The diagrams for the new edition were drawn by Mr. G. B. Shipton.

L. H. C. T.

December 1951.

CONTENTS

CONTENTS

CONTENTS

THE METHODS OF STATISTICS

INTRODUCTION

THE methods of statistics are used in the investigation of systems consisting of aggregates of units when attention is focused on the behaviour of the aggregate rather than on the individual units. Such an aggregate might be the men in the British Isles and the subject of study their heights. We shall follow the usual English practice of referring generally to the aggregate as the *population* (some writers use the term *universe*) and to the units as .the *individuals*.

If such a system were studied according to what we may call the classical scientific method, exemplified in the methods of classical physics, attempts would be made to discover the laws that determine the height of each individual man, just as Newton's Laws of Motion determine the behaviour of individual particles of matter. The statistician does not make this attempt. Having been given the measurements of the individuals, he treats the data so as to bring to mind the salient features of the population as a whole.

The circumstances that lead to the statistical approach to data are varied. The behaviour of the individuals may be fundamentally indeterminate, as, according to modern views, is that of individual electrons ; it may be so complicated and apparently chaotic that no exact laws can be discovered, as for a good deal of biological variation ; or it may be irrelevant to the purposes of the investigator, as for the errors of the individual observations in an experiment. The study of the behaviour of individuals may be impracticable because of social custom or for some other reason ; it may be merely inconvenient or too costly to undertake ; or no sufficiently powerful technique of investigation may, at the time, be available. Whatever the circumstances, they are not strictly the statistician's concern ; he accepts them and applies his methods. Neither, on a narrow view, is it his business to speculate on the causes of the differences between individuals (although it may be his pleasure and part of his duty as a working scientist to do so). Where statistical treatment is applied the individuals are usually subject to a large number of causes, each producing only a small part of the total variation, but this is not necessarily so. Measurements of the successive positions of an oscillating pendulum, made at equal intervals of time differing from the period of oscillation or some multiple of the period, could be treated statistically ; although no one in his right mind would be likely to do this, for where the study of individuals leads to any results, it usually gives much more information than a statistical study.

The concept of the population is distinctive of statistics, and the reader who has been educated in the classical scientific method will need to make a conscious mental effort in order to apprehend it. The population is an entity that is made up of individuals, and yet is more than their sum, except when they are all exactly alike. An important part of the characteristics of a population comes from the variation between the individuals which must, however, be envisaged as a whole and not as a number of individual differences. The population may have properties not possessed by individuals, just as the average size of a population of families may be 3·67 (say), whereas no individual family can include a fraction of a person ; and a short father may have a tall son although the tendency in the population as a whole is for short fathers to have short sons.

One property of the population, that contrasts with the indeterminacy and apparently chaotic behaviour of the individuals, is its stability and the determinacy of its behaviour. The classic example of this is life insurance ; life is uncertain, and we do not know when an individual will die, but an insurance company dealing with a large number of people—a population—can adopt a sound financial policy because the incidence of death in the population is relatively certain. This contrast in behaviour between the population and the constituent individuals has been a cause of wonder and metaphysical speculation ; to the statistician it is a phenomenon to be accepted with as little (or much) wonder as any other natural phenomenon.

It is the business of the social or natural scientist to discover the laws of behaviour of populations, and of the statistician to co-operate. The tools the statistician has developed for this include mathematical specifications of complicated systems which consist of several populations. These populations contain individuals that vary indeterminately, but themselves vary according to exact laws. Such specification forms a large part of the methods dealt with in this book, and it is because he works in this complicated kind of situation that the statistician, if he is to be effective, needs to go outside his narrow terms of reference, and concern himself with the non-statistical aspects of any investigation.

One important field in which these methods are required is experimentation. The statistical method has one antithesis in the classical scientific method and another in the experimental method. The experimental method consists in isolating certain factors, varying perhaps one or two at a time in a determinate manner, keeping the others more or less constant, and making observations. Methods of analysis based on the classical scientific method serve for dealing with the resulting data. The statistical method of investigation involves making what inferences are possible from observations on systems in which the variations in the factors cannot be controlled. This, in a considerable degree, is the condition under which most sociologists and biologists work. In these circumstances some of the irrelevant variations are treated as the indeterminate individual variations within populations, and so the methods of statistical analysis find application.

In fact, however, no investigation is either purely experimental or purely statistical, using the words in the above special sense, for whereas perfect experimental control is unattainable, all variations can be controlled in some degree, either by applying experimental methods or by selection and arrangement. Partial experimental control occurs in a manurial field trial, where the agriculturist varies the quantity and kind of fertiliser, and keeps some of the other factors such as irrigation relatively constant ; but he cannot control all factors. There is control by selection and arrangement in an investigation where children are grouped according to age, and the mean height of each group is calculated to determine the relation between height and age. The only known way of treating the data of such investigations is by the methods of statistics, and we shall see that it is important to arrange the investigation so that it is amenable to such treatment.

This is one of the most important and extensive applications of statistics.

To the experimentalist the uncontrollable variations are experimental errors, to be discounted and ignored as far as possible. This is not the attitude of the statistician to a collection of data. There are no " true value " and " errors " ; all the values are equally real and significant, and the variation is an important characteristic of the population.

Although the methods of statistics are based on the concept of the population, in practice we seldom deal with complete populations ; indeed, they often exist only in imagination. We deal with limited numbers of individuals which are taken as representative of the populations—with samples ; and sometimes the samples are quite small, containing fewer than ten individuals. A sample represents a population with a degree of error, and an important branch of statistics is the " Theory of Errors" of samples.

Because of sampling errors, inferences from the sample about the population cannot be exact ; but it is not to be imagined that statistical theory is necessarily vague and lacking in precision in its ideas. The theory of errors ultimately reduces all sampling experience to a common measure, a probability ; and up to that point it is in principle rigorous. It is true that many simplifying approximations are made, and that the theory, not having reached finality, has not achieved sufficient rigour to satisfy even its authors, the mathematical statisticians. However, the approximations do not introduce serious inaccuracies, and the practical statistician is likely to be more impressed with the degree of rigour that has been achieved than with what remains unachieved. There must, however, be uncertainties in dealing with quantities subject to indeterminate variation, but they lie in the interpretation rather than in the calculation of the probabilities. Fisher (1935) draws a distinction between inferences that are uncertain and mathematical processes that are not rigorous. Statistics deals with uncertain inferences, but it may be mathematically rigorous.

In this book we take the raw data as given, except in the last chapter. In the social and economic fields it is part of the statistician's work to deal with the collection of data, and with their digestion in the form of index numbers or rates designed to express the social or economic phenomena under investigation. This part of the work depends more on special knowledge of the field of application than on general statistical principles, although it depends somewhat on both, and is outside the scope of this book. We shall, however, have occasion to point out conditions that must be satisfied in designing an investigation in order to make the data amenable to the methods of statistics.

The practice of statistics requires some equipment. In addition to the charts and tables given in the appendix to this book frequent use will need to be made of tables of squares, of which the best is

Barlow's Tables of Squares, etc. (4th edition, 1947).

Other tables referred to in the text will need to be used according to the special needs of readers ; three generally useful collections are :

Tables for Statisticians and Biometricians, Part I, edited by K. Pearson,*

Statistical Tables for Biological, Agricultural and Medical Research, by R. A. Fisher and F. Yates, and

Five-Figure Logarithmic and Other Tables, by F. Castle.

A lot of computing is necessarily involved, and readers will be much hampered without access to a calculating machine to perform at least the ordinary processes of addition and multiplication. Slide rules have only a limited use. Many labour-saving devices such as graphs and slide rules involve a sacrifice of accuracy, and they must therefore be used with restraint and discrimination. Broadly, when a simple calculation gives a final result, as in determining a ratio, the effect of errors of approximation can be seen and relatively approximate methods can often be used legitimately. But when the calculation is complex or the result may later be used in further calculations, the effects of errors often become magnified, and it is well to be on the safe side and use ample accuracy.

Arithmetical correctness is vital ; and readers must be prepared at some pains to develop systematic and careful methods of computation.

* These tables are out of print and will not be reissued. They are being replaced by a completely revised edition, the first volume of which is understood (in March 1952) to be ready for press. The new edition will contain those of the old tables that are in current use together with a number of tables published recently in *Biometrika*.

CHAPTER I

FREQUENCY DISTRIBUTIONS AND MEASURES

IN this chapter we shall be concerned with methods of bringing out and describing the characteristics of certain kinds of population. In practice the populations may be represented by samples, but we shall not need at this stage to distinguish between the two beyond noting that samples do not represent the corresponding populations precisely, and may show irregularities and idiosyncrasies not characteristic of the populations.

We deal here only with populations of discrete individuals in which each individual provides one reading of some quality that has been observed or measured. The individual may be an entity that is commonly recognised as a simple unit, such as a man or an electric lamp, or an apparently complex or compound one, such as a family or a box of matches. The observed quality is called the *character* or *attribute* of the individual. The character may be measured and expressed quantitatively, as the height of a man may be expressed in inches, or it may be described in qualitative terms, as is the hair colour. The term " attribute " is sometimes reserved for a qualitatively expressed character. The quantitative measure of a character is called the *variable* or *variate*, and it may be continuously variable, as is a measurement of length or time, or variable in finite discrete steps, as is the number of children in a family. More than one character may be observed for each individual, and in later chapters we shall show how to deal with the data when this is done.

An undigested collection of readings of a single character made on the individuals of a population is difficult to present and interpret : it is impossible to see the wood for the trees. As in the formation of any scientific theory or description of a complex phenomenon, it is necessary to summarise, or to isolate a few important features for description, discarding the irrelevant. There are two main stages in the process of statistical summarisation : (1) the orderly presentation of the data in the form of tables and diagrams, and (2) the calculation of statistical measures that describe the features of the data ; these are dealt with in turn.

FREQUENCY DISTRIBUTIONS

1.1. As an example of the kind of data we have in mind for this chapter consider Table 1.1, ignoring the rows labelled Means and

TABLE 1.1

54	55	41	70	42	50	53	31	49	47
49	59	51	56	40	52	52	56	41	28
50	49	57	57	44	53	72	56	53	60
53	54	32	47	41	43	56	59	53	47
70	62	56	44	54	49	50	35	53	38

Means .	55·2	55·8	47·4	54·8	44·2	49·4	56·6	47·4	49·8	44·0
Ranges.	21	13	25	26	14	10	22	28	12	32

54	27	39	52	49	57	28	48	36	48
27	46	58	65	49	38	51	42	48	47
48	60	66	60	44	55	49	46	55	42
41	62	59	41	49	56	50	62	53	69
47	48	63	62	64	47	53	59	47	46

Means .	43·4	48·6	57·0	56·0	51·0	50·6	46·2	51·4	47·8	50·4
Ranges.	27	35	27	24	20	19	25	20	19	27

Ranges. These data were artificially constructed, and may be taken as representing the measurements of some unspecified character made on a sample of 100 unspecified individuals—they might, for example, have been measurements of the lengths or weights of 100 animals, some dimension measured on 100 mass-produced articles of a given kind, or the strengths of 100 pieces of some material tested to destruction. A sample of 100 is very small for representing all the statistical features of a population, but it will serve the purposes of exposition.

First, we treat the order in which the figures are given as irrelevant (in later chapters we shall have to take account of order), and pay attention only to their magnitude. One natural thing to do is to rearrange them in order of magnitude and then number the values 1, 2, 3, . . . 100. These numbers may be termed the *ranks*. Table 1.1 rearranged in this way produces the result:

Rank :   1   2   3   4   98   99   100
Value :   27   27   28   28   70   70   72

This is termed a *cumulative frequency distribution* because each rank number gives the cumulative number (or cumulative *frequency*—in statistical language a frequency is a number) of individuals having values equal to or less than the corresponding value in the distribution ; e.g. 99 individuals have values equal to or less than 70 units. The values may then be plotted against the ranks and the points joined by a zig-zag of straight lines, or a smooth curve can be drawn through them to give a *cumulative frequency diagram* or *ogive* (a term which is now used but rarely). The shape and position of this curve describe the characteristics of the population.

If the sample contains something like 1 000 individuals or more, as it often does, it would be intolerably laborious to arrange them all in order, and the points on the diagram would be too close together to be distinguished. The smooth curve is usually fairly regular in shape and its outline is sufficiently well defined if only a few points are plotted—between, say, ten and twenty points. We may dismiss as irrelevant detail the exact shape of the curve between the points. The most convenient way of doing this is to choose values of the variate spaced between the lowest and highest, and count the number or frequency of individuals having values equal to or less than each chosen value, which is the cumulative frequency corresponding to that value. It is usually convenient, but not essential, for these values to be equally spaced. If we treat the data of Table 1.1 in this way and choose as values of the variate 29, 32, 35, . . . 71, 74, the corresponding cumulative frequencies are 4, 6, 7, . . . 99, 100. The reader is recommended to form cumulative frequency distributions for Table 1.1, and to plot the diagrams, using the set of chosen values of the variate proposed above, and also others (e.g. 27, 30, . . . ; and 28, 32, . . .). The small differences between these diagrams may be dismissed as irrelevant, being due to differences in arbitrarily chosen conditions. There are some points of detail that arise in making cumulative frequency distributions ; these will be considered later.

The cumulative frequency distribution is not so much used as the *frequency distribution* (without qualification). This is formed by dividing the total range of variation between the lowest and highest values into ten to twenty *sub-ranges* or *class intervals*, usually choosing equally spaced values of the variate to form the boundaries, and recording the frequencies of individuals in the sub-ranges. For the data of Table 1.1 we might choose sub-ranges to correspond to the values of the variate previously chosen in making the cumulative frequency distribution; these sub-ranges would be 27-29 inclusive, 30-32, 33-35, . . . 71-74; and the corresponding frequencies would be 4, 2, 1, . . . 1. The reader is recommended to form the complete distribution and enter it into a table of the form shown in Tables 1.1a. Other tables may also

TABLE 1.1a—FREQUENCY TABLES

(i) *Height of Recruits in U.S. Army in Inches (quoted by Pearson, 1895)*

Height...	51–	52–	53–	54–	55–	56–	57–	58–	59–	60–	61–	62–	63–	64–
Frequency	1	1	2	1	3	7	6	10	15	50	526	1 237	1 947	3 019

	65–	66–	67–	68–	69–	70–	71–	72–	73–	74–	75–	76–	77–	Total
	3 475	4 054	3 631	3 133	2 075	1 485	680	343	118	42	9	6	2	25 878

(ii) *Number of Leaves per Whorl in Ceratophyllum (Pearl, 1907)*

Leaves	5	6	7	8	9	10	11	12	Total
Frequency of Whorls ...	6	169	258	495	733	617	48	2	2 328

(iii) *Lengths of Words from* Concise Oxford Dictionary

No. of Letters in Word	1	2	3	4	5	6	7	8
Frequency of Words	1	1	26	81	100	96	89	61

	9	10	11	12	13	14	15	Total
	68	42	31	13	11	3	1	624

(iv) *Size of Spinning Firms Employing more than 10 Persons (Census of Production, 1930)*

No. of Persons Employed in Firm	11–24	25–49	50–99	100–199	200–299	300–399
Frequency of Firms	68	106	179	196	185	67

	400–499	500–749	750–999	1 000 and over	Total
	47	42	13	8	911

(v) *Degree of Cloudiness at Greenwich, 1890-1904, for Month of July (quoted by Pearse, 1928)*

Cloudiness ...	0	1	2	3	4	5	6	7	8	9	10	Total
Frequency of Days	320	129	74	68	45	45	55	65	90	148	676	1 715

(vi) *Number of Rays of Chrysanthemum Leucanthemum (Tower, 1902)*

Rays	16	17	18	19	20	21	22	23	24	25	26	27	28
Frequency of Flowers	1	—	—	2	8	17	23	22	21	22	19	16	14

	29	30	31	32	33	34	35	36	37	38	39	Total
	12	10	16	18	29	20	6	6	—	—	2	284

be formed with different sets of sub-ranges. The frequency distribution contains all the relevant information provided by the original data, except that the value of the variate for each individual is not specified exactly ; for example, no attempt is made to distinguish between the values 27, 28 and 29. This loss in accuracy is quite unimportant, considering that the values range between 27 and 72, and it is a legitimate sacrifice to make in the process of summarising the data.

Frequency distributions may be plotted into *frequency diagrams*, which are much more readily apprehended than the corresponding tables. One method is to mark off distances along the *x*-axis proportional to values of the variate, and then at the place corresponding to the centre of each sub-range, to raise an ordinate proportional in height to the corresponding frequency. These ordinates may be left to look like the uprights of a fence of varying height as in Figs. 1.1 (ii) and (iii) or their tops may be joined by a zig-zag of straight lines to form a *frequency polygon* as in Figs. 1.1 (i) and (vi). Another method is to raise on that part of the abscissa representing each sub-range a rectangle proportional in area to the corresponding frequency, the set of rectangles forming a *histogram* as in Fig. 1.1 (v). Fig. 1.1 (iv) shows the outline of a histogram. The frequency polygon and histogram are practically equivalent when the sub-ranges are equal ; when they are not the histogram should be used. These and other matters of detail will be dealt with below.

The frequency diagrams for Tables 1.1*a*, in Fig. 1.1, are all fairly simple and regular in outline. It is fortunate that most (not all) frequency diagrams encountered in practice are so, for it makes them fairly easy to apprehend and remember, and it is only for comparatively simple distributions that standard statistical methods have been developed. Moreover, a diagram of simple form is a very economical summary of the original data—more economical even than the frequency table. It is important for readers to learn how to read a frequency diagram, and as an aid to this the diagrams of Fig. 1.1 will be discussed.

If we consult Table 1.1*a* (i) we see that the American recruits of some time previous to 1895 varied between 51 and a fraction over 77 inches. The diagram in Fig. 1.1 (i) is low at the two extremes, but rises fairly steadily to a peak at 66-67 inches, showing that there were very few extremely short or extremely tall recruits,

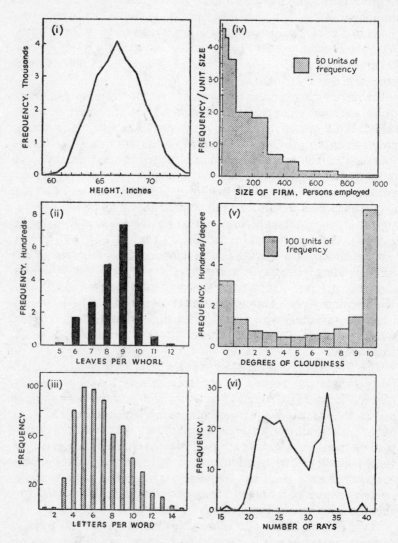

FIG. I.I. Typical frequency diagrams. The data are in Table I.Ia.

that a fair number were moderately tall or moderately short, and that most tended to the typical height of round about 66·5 inches. The variation above and below this typical height is almost symmetrical. This shape of distribution is by far the most common, and it is only for populations distributed according to a mathematical formula which gives a curve somewhat like Fig. 1.1 (i), the so-called " normal " distribution introduced in the next chapter, that most of the methods described in this book apply.

When apprehending such a distribution it is necessary to note only the typical value of the variate [about 66·5 inches in Fig. 1.1 (i)] and the spread about this [roughly 7-9 inches above and below the typical value in Fig. 1.1 (i), if the very few individuals at the very extremes are ignored].

As an example to show how such distributions can arise, imagine a marksman to be shooting repeatedly at a target marked off in vertical stripes, the aim being at the central one. Shots would probably be peppered over the target, and if there were no bias most would be in the central stripe, rather fewer in the next adjacent stripes, still fewer in the next stripes, and so on, very few indeed being in the stripes farthest away from the centre. Indeed it can be imagined that a frequency diagram of the number of shots per stripe plotted against the distance from the centre would be not unlike Fig. 1.1 (i). The concentration of shots towards the centre would be the result of the marksman's aim and the spread about the centre the result of a multitude of disturbing factors, the amount of spread depending largely on the quality of marksmanship.

There are several similar experiments that can be imagined, and some people who find the idea of a frequency distribution and all that it stands for somewhat elusive are helped by them. Presumably it is easier to conceive of the distribution as an entity in spite of the uncontrolled variation if a homogeneous causal system can be imagined as producing it ; and it is easier to accept a distribution as a natural phenomenon and not a statistical kind of monstrosity if one can imagine how it came to be. Undoubtedly systems of causes such as that described, i.e. systems resulting in an aim at some central value with a complex of small, sporadic disturbances, do occur. Frequently, especially when the distribution is simple in shape, there is little profit in attempting to study the causes of the variation between particular individuals : the variation must then be studied as a whole. But this is not necessarily the case, and readers will be better statisticians when they can hold the concept of the frequency distribution in its purity, without forming images of cause systems.

Figs. 1.1 (ii) and (iii) of the distributions of leaves per whorl and lengths of words are examples of asymmetrical or *skew* distributions, in which the spread is not the same on both sides of the peak value. The distribution of Fig. 1.1 (ii) is *negatively* skew (the longer " tail " is in the negative direction) and the other is *positively* skew. When regarding such a diagram we have to note the spreads in the two directions separately. Fig. 1.1 (iv) shows an extremely skew distribution of the sizes of spinning firms in which the peak value is at one extreme. Distributions of this shape are fairly common in economic statistics—for example, the lowest income groups contain most people and the very rich are very few in number. The distribution of degrees of cloudiness in Fig. 1.1 (v) is of a very unusual form ; it shows that in July the sky is usually either nearly completely overcast or nearly completely clear, and that comparatively seldom is there a moderate degree of cloudiness. Figs. 1.1 (i) to (v) are regular in outline and suggest a homogeneous variation that cannot be separated out into a few parts. Fig. 1.1 (vi) of the distribution of rays per chrysanthemum shows irregularities of outline, some of which we may dismiss as idiosyncrasies due to the comparative smallness of the sample (284) ; but there are two well-marked peaks suggesting a mixture of two distinct types of chrysanthemum. Occasionally distributions of still more irregular shapes are encountered, but they are outside the scope of the ordinary methods of statistics and require special treatment.

Frequency distributions with a quantitative variate are the simplest kind of statistical system of a population made up of indeterminate individuals. They are also the base from which have been developed the methods in this book. Moreover, they are very useful practically, and in many fields it is possible to go quite a long way with nothing more elaborate in the way of statistical tools.

A frequency distribution may be formed when the character of the individuals is described qualitatively. For example, the causes of a large number of road accidents may be grouped into a few broad classes and the frequency of accidents of each class be recorded. Such a distribution can be represented in a diagram of vertical columns after the manner of Figs. 1.1 (ii) and (iii), but the shape of the diagram will have no significance, for the classes bear no quantitative relation to each other, and the disposition of the columns along the x-axis is purely arbitrary. If the character may be regarded as a continuous variable qualitatively described (e.g. dark, medium and fair for shade of hair) it is often possible to give the categories numbers and treat the variable as quantitative. This, in effect, is what has probably been done for the degrees of cloudiness of Fig. 1.1 (v). A method is available for giving such data a scale such that the frequency distribution is of the common shape of Fig. 1.1 (i) (see K. Pearson, 1914, pp. xvi and xviii).

Frequency Distributions—Points of Detail

1.11. When the variate is continuous the sub-ranges of the distribution are usually chosen equal, and the choice of their width, and hence of the number of classes into which the total variation is divided, is a matter for compromise. Too many classes give too much detail, and the result is a distribution so overlaid with irregularities that its form is obscured ; too few classes also result in the form of the distribution being lost. If there are several thousands of individuals in the total, 20-25 classes are appropriate, and if there are only one or two hundreds of individuals, ten or even fewer classes are enough ; intermediate numbers of individuals require intermediate numbers of classes. An overriding consideration is that the sub-ranges should not be so small as to be of the same order of magnitude as the errors with which the individual measurements are made. If, for example, the variate is age, it is usually inadvisable to let the sub-ranges be less than one year in width, for many people give their age last birthday, and the frequencies in the groups representing fractions of a year are apt to be too low compared with those in groups representing integral numbers of years.

The sub-ranges of a continuous variate must be continuous ; there can be no gap between the highest value in one and the lowest in the next. Suppose, for the sake of argument, that the data in Table 1.1 are measurements of a continuously variable quantity ; then the statement of sub-ranges suggested above, viz. 27-29, 30-32, . . . is inadequate. Where does a value of 29·6, say, go ? Usually, such data are recorded according to one of two conventions. First, as usually happens for age, each recorded number represents all values between that number and the next highest, so that all values from, say, 29·0 up to (but excluding) 30·0 are recorded as 29, and the actual sub-ranges corresponding to the proposed groupings are 27-30, 30-33, . . . More often, each value is recorded " to the nearest unit," so that 29, for example, refers to all values just exceeding 28·5 and just less than 29·5. Had the data of Table 1.1 been recorded according to this convention, the proposed grouping would correspond to actual sub-ranges of 26·5-29·5, 29·5-32·5, . . . Occasionally it is hard to decide where to put an individual that apparently falls exactly on a boundary between two sub-ranges. It is far preferable to avoid this situation by having in mind the problem of grouping when collecting the data ; but when it is unavoidable the best method is to allocate one-half of an individual to each adjacent sub-range. It is, of course, indicative of slipshod work to record data without a clear definition of and an adherence to some convention in these matters.

Unequal sub-ranges are appropriate when, as for the data of the size of spinning firms in Table 1.1a (iv), the frequencies change much more with the variate in one region than another. Increased detail is thus given where it is most needed. Distributions so arranged are more difficult to handle in subsequent statistical analysis than those with equal sub-ranges, and so, unequal sub-ranges should be used with restraint.

Another way of dealing with very skew data is to subject the variate to some mathematical transformation. If, for example, the distribution is formed with log x as variate instead of x, the measured variate, the effect on the frequency diagram is to expand the scale for low values of the variate and contract that for high values. Suitable transformations may be found by trial and error if desired, or better, from theoretical considerations. For example, the sizes of certain particles may be measured by diameters, whereas the particle volumes may have more technical significance ; and that would suggest cubing the diameters before making a frequency distribution. There is nothing sacrosanct about the linear scale, and transformations have their uses ; but the linear measure often has the greatest technical significance, and in my view that consideration rather than the shape of the resulting frequency distribution should usually decide what mathematical function of the measured variable to use. If a transformation is used, it should be made on the ungrouped data, or on data grouped finely with many groups and narrow sub-ranges.

When the variate is discrete the best sub-range is often the unit of variation—e.g. one sub-range for each number of leaves in Table 1.1a (ii).* But if this leads to too many sub-ranges, some may be combined. Thus the size of spinning firms in Table 1.1a (iv) is measured by the number of people employed, and the variate is discrete ; but it would be silly to have over 1 000 sub-ranges.

In making a histogram, since rectangular areas are proportional to frequencies, the height of each rectangle is proportional to the frequency divided by the sub-range. This method of plotting makes the highest part of Fig. 1.1 (iv) that corresponding to the group of spinning firms of smallest size, even though that group has not the largest frequency [Table 1.1a (iv)]. The frequency in each group depends partly on the width of the sub-range, and without a correction for this we could make the shape of the diagram almost anything we pleased by choosing unequal sub-ranges arbitrarily. The method of plotting a histogram here described gives a diagram of substantially the same shape, whatever the grouping (provided there are enough groups). Any reader who feels doubt on this point is recommended to rearrange and plot a diagram of the data of Table 1.1a (i) with, say, the following unequal sub-ranges : 50-55, 55-60, 60-63, 63-65, 65-66, 66-67, 67-68, 68-70, 70-73, 73-78 inches. He could try first to plot a frequency polygon, and then a histogram in the way just described.

When the variate is continuous, a histogram or frequency polygon is appropriate as it has a continuous outline. When the sub-ranges are equal, it matters little which of these two forms is used, except that if two distributions are superimposed for comparison, the polygon gives outlines that are easier to distinguish. When the variate is discrete the separate columns of Figs. 1.1 (ii) and (iii) are preferable, since they represent the idea of discontinuity. It would, however, be pedantry to treat the sizes of spinning firms in Fig. 1.1 (iv) in this way ; the gaps between the

* The illogicality of describing a single value with no extent as a sub-range is due to the application to discrete variates terms suitable for continuous variates.

sub-ranges are too small to show on the diagram, and the variate may be regarded as substantially continuous.

It is important to distinguish clearly between the variate and the frequency in a frequency distribution. Confusion easily arises when the variate is a pure number, as is the size of spinning firms in Table 1.1a (iv).

A useful form of distribution related to the frequency distribution is what may be termed a *weight* or *value* distribution. Such would result, for example, if Table 1.1a (iv) were converted to show the total numbers of persons employed in the firms in the various sub-ranges of size. We shall not deal further with this type of distribution.

Cumulative frequency tables can easily be made from frequency tables such as are given in Table 1.1a. If the variate is continuous the cumulative frequencies are the numbers of individuals having values *less than* the corresponding boundary values of the sub-ranges ; or the counting can start from the other end of the distribution and the cumulative frequencies be the numbers of individuals having values *greater than* corresponding boundary values. Only when the variate is discrete are the cumulative frequencies the numbers of individuals having values *equal to or less than* or alternatively *equal to or greater than* certain values. Table 1.11 shows a cumulative frequency distribution corresponding to Table 1.1a (i), and the left-hand part of Fig. 1.11 the corresponding diagram, where the frequencies are expressed as decimal fractions of the total.

TABLE 1.11

FREQUENCIES OF RECRUITS IN U.S. ARMY SHORTER THAN VARIOUS LIMITS OF HEIGHT IN INCHES

Height	Frequency	Height	Frequency	Height	Frequency
52	1	61	96	70	23 193
53	2	62	622	71	24 678
54	4	63	1 859	72	25 358
55	5	64	3 806	73	25 701
56	8	65	6 825	74	25 819
57	15	66	10 300	75	25 861
58	21	67	14 354	76	25 870
59	31	68	17 985	77	25 876
60	46	69	21 118	78	25 878

Cumulative diagrams are sometimes plotted on what is known as *probability paper*, with a grid similar to that shown in the right-hand portion of Fig. 1.11. The scale for the variable is the ordinary

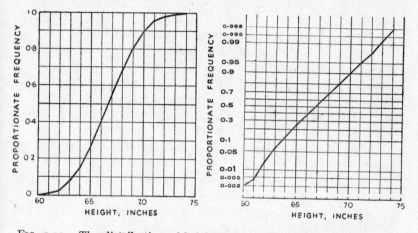

FIG. 1.11. The distribution of heights of recruits [Table 1.1a (i)] represented as a cumulative diagram. The left-hand diagram is on an ordinary linear grid and the right-hand one on a " probability " grid.

linear scale and that for the frequency (specified as percentages of the total) is so arranged that for distributions of exactly the " normal " form (see Chapter II) the cumulative diagram is a straight line. The frequency scale is compressed towards the centre of the range and opened out towards the extremes ; proportionate frequencies of zero and 1·0 do not appear—they are at an infinite distance from the central value of 0·5. One convenience of this paper is that since most distributions are nearly normal and the corresponding curves are nearly straight lines, they are easier to draw than the ogive for the graphical performance of some statistical calculations.

FREQUENCY MEASURES

1.2. Frequency distributions, especially when represented as diagrams, convey to the mind the essential characteristics of a population or sample, but they contain too much detail for precise treatment and accurate comparisons. It seems that the greater the precision with which the mind is required to work the fewer are the quantities with which it can deal. It is necessary to reduce the frequency distribution to a few numerical measures, and this may be done in two ways. The first is to carry a stage further than the formation of a frequency distribution the summarisation of the original data, measuring one or two features of the distribution and ignoring the others as irrelevant for the purposes of the particular enquiry. The second is to find a mathematical formula containing a number of parameters, that is a good approximation to the distribution curve. The values of the parameters that make the formula fit a given frequency distribution are called the *frequency constants* of that distribution. A whole body of statistical theory has been built up on this second approach which will be introduced in the next chapter.

If the frequency distribution is of a complicated or unusual form, e.g. many-peaked, special methods of expression may be necessary, but for most empirical purposes and for distributions commonly met with, use may be made of standard frequency measures that will be described in the sections following. The investigator should always keep the practical problem in mind, whether or not he uses standard measures, and choose appropriate ones. There is no virtue in calculating frequency measures in a blind, routine manner. For some investigations it may be necessary to use measures that derive from technical theory. Thus, according to the kinetic theory of gases, the correct description of the frequency distribution of velocities of molecules for the purpose of expressing energy relationships is the mean of the squares of the velocities. Measures arising in this kind of way are special to the subject of application and cannot be dealt with here.

Proportionate or Percentage Frequencies, Percentiles

1.21. Sometimes the total number of individuals in a distribution and the actual frequencies are of significance, sometimes they are not ; and when they are not the frequencies are expressed as proportions or percentages of the total. Thus as an index of the economic burden of maintaining the young and old of a community it is the proportion or percentage of people of dependent age (say up to 15 and over 65 years) that matters, not the frequency ; but the military strength (old style) of a nation is the frequency of able-bodied men of military age, not the proportion.

For many purposes the limited interests of the investigator are best served by giving the frequency above or below some value of the variate, or the frequency between two values, just as the engineer may be content to know the proportion of a given mass-produced article having some dimension outside the tolerance limits, and may not be interested in the full frequency distribution. In the inspection of manufactured articles such a proportion is commonly referred to as the *fraction* of *defective* articles, or as the *fraction* (or *proportion*) *defective*. An alternative method of expression is to state values of the variate corresponding to chosen frequencies. Such values are sometimes termed *percentiles* when the frequencies are expressed as percentages of the total, or *deciles* when the frequencies are expressed as tenths (the nomenclature is not well developed and is difficult to handle).

These quantities are all easy to determine when the full frequency distribution is given and the particular values of the variate involved are at the boundaries of sub-ranges. Where they are not, some method of interpolation must be adopted ; but simple graphical interpolation from the cumulative frequency diagram is often good enough.

Frequencies underlie nearly all methods of statistical representation. Whatever constants may be calculated or however elaborate may be the analysis, the final interpretation is in terms of frequencies, and readers should always bear this in mind, even though such an interpretation may not always be given explicitly.

Averages

1.22. The term *average* in this sub-title is intended to cover a range of statistical quantities designed to measure what the *Concise Oxford Dictionary* terms the " generally prevailing rate, degree, or amount." They may also be regarded as specifying a value of the variate of a frequency distribution that may be used as a point of reference, about which the individual readings are scattered ; or if we imagine the frequency diagram drawn on such a scale that the origin of the variate appears, these averages serve to define the *location* of the distribution along the *x*-axis.

The most commonly used measure is the *arithmetic mean*, usually referred to as *the* average or *the* mean, and recognisable to the mechanically minded as the *first moment* of the distribution. It is the sum of all the values divided by the number, and methods of calculating it will be dealt with later. If the variate is x the

c   33

mean is usually denoted by the symbol $\bar{x}$. It is well known and understood, and is much used both empirically and in statistical theory. When introducing statistics to people unfamiliar with statistical ideas we may have to emphasise the inadequacy of the average as a statistical description, but we should not underestimate its importance; it is the most important and most useful statistical measure.

The geometric mean is used somewhat in economic statistics in forming index numbers, but very little otherwise, and the harmonic mean is used scarcely at all.

An alternative measure of position is the *median*, which is in fact the fiftieth percentile or the fifth decile (see section 1.21). If all the observations are ranked in order of value the median may be taken as the value of the middle one if the total number is odd, or a value half-way between the two middle ones if the total number is even. If the total number is large and the data are in the form of a frequency distribution, the median is best estimated from the cumulative distribution. There are 25 878 recruits in the first example of Table 1.1a, and we may estimate the median as the value of the 12 939½th in order—say the 12 940th, and it is between 66 and 67 inches. There are 10 300 recruits less than 66 inches in height, and as an approximation we may estimate the median as $66+(12\ 940-10\ 300)\div4\ 054=66\cdot65$ inches. The median can conveniently be determined from the cumulative diagram.

The *mode* is that value of the variate about which the observations are most concentrated, that is, the value at which the ordinate of the frequency diagram is highest, and for the recruits of Table 1.1a (i), for instance, it is between 66 and 67 inches. It is not always easy to define accurately in a sample, for it may be anywhere in the most frequent group, or if the distribution is very flat at the top, and irregular, it is not even easy to decide which would probably be the modal group in the whole population; moreover, a distribution may have more than one real mode, as has already been illustrated. Usually, however, if there is a single mode, the position can be found by assuming Pearson's system of frequency curves as shown in section 1.24.

When the distribution is symmetrical, the mean, median and mode always coincide, and in all other single-modal cases the median comes between the mean and the mode, the dispersion among these three constants being a measure of the extent of asymmetry of the distribution. For practical purposes the following formula holds approximately if the asymmetry is only moderate :

$$\text{Mean} - \text{Mode} = 3 \ (\text{Mean} - \text{Median}).$$

Of these measures, the mean is the most fundamental from a theoretical point of view and is the only one that can be used in further analysis of the data. For the mere representation of the central tendency of a distribution, the median is sometimes recommended because it is said to be least affected by extreme individuals, but for most symmetrical uni-modal distributions, the mean is the most stable constant and is least affected by idiosyncrasies of the particular sample. This result is derived from the theory of errors. When the variate is the life of the individuals under some test of endurance, e.g. the life of electric lamps when burnt at a standard voltage, the median may be an economical constant to determine ; for when half the individuals have failed, the median value may be determined without any further testing. Since the modal is the most typical value, it may be the most suitable single constant to use when the distribution is very skew.

Variability or Dispersion

1.23. There are several quantities that measure the degree of variability or dispersion of the individual values of the variate.

One way of devising such a measure is to choose a point of reference, which is usually the mean value, about which to measure the dispersion, and to express the individual values as differences or deviations from this. If there are N values of x in a population or sample, the deviations are the N values of $(x - \bar{x})$, and the magnitude of these is the degree of variation. These deviations add up to zero (some have positive and others have negative signs), so that their magnitude cannot be represented by a straightforward average. The mean of the squares of the deviations is one measure of variability, called the *second moment* (written μ_2) or *variance* (written v). Thus, we write

$$\mu_2 = v = \frac{S \ (x - \bar{x})^2}{N}$$

where S means " sum the quantity for all values of x in the population or sample." The square root of this is termed the *standard deviation* and is usually denoted by s or σ. Thus we have

$$s \text{ or } \sigma = \sqrt{\mu_2} = \sqrt{\left(\frac{S\,(x - \bar{x})^2}{N}\right)}$$

The computation of these quantities will be dealt with in section 1.31. We shall see in section 5.1 that it is better to replace N by $N - 1$ in the formula for s; but the difference matters only when N is small.

In descriptive statistics it is sometimes convenient to describe the variation relative to the mean by calculating the *coefficient of variation*, which is the standard deviation expressed as a percentage of the mean.

Another way of obtaining an average figure for the magnitude of the deviations as a whole is to sum them irrespective of sign, divide by the number, and so obtain the occasionally used *mean deviation*. The standard deviation is 1·253 times the mean deviation for " normal " distributions.

A second way of describing variability is to measure the spread of the values as the difference between the highest and lowest in the population or sample ; this is called the *range*. It depends on the size of the sample as well as the degree of variation, tending to be smaller for the smaller sizes ; and is a not very precise measure of variation, since it depends on what the two extreme values happen to be and takes no account of the distribution in between. However, the sample size can be allowed for, and if the data occur as, or can be reduced to, a collection of small samples, the *mean range* for the samples becomes a satisfactory measure of variation. Thus, the data of Table 1.1 are divided into twenty sub-samples of five, and the twenty ranges are entered in the table. The mean range is $(21 + 13 + \ldots 19 + 27) \div 20 = 22\cdot3$. This is a satisfactory measure of variation for comparing with another sample or population provided the other is also divided into sub-samples of five.

If the frequency distribution is of the " normal " form, the mean range for sub-samples of given size is proportional to the standard deviation, and full tables are given in *Biometrika*, XVII (1925), p. 386, of the ratio *mean range/standard deviation* for sub-samples (the prefix " sub " is omitted when there is no risk of confusion by so doing) of between 2 and 1 000 individuals ; an abstract of them is given in Table A towards the end of this book. From this we see that the ratio for samples of five is 2·326, so that an estimate of the standard deviation of the data of Table 1.1 is 22·3/2·326 = 9·6, which is not far from the value of 9·4 calculated from the second moment.

The two methods of estimating the standard deviation are equivalent only when the individuals are well mixed and divided into sub-samples at random. The ratio is not very sensitive to moderate changes in the form of the frequency distribution, and the tables from which Table A is taken may be used in most practical experience, even if the frequency distribution is not quite "normal," provided it is uni-modal and tails off fairly gradually to zero at both extremes.

Another measure of variability, somewhat akin to the range, is the *quartile deviation*, which is the deviation measured on either side of the mean of the quartile values of x, chosen so that ordinates drawn at the median and these values divide the area under a histogram into four equal parts. In other words the quartiles are the 25th and 75th percentiles. If the distribution is asymmetrical, the two quartile deviations are not equal. Their average is the *semi-interquartile distance*. If the recruits of Table 1.1a (i) were placed in order we should have :

6 469½ observations   6 469½ observations
lower quartile value   upper quartile value
6 469½ observations   6 469½ observations.
median value

It would be reasonable to take as the lower quartile the value of the 6 470th individual, which is between 64 and 65 inches. The quartile deviations were among the earliest measures of variability used, but there is no reason why deviations corresponding to other percentiles should not be used, and, indeed, Karl Pearson (1920b) has shown that if the frequency distribution is "normal" the deviations of the ordinates which cut off tails of $\frac{1}{14}$th of the total area determine the dispersion with greatest precision of all measures based on percentiles. All these measures have, however, largely fallen out of use.

So many measures of dispersion may be rather bewildering to the reader until he realises that they are different ways of measuring the same thing, and are related for any given form of distribution. The standard deviation is regarded as the fundamental measure, partly because it appears in theoretical equations, and

37

partly because it is least affected by idiosyncrasies of the sample. The variance is exceedingly important because of the part it plays in more complicated statistical analysis ; but it is not easy for the mind to appreciate because it has the dimensions of the square of the units of the variate. The mean range is a convenient alternative to the standard deviation where the data are plentiful and are presented in the form of small samples. In the routine testing of the products of a factory, for example, four articles may be tested every shift, and the mean range for a number of shifts may be taken as a measure of variability. Statistical methods of the routine control of quality in factory production have been based on the mean range in small samples of standard sizes used directly, without conversion to the standard deviation. (See Dudding and Jennett, 1942.)

There are two ways of making the standard deviation, or any other measure of variation, signify something to the mind. The first is by empirical calibration and experience. Thus the standard deviations of a number of samples of some product may be related empirically to some measure of a quality it shows in use ; for example, anyone with suitable experience of cotton yarns appreciates what degree of " count " variation, as measured by the coefficient of variation, corresponds to a satisfactory or unsatisfactory yarn ; and some engineers can assess the precision of an automatic machine tool by the standard deviation of the dimensions of articles it produces. The other way is to interpret the standard deviation in terms of frequencies. This will be treated in section 2.52, but we may note here that for the " normal " distribution, a total range of about six times the standard deviation embraces nearly all the individuals in a large sample.

Shape

1.24. The shape of a uni-modal frequency distribution may vary in two ways : in the degree of asymmetry, and in the flatness of the mode. This flatness of the mode (or *kurtosis*) is different from that flatness of the curve as a whole which arises from the dispersion, and is illustrated in Fig. 1.24, where there are several curves having the same standard deviation but varying kurtosis. These properties may be measured by constants derived from the third and fourth moments of the distribution. The third moment,

$$\mu_3 = \frac{S(x - \bar{x})^3}{N}$$

and the fourth moment,

$$\mu_4 = \frac{S(x - \bar{x})^4}{N},$$

where the symbols on the right-hand side of the equations have the same meaning as those used in defining the second moment.

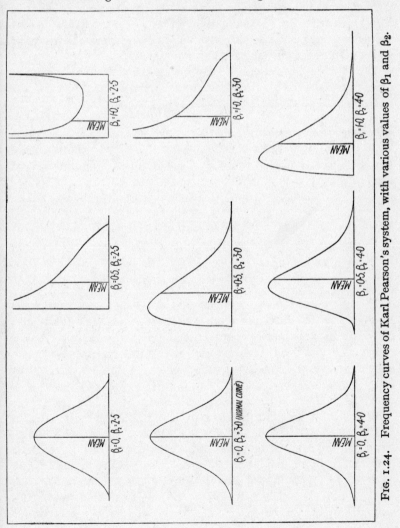

FIG. 1.24.   Frequency curves of Karl Pearson's system, with various values of β_1 and β_2.

39

K. Pearson has derived two constants from the moments, which are independent of the dispersion of the distribution, and describe its shape. They are

$$\beta_1 = \frac{\mu_3{}^2}{\mu_2{}^3} \text{ and } \beta_2 = \frac{\mu_4}{\mu_2{}^2}.$$

β_1 is zero if the distribution is symmetrical, while β_2 is usually about 3 for a curve like that of Fig. 1.1 (i), is smaller if the mode is flatter, and larger if the curve is more sharply peaked. In Fig. 1.24 are given a few smooth frequency curves with different values of β_1 and β_2. They all have positive skewness, and a similar series with negative skewness can be imagined.

The degree of skewness may be simply measured by the quantity

$$\text{Skewness} = \frac{\text{Mean} - \text{Mode}}{\text{Standard Deviation}},$$

which may be positive or negative. The position of the mode, as we have shown, is not easy to define, but if the curve comes within Pearson's system (see section 2.6), the following formula may be used :

$$\text{Skewness} = \frac{(\beta_2 + 3)\sqrt{\beta_1}}{2\,(5\beta_2 - 6\beta_1 - 9)}$$

in which $\sqrt{\beta_1}$ is given the same sign as μ_3. From this we obtain the equation for fixing the mode of a distribution relative to its mean,

$$\text{Mean} - \text{Mode} = \frac{\sigma\,(\beta_2 + 3)\sqrt{\beta_1}}{2\,(5\beta_2 - 6\beta_1 - 9)}$$

The third and fourth moments, or the β ratios calculated from them, serve to characterise well the shape of most uni-modal distributions that are encountered, and Fig. 1.24 shows what a range of shapes can be catered for. Where these moments are not enough, usually where the distributions are more complicated in form, higher ones calculated from higher powers of $(x - \bar{x})$ can be used.

Moments higher than the second are difficult to interpret and clothe with practical significance. They can be used as a short-hand description of shape, and presumably could be used empirically in investigations where, for example, β_1 and β_2 for a number of populations might be related empirically to some quality that is technically important. I do not know of any example of the successful use of the β's in this way and would not expect to find many. A purely empirical use of the standard statistical constants does not seem to have been very fruitful generally.

The higher moments are very important, however, in the theory of distributions. In this theory they sometimes appear in the form of *cumulants* which are more convenient to handle in some mathematical calculations. The second and third cumulants, written κ_2 and κ_3, are equal respectively to the second and third moments, and the fourth cumulant, κ_4, equals $\mu_4 - 3\mu_2{}^2$. As alternatives to the β ratios, Fisher (1925c) uses the quantities

$$\gamma_1 = \pm \sqrt{\beta_1} \text{ and } \gamma_2 = \beta_2 - 3 = \frac{\kappa_4}{\kappa_2{}^2},$$

where γ_1 is given the sign of the third moment. Readers who wish to follow the theory may consult Kendall's *Advanced Theory of Mathematical Statistics* (1943).

COMPUTATION OF MOMENTS
Moments from Ungrouped Data
1.31. It is always possible to compute the mean and the higher moments in a sample by straightforward evaluation of the expressions given in sections 1.22-1.24 as definitions. For example, the mean and second moment are calculated directly in the first three columns of Table 1.31 for a small sample of ten individuals. We have not yet dealt with the theory of methods for such small

TABLE 1.31

x	$(x - \overline{x})$	$(x - \overline{x})^2$	x'	x'^2
67	− 4·8	23·04	− 1	1
70	− 1·8	3·24	0	0
76	+ 4·2	17·64	+ 2	4
73	+ 1·2	1·44	+ 1	1
67	− 4·8	23·04	− 1	1
73	+ 1·2	1·44	+ 1	1
70	− 1·8	3·24	0	0
73	+ 1·2	1·44	+ 1	1
70	− 1·8	3·24	0	0
79	+ 7·2	51·84	+ 3	9
718	0·0	129·60	+ 6	18

samples, and this one is given here merely to illustrate arithmetical processes that are applicable to small and large samples. The sums of the columns are given at the foot of the table, and from them it is seen that the mean $\bar{x} = 71.8$ and the second moment $\mu_2 = 12.96$.

Such calculations are much facilitated by making a transformation of the values of the variate, measuring them as deviations from some arbitrary origin or " working mean " and dividing the deviations by an arbitrary constant ; this last step is equivalent to representing the variation on an arbitrary scale. If x' is the transformed variate, X the arbitrary origin, and h the arbitrary constant or scale,

$$x' = \frac{x - X}{h} \text{ and } x = X + hx' \quad . \quad . \quad . \quad (1.31)$$

Further, let the mean of the values of x' be $\bar{x}'$, and the mean of their sth power be μ_s', so that

$$\bar{x}' = \frac{Sx'}{N} \text{ and } \mu_s' = \frac{Sx'^s}{N}.*$$

Then it may be shown that :

$$\left. \begin{aligned}
\bar{x} &= X + h\bar{x}', \\
\mu_2 &= h^2(\mu_2' - \mu_1'^2), \\
\mu_3 &= h^3(\mu_3' - 3\mu_2'\mu_1' + 2\mu_1'^3), \\
\mu_4 &= h^4(\mu_4' - 4\mu_3'\mu_1' + 6\mu_2'\mu_1'^2 - 3\mu_1'^4).
\end{aligned} \right\} \quad . \quad . \quad (1.31a)$$

To illustrate the use of these equations the mean and second moment have been calculated for the data of Table 1.31. The arbitrary origin $X = 70$, the constant $h = 3$, and the values of x' are given in the fourth column. From their sum, $\bar{x}' = 0.6$ and

$$\bar{x} = 70 + 3 \times 0.6 = 71.8.$$

The sum of the values of x'^2, given in the fifth column, gives $\mu_2' = 1.8$, and from equation (1.31a),

$$\mu_2 = 9(1.8 - 0.36) = 12.96.$$

These results agree with those calculated directly, as indeed they

---

* The letter μ means that the constant is the mean of some power of deviations, the subscript s denotes the order of the power (e.g. for the second moment, $s = 2$) and the prime indicates that the deviations are from an arbitrary origin in arbitrary units. Consistent with this notation $\bar{x}' = \mu_1'$. Where there is no prime, the deviations are measured from the mean in the units of the variate, and μ_s is the sth moment.

should. Readers are recommended to calculate the third and fourth moments for Table 1·31 by the two methods.

1.311. The proof of equations (1.31a) depends on applying the ordinary rules of addition to summations denoted by the sign S.* The first is that the summation of a compound term itself made up of the sum of several terms is equal to the sum of the summations of the separate terms. For example,

$$S(X + hx') = SX + Shx'.$$

The second rule is that the summation of a term that is multiplied by a factor constant for all values of the term summed, is equal to that constant multiplied by the summation of the term. For example,

$$Shx' = hSx'.$$

The general significance of these rules should be appreciated.

From equation (1.31) and the above examples of the summation rules the first part of equation (1.31a) follows easily. It also follows that

$$x - \bar{x} = h(x' - \bar{x}'),$$

and

$$\mu_s = \frac{S(x - \bar{x})^s}{N} = \frac{Sh^s(x' - \bar{x}')^s}{N}.$$

Taking the constant term outside the S sign and expanding the term in brackets by the binomial theorem, we find that

$$\mu_s = \frac{h^s}{N}S\left\{ x'^s - sx'^{s-1}\bar{x}' + \frac{s(s-1)}{2!}x'^{s-2}\bar{x}'^2 + \dots \right.$$
$$\left. (-1)^{s-1}sx'\bar{x}'^{s-1} + (-1)^s\bar{x}'^s \right\}.$$

Summing this term by term, and remembering that $\bar{x}' = \mu_1'$, and is constant for all individuals in the sample, we combine the last two terms, and find that

$$\mu_s = h^s\left\{ \mu_s' - s\mu_{s-1}'\mu_1' + \frac{s(s-1)}{2!}\mu_{s-2}'\mu_1'^2 + \dots (-1)^{s-1}(s-1)\mu_1'^s \right\}.$$

If s is successively put equal to 2, 3 and 4, the last three of equations (1.31a) result.

---

* Readers will do well to master these rules for the sake of following later chapters.

Moments from Grouped Data

1.32. When calculating the moments of a frequency distribution, it is usual to assume that all the individuals in any one group have the central value of that group, i.e. the value midway between the limits of the sub-range. For Table 1.1a (i) the central values are 51·5, 52·5, etc., inches. These values may be transformed as shown in section 1.31. Then to calculate the moments, instead of summing over all individuals, it is possible to multiply the appropriate power of the transformed group value by the frequency and to sum these products over all groups. Let x_t' be the tth group value (the subscript denotes that the transformed variate can only take discrete values corresponding to the central values of the groups), n_t the frequency in that group, and S_t be the summation over all groups, then for such data,

$$S_t n_t = N \quad \text{and} \quad v_s' = \frac{Sx'^s}{N} = \frac{S_t n_t x_t'^s}{N} \quad . \quad . \quad . \quad (1.32)$$

The letter v' is used for the mean of a power of a transformed variate calculated from grouped data where μ' would be used if the data were ungrouped.

For example, the data in Table 1.31 may be grouped and the sum of the fourth column is

$$2 \times (-1) + 3 \times 0 + 3 \times 1 + 1 \times 2 + 1 \times 3.$$

Using equations (1.32) and applying equations (1.31a) to the resulting means as shown above, it is possible to compute the crude mean and moments from grouped data. These moments are denoted by v_2, v_3 and v_4. For a continuous variate some of the crude moments v differ slightly from the true moments denoted by μ, even when calculated from very large (infinite) samples, because the discontinuous form of a frequency distribution with finite groups is only an approximation to the continuous form that is possible with a continuous variate. Sheppard's corrections, when applied to such crude moments calculated from a table with uniform sub-ranges, give values that approximate more closely to the true moments. The corrected mean and moments so obtained are :

$$\left. \begin{array}{l} \bar{x} + \textit{crude mean,} \\ \mu_2 = v_2 - \frac{1}{12}h^2, \\ \mu_3 = v_3, \\ \mu_4 = v_4 - \frac{1}{2}v_2 h^2 + \frac{7}{240}h^4. \end{array} \right\} \quad . \quad . \quad . (1.32a)$$

and

The above transformations make the computation of moments

from grouped data a comparatively easy matter if the arbitrary origin X is chosen to be the central value of one of the groups near the centre of the whole distribution and h is made equal to the sub-ranges, so that the values of the transformed variate x_t' are 0, 1, 2, 3 ... -1, -2, -3 ... etc. The corrections (1.32a) can then be applied to the arbitrary moments, putting h equal to 1, and the final true moments be found by multiplying by h, h^2, h^3 and h^4; the β coefficients, being ratios, are found directly.

The whole process is followed in the example of Table 1.32, the data being the heights of 1 078 fathers (Pearson and Lee, 1903). Column (1) contains the sub-ranges, and column (2) the values of the centres of the sub-ranges in the arbitrary units, x_t'. Column (3) contains the frequencies (the 0·5 frequencies arise because when an observation falls exactly on the border-line between two groups, a half is put into each), and columns (4), (5), (6) and (7) are obtained successively from the previous one by multiplying by the corresponding units in column (2). In column (4) $-27 = 3 \times -9$, in column (5) $243 = -27 \times -9$, in column (6) $-2\,187 = 243 \times -9$ and in column (7) $19\,683 = -2\,187 \times -9$, and so on for the other rows. The arithmetic may be checked by multiplying each frequency directly by $x_t'^4$, and so checking column (7) term by term; if that is correct the other columns from which that was obtained must almost certainly be right. The sums of these columns (paying regard to sign) give the ν' coefficients, and these are corrected step by step below the table. The resulting moments are in inch-units already, since the sub-groups are 1 inch wide. The mean $-$ mode is found from the formula in section 1.24; $\nu_1' = -0\cdot302\,4$, and so the mean is 0·302 4 inch less than the arbitrary origin, which is 68·0 inches (the centre of the group at which $x_t' = 0$). Hence *mean height* $= 68\cdot0 - 0.302\,4 = 67\cdot697\,6$ inches. We shall refer to columns (8) to (13) of Table 1.32 in the next chapter.

In this example the constants have been calculated correct to several decimal places. This has been done advisedly, for when complicated computations are performed, errors due to " dropping figures " too soon are apt to accumulate and become very large, and it is always well to be on the safe side. The number of figures used in computing this example is near the minimum advisable. The final result may be " rounded off " to a few figures, if it is not going to be used in further calculations.

TABLE 1.32

(1)	(2)	(3)	(4)	(5)	(6)
Stature in Inches	Arbitrary Units x_t'	Frequency n_t	$n_t x_t'$	$n_t x_t'^2$	$n_t x_t'^3$
58·5–	−9	3	− 27	243	−2 187
59·5–	−8	3·5	− 28	224	−1 792
60·5–	−7	8	− 56	392	−2 744
61·5–	−6	17	−102	612	−3 672
62·5–	−5	33·5	−167·5	837·5	−4 187·5
63·5–	−4	61·5	−246	984	−3 936
64·5–	−3	95·5	−286·5	859·5	−2 578·5
65·5–	−2	142	−284	568	−1 136
66·5–	−1	137·5	−137·5	137·5	− 137·5
67·5–	0	154	—	—	—
68·5–	1	141·5	141·5	141·5	141·5
69·5–	2	116	232	464	928
70·5–	3	78	234	702	2 106
71·5–	4	49	196	784	3 136
72·5–	5	28·5	142·5	712·5	3 562·5
73·5–	6	4	24	144	864
74·5–	7	5·5	38·5	269·5	1 886·5
Total	—	1 078	−326	8 075	−9 746

$$\nu_1' = -326/1\,078 = -0.302\,41$$

$$\nu_2' = 8\,075/1\,078 = 7.490\,72$$
$$-\nu_1'^2 = -0.091\,45$$

$$\nu_2 = 7.399\,27$$
$$-0.083\,33$$

$$\mu_2 = 7.315\,94$$
$$\sigma = 2.704\,8 \text{ inches}$$

$$\nu_3' = -9\,746/1\,078 = -9.040\,8$$
$$-3\nu_2'\nu_1' = +6.795\,8$$

$$-2.245\,0$$
$$+2\nu_1'^3 = -0.055\,3$$

$$\nu_3 = \mu_3 = -2.300\,3$$
$$\beta_1 = (-)0.013\,513$$

TABLE 1.32—*continued*

(7) $n_t x_t'^4$	(8) $w=\dfrac{x_t-\bar{x}}{\sigma}$	(9) A_w	(10) NA_w	(11) n_t (expected)	(12) z	(13) $y=\dfrac{Nz}{\sigma}$
19 683	−3·030 8	0·001 22	1·3	1·3	0·004 0	1·6
14 336	−2·661 0	0·003 90	4·2	2·9	0·011 6	4·6
19 208	−2·291 3	0·010 97	11·8	7·6	0·028 9	11·5
22 032	−1·921 6	0·027 33	29·5	17·7	0·063 0	25·1
20 937·5	−1·551 9	0·060 34	65·0	35·5	0·119 7	47·7
15 744	−1·182 2	0·118 56	127·8	62·8	0·198 3	79·0
7 735·5	−0·812 5	0·208 25	224·5	96·7	0·286 8	114·3
2 272	−0·442 8	0·328 96	354·6	130·1	0·361 7	144·2
137·5	−0·073 1	0·470 86	507·6	153·0	0·397 9	158·6
—	0·296 7	0·616 65	664·7	157·1	0·381 8	152·2
141·5	0·666 4	0·747 42	805·7	141·0	0·319 5	127·3
1 856	1·036 1	0·849 92	916·2	110·5	0·233 2	92·9
6 318	1·405 8	0·920 10	991·9	75·7	0·148 5	59·2
12 544	1·775 5	0·962 09	1 037·1	45·2	0·082 5	32·9
17 812·5	2·145 2	0·984 03	1 060·8	23·7	0·040 0	15·9
5 184	2·514 9	0·994 04	1 071·6	10·8 ⎫	0·016 9	6·7
13 205·5	2·884 6	0·998 04	1 075·9	6·4 ⎭	0·006 2	2·5
179 147	—	—	—	1 078·0	—	—

$$\nu_4' = 179\ 147/1\ 078 = \quad 166\cdot185$$
$$-4\nu_3'\nu_1' = -\quad 10\cdot936$$

$$\ 155\cdot249$$
$$+6\,\nu_2'\nu_1'^2 = +\quad 4\cdot110$$

$$\ 159\cdot359$$
$$-3\,\nu_1'^4 = -\quad 0\cdot025$$

$$\nu_4 = \quad 159\cdot334$$
$$-\tfrac{1}{2}\nu_2 = -\quad 3\cdot700$$

$$\phantom{-\tfrac{1}{2}\nu_2 =}\ 155\cdot634$$
$$\tfrac{7}{240} = +\quad 0\cdot029$$

$$\mu_4 = \quad 155\cdot663$$
$$\beta_2 = \quad 2\cdot908\ 3$$
$$\text{mean} - \text{mode} = -\quad 0\cdot170\ 1$$
$$\text{mean} = 68\cdot0 - 0\cdot302\ 4 = \quad 67\cdot697\ 6 \text{ inches}$$
$$\text{mode} = \quad 67\cdot867\ 7 \text{ inches}$$

CHAPTER II

DISTRIBUTIONS DERIVED FROM THE THEORY OF PROBABILITY

PROBABILITY

2.1. There are events about which our knowledge is so complete that we are able to predict with certainty whether or not they will occur ; but there are also events about which we know something, but not enough to allow of certain prediction ; the latter are the province of probability. The reliance we can place on a prediction varies in degree for different events, depending on the amount of knowledge we have of the determining factors, and a measure of the degree is called the probability. A probability is usually described as belonging to the event, but by implication if not explicitly it also belongs to the available data of the determining factors.

Probability is expressed on a somewhat arbitrary scale of numbers varying between unity and zero, a value of 1 or 0 corresponding to certainty that the event will or will not occur, and intermediate values to intermediate degrees of certainty ; a probability of 0·5 means that the event is as likely to occur as not. Some writers, notably Jeffreys (1939), have used such a measure in developing a calculus of probabilities for dealing with, among other things, the relations between propositions and the data on which they are based. This use has not received universal acceptance ; but in this book we are concerned with a more restricted use, about the validity of which there is virtually no dispute. We use the results of the mathematical theory of probability, and interpret and apply them statistically.

Mathematical Probability

2.11. In mathematical theory probability is defined in somewhat the following terms (the exact terms of the definition varying with the writer) ; if of a total of $m + n$ things, m possess a given characteristic, the probability of that characteristic is $m/(m + n)$. An alternative form of statement is that the chances are m to n for the characteristic. The measure of probability so defined has a scale similar to that mentioned in the previous section, extending between 1 and 0.

The mathematical theory is not concerned, in general, with determining probabilities, nor with interpreting them; but in most expositions it is usually illustrated by application to particular examples which, in effect, restrict the generality of the definition somewhat. It is usual to imagine an experiment like that of throwing a six-sided die. The throws are the things, the numbers of spots on the sides that remain uppermost after the successive throws are the characteristics, and (a restriction) the die is usually assumed to be unbiased so that each side is equally likely to turn up. The terms are generalised by referring to the throw as a trial, the turning up of a particular side as the occurrence of a particular event or a success, and the turning up of any other side as a non-occurrence or failure. The probability of occurrence of, say, a six is $\frac{1}{6}$. Other idealised games of chance suggest other typical experiments : drawing blindfold from a bag of well-mixed balls that differ only in colour, or drawing cards from a well-shuffled pack, or spinning a perfectly balanced roulette wheel.

The calculus of mathematical probabilities is purely concerned with finding the probability of composite events knowing those of the simple components, and as such it is an exercise in permutations and combinations, enumerating the chances for and against the composite event. There are two fundamental rules that should be understood.

Rule I.—The probability of occurrence of one or other of a number of events, only one of which can occur at a time, is the sum of the probabilities of the separate events. For example, it is easy to see that when throwing a die, two of the six equally likely chances favour the turning up of either a five or a six and that the probability is $\frac{1}{6} + \frac{1}{6} = \frac{1}{3}$.

Rule II.—The probability of the simultaneous occurrence of a number of *independent* events is the product of their separate probabilities. Thus, when throwing two dice, there are 36 equally likely possibilities, and of these, only one is favourable to a double six ; the probability of a double six is $\frac{1}{36}$, and this is $\frac{1}{6} \times \frac{1}{6}$.

Rule II is here given in a restricted form that is simpler than the general form, but is sufficient for our purposes. The word *independent* has its ordinary English meaning, but it will be seen later that in practice we use conformity to the rule as a test, and therefore virtually as a definition, of independence.

Statistical Probability

2.12. The mathematical laws of probability find much use in the theory of statistics for calculating the relations between samples and populations. Superficially, and from the statistical standpoint, the drawing of a sample of, say, 1 000 men from the population of England is very like drawing balls from a bag, and it is assumed that the technique of sampling may be made to satisfy the essential conditions for the application of the laws of mathematical probability. Then the occurrence of an event becomes the drawing of an individual of a given character, the set of equally likely chances becomes a population of equally likely individuals, and a given combination of events becomes a sample of given composition.

On this, the statistical view, the probability of drawing an individual of a given character is the proportion of individuals in the population having that character ; statistical probability is a proportionate frequency. We quite commonly attach a probability to an individual, stating what is the probability of its having a given characteristic ; but such a form of statement should not disguise the fact that in reality we are saying something about the proportionate frequencies in a population. We epitomise the population in an individual. Indeed, I believe that at bottom we interpret all probability statements in this way, and that, for example, when we say that the probability of a given horse winning a given race is one-fifth, we imagine a very large number or population of races run under the same conditions, in one-fifth of which races the given horse wins.

This interpretation of probability is a little more concrete and so is perhaps a little more satisfying to the practical mind than the general description as a ratio expressing a degree of confidence or knowledge, or a ratio of things, but it is still not quite satisfactory. A population is rarely known, even when it is as concrete as a bulk of corn, for if it were known, there would be no question of sampling. However, it has been found in statistical experience that small samples from the same population, which we shall assume to be very large compared with any samples that are likely to be drawn, vary among themselves considerably, but that as they increase in size they become more stable and are less subject to sporadic variations. It is assumed that this tendency continues indefinitely as the size of the sample increases and that there is a single limiting form to which a sample from a given population tends as the sample increases in size. This limiting sample is what the statistician conceives of as the *infinite population,* and in more ordinary language may be described as the result that would be obtained in the " long run " of experience. The probability of a given kind of individual is the proportion of individuals of that kind in this infinite population. We do expect, in the long run, that events having given probabilities will occur and fail in substantially the relative proportions specified by the probabilities.

The infinite population as a concept is seen to be distinct from the bulk that is being sampled, and is an abstraction in that its physical existence cannot be shown ; indeed one can think of an infinite population of throws of a die before one throw has been made. The infinite population depends on the technique of sampling as well as on the bulk, and any difference between the infinite population and the bulk arising from this technique is called *sampling bias.* Since the interest usually lies in the characteristics of the bulk, it is important to eliminate sampling bias as far as possible. This is mentioned further in section 12.22.

Randomness

2.13. Although we use the word *random* and ideas associated with it very much in statistics, there does not seem to exist a single satisfactory definition. An attempt is made in this section to give a description of all that goes with the word that will be good enough for practical purposes. In defining statistical probability we took notice of only the limiting form of the frequency distribution of individuals drawn from a population ; randomness is a property of the order in which they are drawn.

The first thought that comes when we say " random order " is probably the kind of order produced by a physical process like that underlying an idealised game of chance. We think of a constant causal system for all trials so that, for example, the die or the composition of the bag of balls remains constant ; and of a choice at each trial that is blind and independent of the result of every other trial. In statistical practice there is an important place for considering and establishing physical conditions likely to produce randomness. There cannot be degrees of randomness, and if a randomising process puts results in a random order, there is no point in putting them through a second process ; but since we cannot always be confident that a first process has produced randomness, it is often worth while using a second in order to make sure. Moreover, two processes which individually do not produce complete randomness may in combination produce an order that is indistinguishable from random.

Actual experiments with dice and similar apparatus are laborious and difficult to perform, and it is convenient to use the results of three particular experiments, which have been placed on record as *random numbers*. Each set of results consists of a very long series of the digits o to 9, each occurring substantially an equal number of times, and in an order that statisticians, after investigation, accept as random. The first series (Tippett, 1927) contains 40 000 numbers taken from the figures of the areas of parishes given in British census returns, the first two and last two digits in each figure of area being omitted to avoid bias through a possible preference for " round " numbers such as 00 and 50 ; the numbers were somewhat mixed up before inclusion in the series in the hope of ensuring randomness. The second series (Fisher and Yates, 1943) consists of 15 000 numbers taken from the 15th-19th digits in some 20-figure tables of logarithms. The third series (Kendall and Babington-Smith, 1939) consists of 100 000 numbers obtained from a machine. The machine consists of a circular disc marked off in ten equal segments numbered consecutively from o to 9 and rotated by an electric motor. It was rotated in ordinary light and at intervals was momentarily made to appear stationary by a flash from a neon lamp ; the number of the segment opposite a fixed pointer on the machine at the moment of illumination was recorded. The instants of illumination were randomised by an apparatus consisting of an electrical resistance made of a network of pencil lines drawn on paper, and included in the lamp circuit. The observer moved a metal stylus slowly anywhere over the paper ; when it touched a line a charge was added to a condenser, and when the accumulated charge became sufficient the neon tube flashed, the condenser became discharged, and the process was repeated.

A second approach to randomness is more theoretical, and is concerned with recognising randomness without considering how it was produced. Many sets of selections may be made of many results in a given order. For example, if the results are derived from the tossing of a coin, one set may be groups of consecutive pairs, and another set groups of consecutive threes. Within each set the groups may be classified into types ; for the consecutive threes of coin tosses there are eight types, viz. (we write H for heads and T for tails) : HHH, HHT, HTH, HTT, THH, THT, TTH, TTT. In a long series of tosses there will be many groups of three and the types will occur with relative frequencies that can be counted ; the limiting values of these frequencies in an infinite series are the statistical probabilities of the types. A series is regarded as random if, for every set of selections, the statistical probabilities of the types of group are related to those of the individual results according to the rules of mathematical probability. This implies also the independence of the results in a random series, as stipulated in Rule II (section 2.11). It will be noticed that randomness so described has nothing to do with bias —randomness and bias are not incompatible.

This view of randomness cannot be more than an idea, since we can neither have an infinite series nor investigate an infinite number of sets of selections. If, however, we have a long but finite series of results, and on dividing them up into even as few as one set of selections, find the relative frequencies near to those calculated from the mathematical theory, we regard the series as having passed a test of randomness, and until the contrary is demonstrated, we regard the process by which they were obtained as a random process. The longer the series and the more the sets of selections investigated, the greater is our confidence in these conclusions.

A finite series, however long, can be regarded as one of a set of hypothetical selections from an infinite random series, and it will be one of a type having a certain probability of occurrence. All types are theoretically possible (Eddington has entertained the diverting possibility of an army of monkeys strumming on typewriters and producing the books in the British Museum), but as reasonable people we are prepared to act as though very improbable types are impossible, and to regard the corresponding series as non-random.

Thus, although the term randomness is strictly applicable only to an infinite series, we apply it loosely to finite series (preferably long ones), using the mathematical laws of probability as tests of randomness, or what amounts to much the same, of the independence of the individual results. Naturally these tests have been much applied to the results of the traditional random processes, particularly the games of chance. Dice have been thrown and coins tossed by different experimenters many thousands of times in the aggregate, and thousands of runs of roulette wheels have been observed. In the early experiments the mathematical theory was presumably on trial. Good agreement between theory and experiment was often obtained, and where discrepancies occurred it was usually possible to suggest reasons why the particular experiment failed. As a result, there is now confidence that randomness that will pass mathematical tests is physically possible, and where tests are made it is the experiment that is on trial. The mathematical laws are no longer a theory to be either accepted as true or rejected as false ; they provide a basis for analysing statistical experience, and are useful because they describe an important element in that experience. Incidentally, the experiments have shown that considerable trouble must be taken to secure randomness ; for example, the perfunctory shuffling of playing cards that takes place between hands of bridge or whist is far from sufficient to produce a random arrangement. On the other hand, the three series of so-called random numbers mentioned above have passed searching tests.

Sometimes randomness is assumed and the mathematical laws of probability are used to calculate the consequences. The chief example of this second use is in the theory of random sampling. A *random sample* from an infinite population is a particular selection from an infinite random series ; and the fact that in a very extensive use the theory has not been found wanting, is perhaps the best justification for the application of the laws of probability and of the idea of randomness, as well as for the postulate on which the definition of statistical probability is based.

In order to give readers an impression of what randomness looks like, Fig. 2.13 has been prepared. The middle section of the figure was prepared on a piece of graph paper containing $80 \times 45 = 3\,600$ squares. To each square was assigned a digit taken from Tippett's random numbers ; a dot was put in each square to which the digit 1, 2, 3, 4 or 5 had been assigned and the others were left blank. If the 3 600 squares were placed in order,

FIG. 2.13. In the centre diagram the dots are randomly distributed over the paper; in the right-hand one the distribution is more uniform; and in the left-hand one there is a patchiness with a random distribution superimposed.

joining, say, the columns, we would have a random series of dots and no-dots, the probability of a dot being one-half. The arrangement into columns gives a random distribution of dots in two dimensions, which is reproduced in the figure without the framework of squares. Readers will note the absence of a regular pattern, the " over-all-ness " of the distribution, and its patchiness.

It is interesting to contrast this with a non-random distribution. Readers will be able to imagine many systematic non-random arrangements of the dots, so that they fall, say, uniformly into rows and columns, or along diagonals, or are concentrated, say, in the corners, or trace the outline of a face, and so on. The left-hand section of Fig. 2.13 illustrates a fairly common type of non-random distribution. The 3 600 squares were assigned random numbers as before, but in addition the squares were divided into blocks of $4 \times 5 = 20$, and each block was assigned at random either the number 3 or 7. There were 180 blocks, 84 being assigned the number 3 and 96 the number 7, the difference from 90 being due to chance. Then, in those blocks marked 3, dots were put in the squares to which the digits 1, 2 and 3 had been assigned ; and in the other blocks dots were put in the squares to which 1, 2, 3, 4, 5, 6 and 7 had been assigned. Thus there are about 1 800 dots as in the middle section of Fig. 2.13, but their distribution is not random because the probability of the square having a dot varies from 0·3 to 0·7 according to which block it belongs to. The distribution contains two elements of randomness superimposed : a random distribution of the two types of block and a random distribution of dots within each block, and the result is a distribution which is noticeably more irregular than that in the middle section of Fig. 2.13.

The distribution in the right-hand section is more regular than the random one. It is made by dividing the squares into blocks of ten squares made up of pairs of columns of five, and putting dots in five squares chosen at random from each block with the aid of the random numbers. This time there are exactly 1 800 dots. Comparison of the three sections of Fig. 2.13 shows that for simple randomness there is a correct degree of patchiness or irregularity.

2.14. The foregoing discussion of probability and randomness may be summed up roughly in the following terms. It is assumed that in the long run of experience the proportions of occurrences of different kinds of chance events will tend to have stable values that define the infinite population. The long run proportion of any one kind of event is its probability. In practice all probability statements are interpreted in terms of proportionate frequencies in the long run of experience, even when used to measure a degree of subjective confidence that the event will happen. Thus, an event that happens frequently in the long run has a high probability, and on any single occasion we have a considerable degree of confidence that an event with a high probability will happen. Simple events are combined at random when the relations between the probabilities of the composite and simple events satisfy the laws of mathematical probability, and randomness can be produced by carefully operating the recognised processes such as underlie games of chance.

Many theoretical frequency distributions have been derived from the above-mentioned laws of mathematical probability, some of which are required for the solution of special problems. We shall deal with a few of the simpler distributions that are the basis of the general methods of statistics.

BINOMIAL DISTRIBUTION

2.2. If we had four perfect dice and threw them together, noting the number of sixes that turned up, we should find at different throws, four, three, two, one and zero sixes ; and if we made enough throws we could form a frequency distribution in which the variate was the number of sixes per throw, or alternatively the number of " not-sixes," and the individuals were throws. This is the distribution dealt with in this section. In order to obtain this distribution generally we shall refer to the throw of four dice as a *set of n trials* $(n = 4)$, the casting of a six as a *success* and the casting of some other number as a *failure*. Then, if the probability of a success is p and that of a failure is q $(p + q = 1)$, the probability that $(n - s)$ *particular* independent trials will be successes and s will be failures is, by Rule II of mathematical probabilities, $p^{n-s}q^s$. According to the theory of combinations, there are

$$\frac{n(n - 1) \ . \ . \ . \ . \ . \ (n - s + 1)}{s\,!}$$

ways in which $(n - s)$ successes and s failures occur in a set of n, and by Rule I we must add the corresponding probabilities to determine the probability that *any* $(n - s)$ trials will be successes and any s failures. Thus, in a set of n independent trials the probability of $(n - s)$ successes and s failures is

$$\frac{n(n - 1) \ldots \ldots (n - s + 1)}{s\,!} p^{n-s} q^s \quad \ldots \quad (2.2)$$

These probabilities are set out in Table 2.2 and form the proportionate frequencies in what is termed the *binomial frequency distribution*, so called because the proportionate frequencies are

TABLE 2.2

Number of Successes per Set	Number of Failures per Set	Proportion of Sets
n	0	p^n
$n-1$	1	$np^{n-1}q$
$n-2$	2	$\dfrac{n(n-1)}{2\,!}p^{n-2}q^2$
$n-3$	3	$\dfrac{n(n-1)(n-2)}{3\,!}p^{n-3}q^3$
⋮	⋮	⋮
0	n	q^n
Total	... ...	1

the terms in the expansion of the binomial $(p + q)^n$. The variate of this distribution is discrete, and all the proportionate frequencies may be described in terms of the constants p (or q) and n.

In our example of throwing four six-sided dice, there are $\dfrac{4 \times 3}{1 \times 2} = 6$ ways in which two successes and two failures may occur; they are SSFF SFSF SFFS FSSF FSFS FFSS. Each way has a probability of $(\frac{1}{6})^2 (\frac{5}{6})^2 = \frac{25}{1296}$, and the probability

of two successes and two failures is $\dfrac{6 \times 25}{1\,296}$. This, together with

the other probabilities, is entered in Table 2.2a; they are the terms in the expansion of the binomial $(\frac{1}{6} + \frac{5}{6})^4$.

TABLE 2.2a

Number of Sixes ...	4	3	2	1	0	Total
Proportion of Throws ...	$\frac{1}{1296}$	$\frac{20}{1296}$	$\frac{150}{1296}$	$\frac{500}{1296}$	$\frac{625}{1296}$	1
Percentage of Throws ...	0·08	1·54	11·57	38·58	48·23	100·00

It is a matter of algebra to calculate the moments of the general distribution given in Table 2.2 ; they are :

Mean Number of Successes, $l = np$,

Second Moment, $\mu_2 = npq = l\left(1 - \dfrac{l}{n}\right)$,

whence

Standard Deviation, $\sigma = \sqrt{(npq)} = \sqrt{l\left(1 - \dfrac{l}{n}\right)}$,

Third Moment, $\mu_3 = npq(q - p), \beta_1 = \dfrac{(q - p)^2}{npq}$,

$$\quad \cdots \quad (2.2a)$$

Fourth Moment, $\mu_4 = npq\{1 + 3(n - 2)pq\}, \beta_2 = \dfrac{1}{npq} + \dfrac{3(n - 2)}{n}$.

It will be noted that the second and fourth moments are symmetrical in p and q, i.e. the result is the same whether the successes or failures are the variate, and that for the third moment the interchange of p and q merely alters the sign.

The computation of a binomial distribution requires some skill and practice in all but the simplest cases. It is a good plan to obtain separately the coefficients $n(n - s) \ldots (n - s + 1)/s!$ and the products $p^{n-s}q^s$. The coefficients should be computed exactly, or taken from a table such as that given by Fry (1928). The products may be developed term by term starting with p^n and multiplying each term by q/p to obtain the next, until q^n is reached ; this may then be recomputed directly as a check. If n is at all large, large numbers are involved, and a calculating machine is almost a necessity. Tables for values of *n* up to 20 are published by the National Bureau of Standards (1949).

POISSON SERIES

2.3. A binomial distribution may be imagined in which the probability of a failure, *q*, is very small, that of a success, *p*, is nearly equal to unity, and the number of trials per set, *n*, is exceedingly large, so that the mean number of failures per set, $m = nq$, is of moderate dimensions. Then for any moderate value, *s* is negligible compared with *n*, and $(n - s)$ may be equated to *n*. On doing this in expression (2.2) we see that the probability of *s* failures is

$$\frac{n^s q^s}{s!}(1 - q)^n = \left(1 - \frac{m}{n}\right)^n \frac{m^s}{s!}$$

and the limit of this as *n* approaches infinity is

$$\frac{m^s}{s!}e^{-m} \quad \cdot \quad \cdot \quad \cdot \quad \cdot \quad \cdot \quad \cdot \quad \cdot \quad \cdot \quad (2.3)$$

where *e* is the exponential base = 2·718 28 . .

The expansion of this for different values of *s* is the *Poisson Limit to the Binomial* or the *Poisson Series* or the *Law of Small Numbers*.

This distribution is defined entirely by the one constant *m*, which is the mean. The other moments are given by the limits to equations (2.2a) as *n* approaches infinity, and of these it is only important to note that the second moment, which may be written $(1 - m/n)m$, equals the mean.

To calculate the terms of the series for a given value of *m*, the expression (2.3) may be evaluated with the aid of logarithms, but there are also tables. Soper's tables in Karl Pearson's collection (1914) give values of the expression to six decimal places for values of *m* from $m = 0·1$ increasing in steps of 0·1 to $m = 15·0$. Molina's tables (1943) are more extensive, going up to $m = 100$. For approximate work where the probability is required to two decimal places only, Chart A given at the end of this book may be used.

Exponential Distribution of Intervals Between Events

2.31. In sections 2.2 and 2.3 we have divided our experience into uniform sets of *n* trials and taken the number of successes or failures as the variable ; when the trials and events are ordered in space or time an alternative procedure is to count the number of trials (or length of interval) between consecutive successes, thus treating the size of the set as the variable and keeping the number of successes per set constant at unity.

The distribution of intervals corresponding to the binomial distribution has not been much used, but that corresponding to the Poisson arises in practical work more often. For this latter distribution the interval u between successive events is a continuous variate, and it is appropriate to use the ideas and notation of the calculus, and to derive the elemental frequency df within the elemental sub-range du surrounding the value u. This is given by the equation

$$df = y\,du = \frac{N}{\bar{u}} e^{-u/\bar{u}} du \quad . \quad . \quad . \quad . \quad (2.31)$$

where N is the total frequency, $\bar{u}$ is the mean interval, e is the exponential base, and y is the height of the frequency diagram at the abscissa u. The diagram is a continuous J-shaped curve with its highest ordinate at $u = 0$, when the height is $N/\bar{u}$, and it tails off to zero height as u approaches infinity. The elemental frequency df may be regarded as represented by an infinitesimal rectangle in a histogram, having a base of du and a height of y. Areas under the curve between given ordinates represent frequencies between corresponding limits of u and may be determined by integration. In particular, the proportionate frequency of intervals longer than u, termed the *probability integral*, is given by

$$\int_{u}^{\infty} \frac{1}{\bar{u}} e^{-u/\bar{u}} du = e^{-u/\bar{u}} \quad . \quad . \quad . \quad (2.31a)$$

Values of this for different values of the ratio $u/\bar{u}$ are given in Table B at the end of this book. With the aid of Table B the continuous distribution of equation (2.31) can be transformed into a grouped frequency distribution, as is illustrated below. It is surprising to note that when this is done with equal sub-ranges the largest frequency is that of the group containing the shortest intervals, whatever the mean interval.

We shall illustrate a simple application of this distribution below ; readers who are interested to study it further may refer to a paper by Morant (1921).

USES OF THE BINOMIAL, POISSON AND EXPONENTIAL DISTRIBUTIONS

2.4. The above distributions provide the most important means of using the mathematical laws of probability for testing randomness, as discussed in section 2.13. As a first example, let us test the distribution of dots in the middle part of Fig. 2.13. The 3 600 small squares were divided into 180 blocks of 20, each being made up of four columns of five squares. The numbers of dots in the blocks were counted and the frequencies in column (2) of Table 2.4 obtained. The reader can form this distribution by joining the marks round the edges of Fig. 2.13 with fine pencil lines and counting the dots in the rectangles so formed. The expected distribution obtained by expanding $(0 \cdot 5 + 0 \cdot 5)^{20}$ and multiplying the terms by 180 is in column (3) of Table 2.4 and agrees reasonably well with the actual distribution. A criterion for testing that the disagreement is not more than can reasonably be attributed to chance will be described in section 4.2 ; columns (2) and (3) pass this test, known as the χ^2 test. The comparison of these distributions in Table 2.4 is a typical test of randomness that has been performed on the three series of random numbers referred to in section 2.13, and we have here gone a little way—a very little way—towards testing the randomness of the one used in constructing Fig. 2.13.

We can now see more clearly the impossibility of proving randomness by these tests. It is easy to imagine a diagram like Fig. 2.13 with 180 blocks of 20 squares, one block containing 16 dots, three blocks 15 dots, and so on, in conformity with column (3) of Table 2.4, but with the blocks arranged in a pattern, the blocks with most dots being in, say, the top left-hand corner and those with fewest dots being in the bottom right-hand corner. This type of non-randomness would be disclosed by another grouping of squares into blocks, but very many groupings would be needed to ascertain that all types of non-randomness were absent.

It is interesting to treat in the same way the non-random distribution of dots in the lowest section in Fig. 2.13. The frequency distribution is in column (4) of Table 2.4, and it differs markedly from that in column (3). From our knowledge of the way in which the distribution of dots was made, we would expect the frequency distribution to be made by averaging the two binomial series $(0.3 + 0.7)^{20}$ and $(0.7 + 0.3)^{20}$. Such a combined distribution is in column (5) of Table 2.4, and according to the χ^2

TABLE 2.4

Number of Dots per Block	Frequency of Blocks			
	Random Actual	Expected $(0.5+0.5)^{20}$	Non-random Actual	Expected $\frac{1}{2}(0.3+0.7)^{20}$ $+\frac{1}{2}(0.7+0.3)^{20}$
(1)	(2)	(3)	(4)	(5)
20	—	0.0	—	0.1
19	—	0.0	—	0.6
18	—	0.0	5	2.5
17	—	0.2	7	6.4
16	1	0.8	16	11.7
15	3	2.7	12	16.1
14	4	6.7	19	17.3
13	18	13.3	16	14.9
12	27	21.6	12	10.6
11	23	28.8	4	7.0
10	33	31.8	4	5.6
9	33	28.8	5	7.0
8	19	21.6	6	10.6
7	8	13.3	16	14.9
6	8	6.7	19	17.3
5	3	2.7	16	16.1
4	—	0.8	15	11.7
3	—	0.2	5	6.4
2	—	0.0	3	2.5
1	—	0.0	—	0.6
0	—	0.0	—	0.1
Total ...	180	180.0	180	180.0

test of section 4.2 the frequencies in columns (4) and (5) are in reasonable agreement.

In the foregoing examples we have been investigating not only randomness of order but also the consistency of the distributions with the known probabilities of 0·5, 0·3 and 0·7. In practice the probabilities often have to be estimated from the data. In order to provide data for illustrating this, a special experiment was made by incubating 800 cabbage seeds on filter paper in rows of ten, and after eight days the number of germinated seeds in each row was counted ; the data were formed into the frequency distribution of

TABLE 2.4a

Number of Seeds Germinated per Row	Frequency of Rows	
	Actual	Expected
0	6	6·9
1	20	19·1
2	28	24·0
3	12	17·7
4	8	8·6
5	6	2·9
6	—	0·7
7	—	0·1
Total ...	80	80·0

the second column of Table 2.4a. If the germinated seeds were distributed at random among the rows, this frequency distribution would be expected to be binomial with $n = 10$. The probability p of a single seed germinating is estimated from the relationship between the mean l, n and p given in equations (2.2a). The mean number of germinated seeds per row is $(0 \times 6 + 1 \times 20 + \ldots 5 \times 6) \div 80 = 2·175$, and the estimate of p is therefore $2·175 \div 10 = 0·217\ 5$. The proportionate frequencies of the expected binomial distribution are given by the expansion of $(0·217\ 5 + 0·782\ 5)^{10}$, and these multiplied by 80 are the expected frequencies of Table 2.4a. The agreement between the actual and expected frequencies is quite good, and as far as may be judged from this limited experience the variations in germinated seeds from row to row were random ; the seeds were well mixed and independent and conditions were uniform, so that there was a constant probability of any one germinating.

It may be objected that since the expected distribution was derived from the actual by choosing p to make the two means equal, the closeness of agreement signifies nothing. This objection is not valid, however, since the two distributions have only been made to agree in two respects, mean and total frequency, and they have not been made to agree in form ; that agreement is a consequence of randomness.

Another test of randomness is that the various moments should bear the same relations to each other as those of the theoretical binomial distribution given in expression (2.2a). The most important relationship is that between the second moment and the mean. The second moment or variance of the actual distribution in Table 2.4a, calculated by the technique of paragraphs 1.31 and 1.32, is 1·744, and $l(1 - l/n)$, which may be termed the expected variance, is 1·702 ; again the agreement is good.

TABLE 2.4b

Number of Cells per Square	Frequency of Squares	
	Observed	Expected
0	—	3·71
1	20	17·37
2	43	40·65
3	53	63·41
4	86	74·19
5	70	69·44
6	54	54·16
7	37	36·21
8	18	21·18
9	10	11·02
10	5	5·16
11	2	2·19
12	2	0·86
13	—	0·31
14	—	0·10
15	—	0·03
16	—	0·01
Total	400	400·00

The almost classical example of a Poisson distribution is that given by counts of yeast cells in the squares of a haemacytometer. The liquid in which the yeast cells are suspended can be regarded as consisting of aggregates of molecules of the liquid about equal in size to the yeast cells which are sparsely distributed among them. Then the probability that any aggregate taken at random is a yeast cell (the aggregate being a *trial* and the yeast cell a *failure* in the language of the theory) is extremely small ; but there are very many such aggregates in the liquid under one square in the haemacytometer (i.e. in the *set*), so that the mean number of yeast cells per square is finite. Consequently, if the cells are distributed independently and at random through the suspending liquid the frequency distribution of number per square should be the Poisson Series. Table 2.4b gives the distribution of the counts in 400 cells found by " Student " (1907). The mean number of cells per square is 4·68, and from Soper's tables the Poisson Series having a mean (m) of the same value is constructed, the separate terms being multiplied by 400 to give the expected frequencies of the above table. Thus, for $m = 4·6$, 0·010 052 of the squares should have zero cells and for $m = 4·7$ this frequency is 0·009 095 ; hence by linear interpolation, for $m = 4·68$ it is 0·010 052 − 0·8 × 0·000 957 = 0·009 286, and this multiplied by 400 gives the expected frequency of 3·71. The agreement between the two distributions is quite good. The second moment of the observed distribution is 4·46, and is nearly equal to the mean.

In general, the Poisson distribution would be expected to apply where events occur at random and under constant conditions in a medium (usually space or time) that may be divided into a number of equal zones, provided that relative to the size of the zone the medium is continuous (i.e. there is a very large number of elemental units of medium per zone) and the events are rare " points," i.e. there is room in each zone for an exceedingly large number of events although the actual number in any zone is moderate. Examples are the distribution of microscopic and ultra-microscopic particles and bacteria in liquids, the numbers of α-particles emitted from radioactive substances in intervals of time, and counts of weeds or pests in given areas of land in agricultural field trials.

The example of Table 2.4c is taken from Newbold (1926). Accident records were taken for a period of about one year of 247 men engaged in moulding chocolate in a factory, and the distribution of men having 0, 1, 2, . . . accidents is in Table 2.4c. The mean number of accidents per man is $m = 3·813$ 8, and the

66

expected frequencies are as tabulated. The discrepancies are substantial, and the incidence of accidents is not random.

Another example comes from the weaving of cloth. During weaving, a warp thread occasionally breaks, the average rate of occurrence being one or two per 10 000 " picks " (the unit of length), although there is theoretically an independent chance of a break occurring at every pick. If the basic factors affecting warp breaks (e.g. the quality of the warp and the atmospheric humidity) are constant, the distribution of breaks should be random ; we shall test some actual data by the Poisson and exponential distributions. There is on the loom a counter which records the number

TABLE 2.4c

Number of Accidents per Man	Frequency of Men		Number of Accidents per Man	Frequency of Men	
	Actual	Expected		Actual	Expected
0	42	5·5	11	1	0·3
1	44	20·8	12	5	0·1
2	30	39·6	13	1	0·0
3	30	50·4	14	2	0·0
4	25	48·0	15	2	0·0
5	11	36·6	16	—	0·0
6	12	23·3	17	1	0·0
7	15	12·7	18	—	0·0
8	8	6·1	19	—	0·0
9	8	2·6	20	1	0·0
10	8	1·0	21	1	0·0
			Total	247	247·0

of picks inserted as weaving proceeds ; the data were provided by reading this every time a warp break occurred. The total length was divided into 10 000-pick lengths, the number of breaks in each length was counted, and the actual frequency distribution of Table 2.4d was formed. The mean number of breaks per 10 000 picks is 1·279, and the corresponding Poisson distribution, obtained approximately from Chart A, is the expected distribution of Table 2.4d. The discrepancies are scarcely enough to indicate any large departure from randomness. The variance is 1·548, which is only a little more than the expected value of 1·279. We shall later show that these discrepancies are probably significant (section 4.15).

An alternative method is to measure the intervals between successive breaks in 100-pick units. There were 193 intervals and the mean interval calculated without the approximation of grouping was $\bar{u} = 76.803$ 100-pick units. It is convenient to group these intervals in multiples of 0·1 times the ratio $u/\bar{u}$, as shown in the first column of Table 2.4e. The second column was obtained from the first by multiplying by 76·803, the actual distribution in the third by grouping the data according to the second column, and the expected distribution in the fourth from Table B by noting the probability integrals corresponding to the values of $u/\bar{u}$, differencing them, and multiplying by 193. The first frequency of 35·0 is $(1·000 - 0·818\ 7) \times 193$. The two distributions of Table 2.4e are in fair agreement.

TABLE 2.4d

Warp Breaks per 10 000 picks	Frequency of 10 000-pick Lengths	
	Actual	Expected
0	48	41
1	46	52·5
2	30	33·5
3	12	14·5
4	9	4·5
5	2	1
Total	147	147·0

Two questions arise when the same data can be treated in both these ways. The first is the reconciliation of the estimates of m and $\bar{u}$. There were two unbroken series of pick readings, each started and completed by a warp break, totalling 1 482 300 picks, and 195 breaks. But we should regard each break as being associated with one interval, either preceding or following the break, and so should count either the first or last break in each series as belonging to the weaving period outside the 1 482 300 picks, and the mean breaks per 10 000 picks is 193 ÷ 148·23 = 1·302. This differs from the above estimate of 1·279 because the two experiences do not coincide exactly. In one instance the experience of weaving fractions of 10 000 picks was discarded and

there were only 188 breaks in total; in the second instance the
experience of the weaving immediately before the first and after
the last break in each series was discarded. The second question
is : where there is a choice, which test is to be preferred as being
more discriminative? This has not, as far as I know, been
investigated. Probably the result will depend on the nature of the
departure from randomness, if any, to be expected. One would

TABLE 2.4e

Length of Interval		Frequency of Intervals	
$u/\bar{u}$	u	Actual	Expected
0·0–0·2	0 – 15·36	45	35·0
0·2–0·4	15·36– 30·72	30	28·7
0·4–0·6	30·72– 46·08	25	23·5
0·6–0·8	46·08– 61·44	10	19·2
0·8–1·0	61·44– 76·80	15	15·7
1·0–1·2	76·80– 92·16	14	12·9
1·2–1·4	92·16–107·52	5	10·5
1·4–1·6	107·52–122·88	7	8·6
1·6–1·8	122·88–138·24	6	7·1
1·8–2·0	138·24–153·61	5	5·8
2·0–2·4	153·61–184·33	10	8·6
2·4–2·8	184·33–215·05	6	5·8
2·8–3·2	215·05–245·77	8	3·8
3·2–3·6	245·77–276·49	2	2·6
3·6– ∞	276·49– ∞	5	5·2
Total		193	193·0

expect the distribution of intervals to be the better, containing as
it does more detailed information, although in this instance when
the χ^2 criterion of section 4.15 is applied to test the discrepancies
in Tables 2.4d and 2.4e, Table 2.4d comes nearer to showing a
departure from randomness. A difficulty of the division of a given
length of experience into constant lengths as for Table 2.4d is
that if the lengths are short the mean occurrences per length is
low and there are few frequency groups, whereas if the lengths
are long there is a small total frequency ; a compromise must be
struck.

When the binomial, Poisson or exponential distribution fits any data, it is inferred that the variations are due to chance and cannot be reduced or controlled. If some experimental or observational technique that would be expected to show such chance variations is under investigation, it is regarded as satisfactory ; if some natural phenomenon or factory process or other human experience is under investigation the variations are accepted as inherent. Where there are significant departures from the appropriate distribution law, there is justification for investigating the causes of some of the variation, and for attempting to eliminate them. Results like those of Table 2.4c have, for example, given direction to the investigation of accidents, and have led to the discovery of the " accident proneness " of individuals ; and a departure in randomness in some particular records of warp breaks has been taken as evidence that the method of recording was unreliable. A frequent kind of discrepancy is that in which the actual variance is greater than the expected, and this is usually taken as meaning that the conditions are not uniform, so that the probability of a success or an occurrence varies from one set of trials or zones to another. Then the actual distribution is composed of several binomial or Poisson distributions superimposed—the distribution in column (5) of Table 2.4 is a simple example. Another type of departure from randomness is produced when the occurrence of an event increases the probability of further occurrences in the neighbourhood, as, for example, when one diseased individual infects others. The proposing of possible kinds of variation requires technical knowledge of the field of application rather than knowledge of statistics, although statistics is necessary to work out resulting theoretical systems combining random with systematic elements of variation. Readers who are interested to follow up these further questions and to follow further examples may refer to Cochran (1936), Fisher (1936a), Newbold (1927), Neyman (1939), Przyborowski and Wileński (1935), and Tippett (1934).

The binomial, Poisson and exponential distributions also form the basis of theoretical calculations that are applied where randomness has been sufficiently established or is assumed. In the inspection of articles made by a factory, a set of n may be examined and each article be classed as defective or satisfactory ; and it is necessary for establishing a sampling scheme to know, for a given proportion of defective articles in the bulk (i.e. for a given probability, p) what proportions of sets will have zero, one, two and so on defective articles. Randomness is assumed and the binomial or Poisson distribution used. Fry in his *Probability and its Engineering Uses* (1928) shows how the distributions are used in solving problems such as arise in dealing with telephone traffic, where randomness of the occurrence of various events is assumed. The exponential distribution finds some use for calculating the distribution of lengths of molecular chains in high polymer chemistry, the lengths being assumed as formed by randomly distributed cuts in a long chain.

Normal Distribution

2.5. The " normal " distribution may be derived mathematically as another limiting form of the binomial that is approached as n becomes very large, both p and q remaining finite. A binomial distribution may be represented by a histogram with each group centred over the value of the variate corresponding to the number of occurrences per set ; there are $(n + 1)$ groups and the outline of the diagram is of the characteristic stepped form. As n, and hence the number of groups, increases, it becomes necessary to reduce the scale of the variate to keep the diagram within reasonable dimensions and so the steps in the outline become smaller. If this process continues indefinitely, it may easily be imagined that in the limit the steps in the outline coalesce to form a smooth curve ; this is the frequency curve of the *normal* or *Gaussian* distribution. Since it is a continuous curve the variate is necessarily continuous and we may imagine about any given value of x an element sub-range dx, and to regard the area under the curve between ordinates drawn at the limits of the sub-range as an element of frequency, df (say). Then, this elemental strip may be regarded as a rectangle of height y and

$$df = ydx = \frac{N}{\sigma\sqrt{(2\pi)}}e^{-\frac{1}{2}\frac{(x-m)^2}{\sigma^2}}dx \quad . \quad . \quad . \quad . \quad (2.5)$$

where e is the exponential base $= 2.718\ 28\ldots$, x is the variate, and N, m and σ are constants or parameters.* It will be seen later why the equation is written in this particular form and the $\sqrt{(2\pi)}$ and $-\frac{1}{2}$ are not incorporated in the constants. The derivation of this equation from the binomial is purely an algebraic process.

* Subsequently, when e is raised to a power represented by a complicated expression it will be written Exp ( ) where the power is specified in the brackets.

This curve is that given in Fig. 1.24 for $\beta_1=0$, $\beta_2=3$ and in Fig. 2.5. It extends between $x=+\infty$ and $x=-\infty$, since only at those extremes does $y=0$, and it is symmetrical about an ordinate at $x=m$, i.e. about the ordinate at O in Fig. 2.5.

It is now possible to find the various moments of (2.5). The total area under the curve is the total frequency, and on integrating (2.5) between the limits of $x=\pm\infty$ this is found to be N. Hence N in (2.5) is the total frequency. The other moments may be

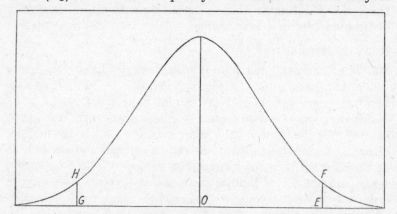

FIG. 2.5. The normal frequency distribution. The two " tails " beyond EF and GH constitute 5 per cent. of the total area.

found from equation (1.32), by substituting df for n_i, the frequency in the sub-group, and integrating instead of summing. Thus the mean is

$$\frac{1}{N}\int_{-\infty}^{+\infty}xdf=m$$

so that the constant m is the mean of the distribution. Similarly the other moments may be found, and the first four are :

$$mean=m$$
$$\mu_2=\sigma^2$$
$$\mu_3=0,\ \beta_1=0$$
$$\mu_4=3\mu_2{}^2,\ \beta_2=3.$$

These expressions for the mean and variance cannot be deduced from those given in (2.2a) for the binomial distribution by writing $n=\infty$, for they would both become infinite ; this is balanced in the derivation of the curve by the ultimate reduction in the scale of the variate, referred to above. The ratios β_1 and β_2, however, are pure numbers, and by putting $n = \infty$ in (2.2a) they reduce to the values given above for the normal curve.

Determination of Normal Frequencies

2.51. Apart from the total frequency, N, any given normal distribution is completely characterised by the two constants m and σ. We are interested in calculating proportionate frequencies between various limits of x. This could be done by integrating (2.5) between the limits if it were possible to evaluate the integral, but as it is not, ordinates must be calculated, and the integration performed by quadrature or by some graphical means. For example, in Fig. 2.5 the proportionate frequency having values less than a value denoted by G on the variate scale is the area under the curve to the left of GH, expressed as a fraction of the total area under the curve ; the proportion between G and E is the area between GH and EF ; the proportion greater than E is the area to the right of EF. This process of integration by quadrature is possible, but laborious. However, tables have been calculated, and these reduce the labour considerably.

A complete set of tables for a range of values of m and σ would be enormous, but by performing a mathematical transformation all normal curves reduce to a standard form. The transformation consists in measuring the variate as a deviation from the mean, divided by the standard deviation. If we write

$$w = \frac{x - m}{\sigma}, \quad . \quad . \quad . \quad . \quad . \quad (2.51)$$

and divide equation (2.5) by N to represent the proportionate frequency, we have

$$df = \frac{1}{\sqrt{(2\pi)}} \operatorname{Exp} \left(-\tfrac{1}{2}w^2\right) dw = z\,dw \quad . \quad . \quad (2.51a)$$

This may be termed the standardised form of the normal curve, and has a mean of zero and a standard deviation of unity. The *probability integral* at w is the area under the curve to the left of an ordinate drawn at w and may be written

$$A_w = \int_{-\infty}^{w} \frac{1}{\sqrt{(2\pi)}} \operatorname{Exp} \left(-\tfrac{1}{2}w^2\right) dw.$$

There are several sets of tables relating A_w, z and w, of which we shall mention only a few that are specially convenient for practical statistical work and readily accessible. Very complete tables of A_w and z for positive equally spaced values of w have been calculated by Sheppard and are included in *Tables for Statisticians and Biometricians*, Vol. I (Pearson, 1914), where our w is called x and our A_w is called $\frac{1}{2}(1 + \alpha)$. To find the probability integral for a negative value of w, use is made of the fact that the distribution (2.51*a*) is symmetrical about an ordinate at $w = 0$. If A_{-w} is the integral at $-w$ and A_w is the integral at w, it is easy to see that

$$A_{-w} = 1 - A_w \quad . \quad . \quad . \quad . \quad . \quad (2.51b)$$

Pearson's tables also give values of w (there termed " deviates of the normal curve ") for values of A_w equally spaced at intervals of 0·001 (each value of A_w is termed a " permille of frequency "). Chart B at the end of this book relates w and A_w and may be used for approximate evaluations.

For some purposes it is convenient to have the sum of the areas under tails beyond given values of w and $-w$, e.g. the sum of the areas to the right of EF and to the left of GH in Fig. 2.5. Since the distribution is symmetrical about the axis $w = 0$, this sum of areas is $2(1 - A_w)$. Fisher and Yates (1943) give tables of w for equally spaced values of $2(1 - A_w)$, and an extract is given in Table C at the end of this book. The same data are given approximately in Chart C by the line for $\nu = \infty$.

To find the probability integral for any value of an actual variate (x in our notation) it is transformed to w by equation (2.51) and the corresponding integral is that required. Thus, if $m = 67·697\ 6$ inches and $\sigma = 2·704\ 8$ inches and it is required to find the probability integral at $x = 60·5$ inches, say, then

$$w = \frac{60·5 - 67·697\ 6}{2·704\ 8} = -2·661\ 0$$

From Sheppard's tables the value of the integral at a deviation of 2·66 is 0·996 09 and at 2·67 it is 0·996 21; so the first difference is 0·000 12, and by linear interpolation the integral for $w = +2·661\ 0$ is

$$A_w = 0·996\ 09 + 0·000\ 12 \times 0·10 = 0·996\ 10.$$

Hence, from equation (2.51*b*), the integral for $w = -2·661\ 0$ is 0·003 90.

The proportionate frequency between any two values of the

variate may be found by taking the difference of the two corresponding integrals. Thus, in the above example the integral
corresponding to $x = 59.5$ is found to be 0·001 22 and the proportionate frequency between 59·5 and 60·5 inches is 0·003 90
$-$ 0·001 22 $=$ 0·002 68.

A normal frequency distribution may be " fitted " to an actual
distribution by putting m and σ equal to the computed mean and
standard deviation respectively and then finding the frequencies in
the sub-groups from the normal probability integrals. The proportionate frequency calculated in the above example is for the
second group of the distribution of heights of fathers in Table 1.32
and has been calculated in this way ; the process is completed in
the later columns of that table. Column (8) gives values of w
corresponding to the limits of the sub-ranges, column (9) gives
probability integrals, in column (10) these are converted to
frequencies by multiplying by the total $N = 1\ 078$, and the normal
or " expected " frequencies in column (11) are the differences of
the values in the previous column. These may be compared with
the actual frequencies, n_t, in column (3). The reader who has not
access to Sheppard's tables may roughly check the results by
reference to Chart B. In order to plot the curve we must find the
ordinates. Sheppard's tables give values of z, the ordinates of the
standardised curve corresponding to the deviations w (see equation 2.51a), and these are given in column (12) of Table 1.32. The
ordinates of the actual curve are obtained by the transformation

$$y = \frac{zN}{\sigma} = 398.55\ z,$$

and these are in column (13). In Fig. 2.51 the curve drawn from
these ordinates is superimposed on the histogram.

Sometimes a frequency or proportionate frequency is given, and
it is desired to find the corresponding value of the variate. The
value of the standardised variate w may be found from Sheppard's
tables, and hence, knowing m and σ, the actual variate be
calculated from equation (2.51).

For example, suppose it is required to know for the data of
Table 1.32 the limit of height such that 20 per cent. of the fathers
are shorter than the limit and 80 per cent. are higher, assuming the
distribution to be normal with mean and standard deviation equal
to the values already computed. Then $A = 0.2$, and since this is

less than 0·5 it corresponds to a negative value of w; we must therefore first find w corresponding to $A = 1 - 0·2 = 0·8$. From Sheppard's tables the value of the variate at which $A = 0·799\ 546$ is 0·84 and the value at which $A = 0·802\ 338$ is 0·85. Hence, by linear interpolation, the value at which $A = 0·8$ is

$$w = \frac{0·8 - 0·799\ 546}{0·802\ 338 - 0·799\ 546} \times 0·01 + 0·84 = 0·841\ 63.$$

Hence the value of w at which $A = 0·2$ is $- 0·841\ 63$ and if this is substituted in (2.51) the limit of height is found to be 65·421 inches.

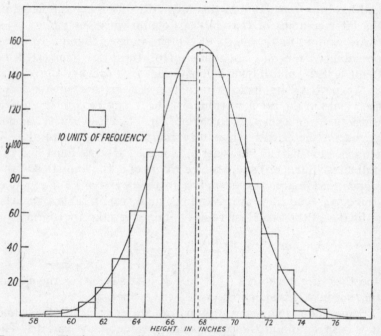

FIG. 2.51. The frequency distribution of heights of recruits [Table 1.1a (i)] represented as a diagram, with the fitted normal curve superimposed.

Relation between Normal Frequencies and Standard Deviation

2.52. A few important values of the probability integral of the normal distribution are given in Table 2.52. The first entry in this table is obvious; the ordinate at $w = 0$ is the axis of symmetry of the curve, and the area up to this ordinate is half the total area.

The second entry of the variate is the quartile deviation ; the proportionate frequency between positive and negative values of this deviation is half the total. The ordinates GH and EF drawn in Fig. 2.5 are at values of the variate corresponding to $w = + 2\cdot0$ and $- 2\cdot0$, and the proportionate area of the two " tails " beyond these limits is 0·045 50 ; i.e. about 5 per cent. of the individuals in a normal population deviate from the mean by twice the standard deviation or more. Similarly, from the last entry in Table 2.52 we see that 99·73 per cent. of the individuals are contained within a total range of six times the standard deviation. These data will assist readers in appreciating the significance of the standard deviation as a measure of variability when applied to a distribution that is approximately normal.

The proportional relations between the standard deviation and

TABLE 2.52

Variate w	Probability Integral A_w	Sum of Two " Tails " $2(1 - A_w)$
0	0·500 00	1·000 00
0·674 49	0·750 00	0·500 00
1·0	0·841 34	0·317 31
2·0	0·977 25	0·045 50
2·6	0·995 34	0·009 32
3·0	0·998 65	0·002 70

other measures of dispersion given above in section 1.23 are true only for normal distributions, although they are roughly applicable also to many distributions that are approximately normal.

Practical Applicability of the Normal Distribution

2.53. The Normal distribution is a continuous curve, and first we must discuss the applicability of frequency curves in general to practical data.

It is assumed that for most infinite populations with a continuous variate, the frequency distribution may be represented by a continuous frequency curve. This is an extrapolation of the practical experience that as the size of the sample is increased the sub-ranges of the distribution may be reduced and the outline of the histogram usually becomes more regular. Where a form of curve can be assumed, the parameters may be estimated from a large sample, and a curve be fitted to the actual distribution, as has been done for Table 1.32.

The normal curve has also been deduced mathematically as the distribution that results from the combination of an infinite number of very small random errors, and this fact together with the fact that the distribution is a special case of the binomial gives it a fundamental status. It is believed by some to represent the deviations due to experimental errors in measurements of a physical constant, and a quantity that is distributed according to this law is sometimes held to be subject only to chance causes that cannot be controlled. Conversely, where a distribution is skew, it is often inferred that superimposed on the chance variations are some larger ones due to a few important causes that may be controlled. I am dubious of this use of the normal distribution. Doubtless normality may be made a definition, and hence a test, of " randomness " just in the way that conformity to the binomial and Poisson distributions has been interpreted, but it is doubtful if for the normal curve such a course has any practical significance. Frequently, when man has done all he can to control the variation in a character and the remaining variations are practically random, the resulting distribution is far from normal. Experimental errors in physical measurements are by no means always normally distributed, and some quantities like the strength of elements of various natural and manufactured materials have essentially skew frequency distributions. It may also happen that the distribution of a quantity is to all intents and purposes normal, and yet a further degree of control may be possible. On the whole, I doubt if in practical use the normal distribution is of more than empirical value ; it is a convenient means of describing any data it happens to fit.

In presenting this view of the place occupied by the normal curve in the statistical scheme, it would be a mistake to underestimate its importance. The curve does in fact represent closely a very large number of experimental distributions and approximately represents many more. It is important, too, because it is the distribution on which most of the statistical theory of errors is based.

Non-normal Curves

2.6. There are several systems of smooth curves for describing data which do not follow the normal law, of which Pearson's is probably the most useful ; all the curves in Fig. 1.24 are of this system. The type is decided upon from the values of the two β ratios, and then these, together with the standard deviation and mean, are used to find the unknown parameters in the equation.

These curves may be made to fit satisfactorily a very wide range of frequency distributions—most of the uni-modal distributions that are likely to be met with in practice ; and so are very powerful. After they were first introduced it became a regular practice to fit all experimental distributions with one of these curves, and the result was very satisfactory to the computer. But no useful purpose seemed to have been served, and now this is done only exceptionally. Sometimes, however, especially in sampling theory, the distribution of some quantity is desired but an equation for it cannot be obtained. Then if, as often happens, the first four moments can be obtained the appropriate frequency curve of Pearson's system can be used as an approximation. Where this has been done and the true distribution has later been deduced, the approximation has been found quite good. This practice may therefore be adopted with some confidence.

These curves must be used with all the caution proper to the use of any empirical formula. They may on occasion give poor approximations ; and it is specially dangerous to use them for extrapolation. There is sometimes a temptation to fit a curve to a body of data and then to use it for calculating the probability of occurrence of an extreme value such as an extremely weak specimen of some engineering material or an exceptional flood : values more extreme than any contained in the original data. Such a practice is very liable to lead to wrong conclusions.

The technique of fitting these curves is fully described in Elderton's *Frequency Curves and Correlation*.

Sampling Distributions

2.7. A sampling distribution results if a large number of finite random samples are taken from an infinite population, some single characteristic of each sample is computed and the computed values are formed into a frequency distribution. For example, the observations of Table 1.1 may be regarded as forming twenty samples of five observations from one population and we may take the mean as the characteristic. The means of these samples are given in Table 1.1, and are formed into a frequency distribution in Table 2.7. This table also gives the distribution of the individual observations.

The distribution of means is called the *sampling distribution* of the mean. Like any other frequency distribution it has a mean, and a standard deviation. The standard deviation of such a distribution is called the *standard error* of the mean and its square is the *sampling variance* of the mean.

Other characteristics of the samples of five could have been calculated, for example the standard deviations or the medians. Each of these would have had its own sampling distribution and standard error.

Most sampling distributions in common use may be deduced mathematically by applying the laws of probability, but given sufficient time and energy one could determine them experimentally by making up an artificial population (say) by writing

TABLE 2.7
FREQUENCY DISTRIBUTIONS

	27–	30–	33–	36–	39–	42–	45–	48–	51–
Individual observations	4	2	1	3	7	7	10	17	13
Means of 5	—	—	—	—	—	3	4	5	2

	54–	57–	60–	63–	66–	69–	72–	Total
	13	8	7	3	1	3	1	100
	5	1	—	—	—	—	—	20

numbers on cards, shaking up in a bag, drawing samples and calculating the means or other statistical measures much in the way in which Table 2.7 was constructed from Table 1.1, except that the scale of the experiment would need to be much larger. This kind of technique is actually used when the distribution cannot be deduced mathematically, also to check some results of mathematical theory and to investigate the errors when some of the assumptions are not justified.

Sampling Distribution of Mean

2.71. We are particularly concerned here with the sampling distribution of the mean in samples of size N drawn from an infinite population in which the individuals are normally distributed. This is itself a normal distribution with a mean equal to the mean of the individuals in the population and a standard error of

$$\frac{\sigma}{\sqrt{N}}$$

where σ is the standard deviation of the individuals.

It will be noticed that as N increases, the standard error of the

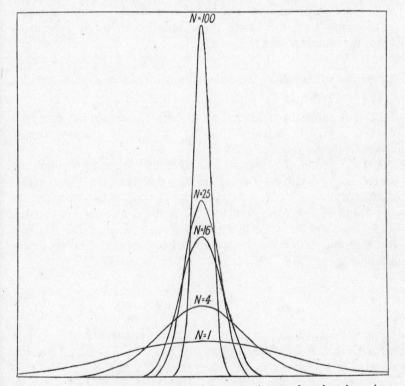

FIG. 2.71.   Sampling distributions of the mean in samples of various sizes.

mean decreases. This is shown in Fig. 2.71, where there are given the sampling distributions of the means of samples of 1, 4, 16, 25 and 100 from a population in which the individuals are normally distributed with an unspecified standard deviation. This population distribution is that in Fig. 2.71 for $N = 1$. For the larger samples, there is less dispersion about the population mean. This is the statistical demonstration of the common experience that a large sample gives a more accurate representation of the population than a small one ; the increase in precision is measured by a reduction in standard error.

The normal probability integral may be used to calculate proportionate frequencies of samples having means within given limits, and Table 2.52 may be used by reading " deviation of sample mean from population mean, divided by standard error " for " variate w." Thus only 0·045 50 or about 1 in 20 of the possible samples have means that differ from the population value by more than twice the standard error.

Deduction of Sampling Distributions of Mean and Standard Deviation

2.72. The sampling distributions of both the mean and standard deviation may be deduced together. The proof is taken from a paper by Irwin (1931).

Let the population mean be $\bar{\xi}$ and the other particulars as stated above. Also let the variate be x and the values in any one sample of N be $x_1 \ldots x_s \ldots x_N$. Since the population distribution is continuous, we cannot state what is the probability of a value x_s, for an ordinate of the frequency curve drawn at x_s has no area, but the probability of a value lying within an elemental range dx_s about a value x_s is

$$\frac{1}{\sigma\sqrt{(2\pi)}} \operatorname{Exp}\left(-\tfrac{1}{2}\frac{(x_s - \bar{\xi})^2}{\sigma^2}\right)dx_s \quad . \quad . \quad (2.72)$$

From the second rule of probability, the probability of a sample having values lying within ranges $dx_1, dx_2 \ldots$ of $x_1, x_2 \ldots$, which we may shortly describe as " the probability of the sample," is

$$\frac{1}{(2\pi)^{\frac{1}{2}N}\sigma^N} \operatorname{Exp}\left(-\tfrac{1}{2}\frac{(x_1 - \bar{\xi})^2 + \ldots (x_N - \bar{\xi})^2}{\sigma^2}\right)dx_1 \ldots dx_N \quad \text{or}$$

$$\frac{1}{(2\pi)^{\frac{1}{2}N}\sigma^N} \operatorname{Exp}\left(-\tfrac{1}{2}\frac{x_1{}^2 + \ldots x_N{}^2 - 2\bar{\xi}(x_1 + \ldots x_N) + N\bar{\xi}^2}{\sigma^2}\right)dx_1 \ldots dx_N.$$

Now if $\bar{x}$ and s are the mean and standard deviation of the sample,* according to sections 1.23 and 1.31,

$$x_1 + \ldots x_N = N\bar{x} \text{ and } x_1^2 + \ldots x_N^2 - N\bar{x}^2 = Ns^2.$$

Substituting these in the exponent of the above expression, we see that the probability of the sample is

$$\frac{1}{(2\pi)^{\frac{1}{2}N}\sigma^N} \operatorname{Exp}\left(-\tfrac{1}{2}N \frac{s^2 + (\bar{x} - \bar{\xi})^2}{\sigma^2}\right) dx_1 \ldots dx_N.$$

Many of the possible samples from this population will have a mean value $\bar{x}$ and a standard deviation s, and to find the probability of a sample with these two constants lying within ranges $d\bar{x}$ and ds of $\bar{x}$ and s we must apply the first probability rule and integrate the above expression for all samples having these two constants. This is a mathematical step involving a transformation to polar co-ordinates in N-dimensional space and a subsequent integration, and leads to the following expression for the probability of a mean of $\bar{x}$ and a standard deviation of s :

$$df = Ks^{N-2} \operatorname{Exp}\left(-\tfrac{1}{2}\frac{N(\bar{x} - \bar{\xi})^2}{\sigma^2}\right) \operatorname{Exp}\left(-\tfrac{1}{2}\frac{Ns^2}{\sigma^2}\right) d\bar{x}\, ds$$

where K is a constant. This is the probability or proportionate frequency distribution of the two statistical constants. Since the term containing $\bar{x}$ does not contain s, and *vice-versa*, the converse of the second rule of probability implies that $\bar{x}$ and s have independent probabilities, and the two distributions may be written separately :

$$\left. \begin{aligned} df &= K_1 \operatorname{Exp}\left(-\tfrac{1}{2} N \frac{(\bar{x} - \bar{\xi})^2}{\sigma^2}\right) d\bar{x} \\ df &= K_2 s^{N-2} \operatorname{Exp}\left(-Ns^2/2\sigma^2\right) ds \end{aligned} \right\} \quad \ldots \text{ (2.72a)}$$

and

By integrating the first expression over the whole range and equating the result to unity, the constant K_1 is found to be

$$\sqrt{N}/\sigma\sqrt{(2\pi)}.$$

Hence the distribution of the mean is a normal one with mean

---

* For the first time it is necessary to distinguish clearly between the population value of a statistical constant and the value estimated from a sample. Usually we shall denote population values by Greek letters and the sample values by corresponding italic letters. This is why we have used $\bar{\xi}$ instead of m in the equation for the normal distribution.

equal to $\bar{\xi}$ and standard deviation equal to $\sigma/\sqrt{N}$. That of the standard deviation is more complicated, and is not much used in that form.

It is convenient here, for later reference, to deduce the sampling distribution of the variance as defined in section 1.23. Let this be $v' = s^2$. Then

$$s = \sqrt{v'}, \; ds = \tfrac{1}{2} \, dv'/\sqrt{v'}$$

and on substituting in the second of equations (2.72a) we find that

$$df = K'_2 \, v'^{\frac{1}{2}(N-3)} \, \mathrm{Exp} \, (-Nv'/2\sigma^2) \, dv' \; . \; . \; . \; (2.72b)$$

The mean value of v' in a large number of samples of size N is

$$\bar{v}' = \int_0^\infty v' \, df = \frac{N-1}{N} \, \sigma^2.$$

Thus, v' tends to over-estimate σ^2, the population value of the variance in the ratio $(N - 1)/N$. A better estimate of the population variance would be

$$v = \frac{N}{N-1} v' = \frac{S \, (x - \bar{x})^2}{N-1}$$

The difference between this formula for estimating variance and that in section 1.23 is unimportant when N is large, but not when N is small ; we shall revert to this topic in Chapter V.

The sampling distribution of the variance forms the basis of methods we shall introduce in Chapter V.

The χ^2 Distribution

2.73. A sampling distribution much used in statistical theory is that of the quantity always denoted by χ^2. In general terms, χ^2 is defined as the sum of the squares of a number of independent values of a quantity w, where w is distributed normally about a mean of zero with unit standard deviation. If there are g independent values of w, the sampling distribution of χ^2 is given by the equation

$$df = k \, (\chi^2)^{\frac{1}{2}(g-2)} \, \mathrm{Exp} \, (-\tfrac{1}{2} \chi^2) \, d \, (\chi^2) \; . \; . \; . \; . \; (2.73)$$

where df is the element of frequency between ordinates drawn at χ^2 and $\chi^2 + d \, (\chi^2)$, k is a constant, and g is termed the *degrees of freedom* (the significance of this term will be discussed in section 4.2).

χ^2 is closely related to Nv', where v' is the estimate of variance defined in section 1.23 for a population with $\bar{\xi} = 0$ and $\sigma = 1$, the only difference being that χ^2 is calculated from deviations from the population mean $\bar{\xi} = 0$, whereas Nv' is calculated from deviations from the sample mean, $\bar{x}$. It can be shown that this difference is accounted for by regarding a χ^2 based on g degrees of freedom as equivalent to Nv' based on $N = g + 1$ observations. If we write in equation (2.72a)

$$N = g + 1, v' = \frac{\chi^2}{g + 1} \text{ and } \sigma = 1$$

we obtain equation (2.73).

There are two main sets of probability tables for χ^2. The first, calculated by Elderton and included in Pearson's *Tables for Statisticians and Biometricians*, gives the probability integral

$$P = \int_{\chi^2}^{\infty} df$$ for integral values of χ^2 and values of n' between 3 and 30, where n' is one more than the degrees of freedom ($= g + 1$). Chart D, at the end of this book, has been constructed from these tables. Fuller tables are given by Hartley and Pearson (1950a). The other tables by Fisher (1925c) give values of χ^2 corresponding to values of P for degrees of freedom (denoted by n) from 1 to 30. An extract from these is in Table D, in terms of our notation. For values of g larger than 30, the quantity $\sqrt{(2\chi^2)}$ may be regarded as normally distributed about a mean of $\sqrt{(2g - 1)}$ with a standard deviation of unity (Fisher, 1925c). The normal probability curve (Chart B) may thus be used for large values of g, putting $w = \sqrt{(2\chi^2)} - \sqrt{(2g - 1)}$, and $P = 1 - A_w$. Thus, according to this approximation for $g = 30$ and $P = 0.05$, $A_w = 0.95$, $w = 1.65$ and $\chi^2 = 43.5$; according to Table D, $\chi^2 = 43.77$ corresponds to a probability of 0.05.

Another special case arises when $g = 1$. Then, if $d(\chi^2)$ is written $2\chi d\chi$, equation (2.73) becomes the equation for the normal distribution, except that since χ extends from zero to infinity, one-half of the normal distribution is used. Thus, if we use the notation of section 2.51 to express the variables of the normal distribution, we have that for $g = 1$ and

$$\sqrt{(\chi^2)} = w, \quad P = 2A_w - 1 \quad \ldots \ldots \quad (2.73a)$$

CHAPTER III

INFERENCE FROM RANDOM SAMPLES

3.1. Much statistical work is concerned with attempts to learn something of the characteristics of populations from measurements made on finite representative samples. We shall deal in this chapter with the principles underlying the methods of using results from samples.

There are different types of sample, but in this chapter we refer only to the simple random sample, as described in section 2.13 : one so taken that every individual in the population has an equal chance of being included, and every individual in the sample is independent of every other. The theory of random sampling describes the relations between samples and the infinite population ; we shall assume that this is the bulk that is being sampled, i.e. that there is no bias. It is sometimes a matter of some practical difficulty to take samples satisfying these conditions ; this question will be dealt with in Chapter XII.

The exposition of the theory of inference in this chapter will be simplified by imposing certain limitations on the discussion. We shall deal with the sampling errors of only the mean and a proportionate frequency ; and certain approximations will be made that are justified only if the samples are large—say larger than twenty. The wider application of the theory will be dealt with in later chapters.

We shall again make the assumption that the sampled population is infinite in the sense that its composition is not appreciably altered by the abstraction of the sample.

TESTS OF SIGNIFICANCE—METHOD

3.2. Errors of random sampling make it impossible for inferences to be made about the population with certainty ; they can be made only with probabilities. Inferences are often made as a basis for some course of action ; in research an experiment may be repeated, or the investigation be pursued in one direction rather than another ; or in commerce a delivery of some material may be accepted by the purchaser, or rejected. In these circumstances man has not learnt to develop a graded infinite series of courses of action appropriate to the infinite series of probabilities between 0 and 1 ; usually he has to choose between two alternatives, although in some applications the technique has been developed for choosing one of three or four courses.

The general scientific method that is applied in situations of this kind is that of framing a working hypothesis and testing it experimentally. As long as the experiments fail to disprove it, so long is the hypothesis accepted. This is the method by which statistical inferences of one important class are made. A hypothetical population of certain characteristics is postulated, and if the sample is such that it could reasonably have come from that population, the hypothesis is accepted. Owing to sampling errors, there is no sharp dividing line between samples that could and could not have come from the hypothetical population. It is only possible to give a probability that a sample like the one observed could have come from the population. If the probability is low, the hypothesis is rejected ; if it is high, the hypothesis is accepted and the deviation between the sample and the postulated population is regarded as being reasonably attributable to errors of sampling.

In carrying out this process, we have to make assumptions—that the observations have been made correctly, that there are no arithmetical errors, that the sampling technique is reliable, that the frequency distribution in the population is of a certain form, and so on. Strictly, these are part of the hypothesis, which may be rejected because one of these is in error. In practice, however, it is convenient to distinguish between the *assumptions* and the *hypothesis*. The hypothesis is tentative and under test : the assumptions are accepted without question. We try to arrange things so that either there are good grounds for accepting the assumptions, or such departures from them as are to be expected do not influence the decision appreciably. Nevertheless, the assumptions should not be accepted too easily, and we should always have it in mind that they may be wrong. Sometimes the hypothesis of one test, if accepted, may become an assumption of another.

If there is some ground for assuming the population to be normal with a given mean and standard deviation, the distribution of the means of samples of any given size is the sampling distribution described in section 2.71, and from the probability integral, the probability of a sample mean deviating from the population mean by more than any value may be deduced. For example, we see from Table 2.52 that the probability of a sample mean differing from the population mean by plus or minus three or more times the standard error is 0·002 70. This is low, and if any actual sample does differ in mean from the population value by more than this amount, we infer that the deviation may not reasonably be attributed to random errors and the hypothesis regarding the population has to be abandoned.

The probability of a random deviation exceeding any given value is in this book called the *level of significance* of the deviation, and is often expressed as a percentage. For example, a deviation of plus or minus three times the standard error is on the 0·27 per cent. level of significance, and one of 1·0 times the standard error is on the 32 per cent. level. The term level of significance is also commonly applied to the value of the deviation, so that according to this usage a deviation of three times the standard error would *be* the 0·27 level.

By way of example we shall assume the lengths of 4 000 hairs of an Indian cotton given by Koshal and Turner (1930) to be an infinite population. This assumption is an approximation, for 4 000 is not infinitely large compared with 1 000, the size of the sample we shall test. The mean length is 2·33 cm. and the standard deviation is 0·480 6 cm. The first thousand hairs were selected by a different method from the rest and gave a mean of 2·54 cm. Is this deviation compatible with the hypothesis that the 1 000 are a random sample from the 4 000 and that the difference in means is due to random errors, or is the difference large enough to indicate that the change in technique has had an effect ? The standard error of the mean is 0·480 6/$\sqrt{1\ 000}$ = 0·015 2, and the deviation of 0·21 cm. is over 13 times the standard error. Sheppard's normal probability tables show that this is far beyond the 0·000 001 level of significance, and the hypothesis is untenable. If we were to correct for the wrong assumption that 4 000 hairs are an infinite population the deviation would be even more highly significant.

Any deviation that is large enough and is on a sufficiently low probability level to lead to a rejection of the hypothesis regarding the population is said to be *statistically significant* and for the above example the mean of the sample is said to be significantly different from that of the population. The question arises : at what probability level does a deviation become statistically significant ? There is no rational probability level at which possibility ceases and impossibility begins, but it is conventional to regard a probability of 0·05 as the critical level of significance. The considerations that govern the choice of this level will be discussed in section 3.3, and it is sufficient here to state that this convention has been found to give a satisfactory rule of action in most circumstances. It will be seen from Table 2.52 that a deviation of twice the standard error corresponds roughly to a probability level of 0·05, so we have the following working rule :

A deviation of a sample mean from a postulated population value of twice the standard error lies on the 0·05 (or 5 per cent.) level of significance, and a deviation greater than this amount is statistically significant.

This rule applies only when positive and negative deviations are considered to be equally likely and no distinction is made between them.

If a deviation is greater than one lying on the 0·05 level, and corresponds to a smaller probability, it is said to be *above* that level ; the smaller the probability level the higher or greater is the significance.

As a measure of dispersion of the sampling distribution of sample means, the quartile deviation is occasionally used instead of the standard error, and is called the *probable error*. The probable error is 0·674 49 times the standard error, and three times the probable error is roughly equivalent to twice the standard error. The probable error has no particular advantages, and as it involves the troublesome factor 0·674 49, it has gone almost completely out of use.

Significance of Difference between Two Sample Means

3.21. The most common situation is one in which the investigator has two samples, and wishes to know if their differences are real or may be attributed to errors of random sampling. Again we shall confine attention to the two means. The appropriate hypothesis is that the two samples are from populations having the same mean, and the probability level of the observed difference is calculated accordingly. Again the hypothesis is accepted if the level is fairly high and there is no statistically significant difference between the means ; if the level is low (say below 0·05), the hypothesis is rejected and the difference is real. To calculate these probabilities it is necessary to know the sampling distribution of the difference between two means.

Let the total numbers of individuals in the two samples be N_1 and N_2. Then it is possible to imagine a sampling experiment in which a very large number of pairs of samples are taken from the respective populations, the number of individuals in the first of each pair being N_1 and the number in the second being N_2. For each sample the mean may be found, and hence for each pair, the difference between the two means. There will be as many differences as there are pairs of samples, and these may be formed into a frequency distribution—the sampling distribution of the difference between two means. This distribution has been deduced mathematically and is normal with a mean value of zero, as may be expected, and a standard deviation (or standard error) larger than the standard error of either sample mean taken separately. If SE_1 is the standard error of the distribution of one series of means and SE_2 is that of the other, the standard error of the distribution of differences is easily deduced from the equations of section 4.15 as

$$SE_{1-2} = \sqrt{\{(SE_1)^2 + (SE_2)^2\}} \quad . \quad . \quad . \quad (3.21)$$

provided the two samples are independent. Further, if σ_1 and σ_2 are the standard deviations of the individuals in the two populations, the standard error of the difference between the two means is

$$SE_{1-2} = \sqrt{\left(\frac{\sigma_1^2}{N_1} + \frac{\sigma_2^2}{N_2}\right)} \quad . \quad . \quad . \quad (3.21a)$$

Usually, σ_1 and σ_2 do not differ appreciably, and it is reasonable to include in the hypothesis the postulate that the two populations are the same, so that $\sigma_1 = \sigma_2$.

In these circumstances, if the two single samples are of the same size they have the same standard error, and the " twice the standard error " criterion leads to the working rule that differences greater than three times the standard error of a single mean are significant ; for if $SE_1 = SE_2$, $SE_{1-2} = \sqrt{2}SE_1$ and $2\sqrt{2}$ is nearly equal to 3.

In order to compute the standard error, it is necessary to know

σ, the standard deviation of the individuals in the population. Frequently this is unknown, and as an approximation an estimate s obtained from the samples is used instead. This practice limits the application of the theory to large samples. Where there are two samples and a common standard deviation is assumed, some combined estimate of s should be used, since the hypothesis is that the samples are from the same population. If s_1 and s_2 are the two sample estimates, a suitable combined estimate is

$$s = \sqrt{\left(\frac{N_1 s_1^2 + N_2 s_2^2}{N_1 + N_2}\right)} \quad \cdots \quad (3.21b)$$

and on substituting this value of s for the values of σ in equation ($3.21a$) we find that

$$SE_{1-2} = \sqrt{\left(\frac{s_2^2}{N_1} + \frac{s_1^2}{N_2}\right)} \quad \cdots \quad (3.21c)$$

Frequently, however, the standard errors of separate means are calculated more or less as a routine and it is convenient to use these directly in equation ($3.21a$) leading to the expression

$$SE_{1-2} = \sqrt{\left(\frac{s_1^2}{N_1} + \frac{s_2^2}{N_2}\right)} \quad \cdots \quad (3.21d)$$

This second course is consistent with the original hypothesis that the samples are from two populations with the same mean and

TABLE 3.21

Country	Number in Sample	Mean Height (inches)	Standard Deviation (inches)	Standard Error of Mean
England ...	6 194	67·437 5	2·548	2·548 ÷ √6 194 = ± 0·032 38
Scotland ...	1 304	68·545 6	2·480	2·480 ÷ √1 304 = ± 0·068 68

possibly different standard deviations. When $\sigma_1 = \sigma_2$ and the samples are large, equations ($3.21c$) and ($3.21d$) lead to results that are not very different, so it is usually safe as well as convenient to use the second. This is used in the following example.

The British Association Report for 1883 gives on page 256

distributions of the heights of men born in England and Scotland ; we shall test the significance of the difference between the two means. The necessary data are in Table 3.21.

The difference in height is 1·108 1 inches, and its standard error is

$$\pm \sqrt{(0\cdot032\ 38^2 + 0\cdot068\ 68^2)} = \pm 0\cdot075\ 9\ ;$$

1·108 1 is 14·6 times 0·075 9, and we thus conclude that Scotsmen are really taller than Englishmen.

Groups of Samples

3.22. The probabilities deduced in accordance with the foregoing theories are only for a single sample or pair of samples taken at random, and when there are several samples the problem of significance is more complicated. If we had a hundred pairs of samples from the same population, giving a hundred differences whose true value was zero, we should expect four or five of them to be greater than twice the standard error ; but if we applied the simple theory and the 0·05 level of significance by " rule-of-thumb," we should erroneously report these four or five as " significant " or real differences. We should thus almost always make an error with regard to the significance of the largest differences ; and there is likewise a tendency to overestimate the

TABLE 3.22

LARGEST $\dfrac{\text{DEVIATION}}{\text{STANDARD ERROR}}$ OF n LYING ON 0·05 LEVEL OF SIGNIFICANCE

n	Deviation / Standard Error
1	2·0
2	2·2
4	2·5
6	2·6
10	2·8

significance of the largest values in any group of samples if the simple theory of the previous sections is applied. However, the theory can be elaborated to give correct estimates of the significance in such circumstances. We shall work out the significance of the biggest n deviations.

Suppose there are n independent differences between pairs of means; e.g. the aim may be to see if several treatments have an effect on some quantity and one of each pair of samples may be an untreated control (a separate one for each pair) and the other be given one of the treatments. We wish to test if the biggest ratio *difference/standard error of difference* is significant. Let the probability that errors of random sampling would give a *single* difference equal to or greater than d (say) be P (as found in the ordinary way from probability tables), and let P_n be the probability that the biggest of n would equal or exceed d. Then $(1 - P_n)$ is the probability that n differences would be less than d, and $(1 - P)$ that *one* random difference would be less; from Rule II (section 2.11) we have

$$(1 - P_n) = (1 - P)^n,$$

whence $P_n = 1 - (1 - P)^n.$

Table 3.22 has been worked out to show what value the largest of n deviations (in terms of the standard error) must reach to lie on the 0·05 level of significance for the normal distribution. For example, for $n = 6$ and $P_n = 0·05$, $1 - P = (0·95)^{\frac{1}{6}} = 0·991\,5$; if both tails contribute to P, the value of A_w is 0·995 8, and from Chart B that of w is seen to be 2·6.

Sometimes we want to know if the difference between the largest and smallest in a group of sample means is significant; such

TABLE 3.22*a*

$$\dfrac{\text{RANGE}}{\text{STANDARD ERROR OF A DIFFERENCE}} \text{ ON 0·05 AND 0·01 LEVELS OF}$$

SIGNIFICANCE

Number of Samples	$P = 0·05$	$P = 0·01$
2	2·0	2·6
4	2·6	3·1
6	2·9	3·4
10	3·2	3·6

a difference is a range. E. S. Pearson (1932) gives some values of the range at various levels of significance and Table 3.22*a* has been calculated from them. When there are four samples, a difference between the largest and smallest mean of 2·5 times the standard error is equivalent to one of twice the standard error for a pair.

We shall illustrate this by the data of Table 3.22b showing the mean corn yield per plot for a number of agricultural plots subjected to five treatments. The standard error of any one mean

TABLE 3.22b

Treatment	Mean Yield per Plot, Grammes
A	295·2
B	297·5
C	276·3
D	272·2
E	271·8

is given as 8·712, and that of any random difference between two means is thus 12·32 grammes. The largest difference is between treatments B and E, and is 25·7 or 2·1 times the standard error. For a single randomly chosen pair of means, this difference would be significant, but here it is the largest difference in a set of five means, and from Table 3.22a we deduce that it is well below the 5 per cent. level of significance.

If it is desired to compare the means of several samples as a whole, there are other and more suitable methods that will be described in Chapter VI ; but if the wish is to compare selected pairs, the above considerations show at least that more stringent tests of significance should be applied than when a single pair is taken at random. These considerations sometimes arise implicitly, without being recognised. Often, in research work, we do not test the small deviations from our hypothesis, but only the big ones, and so implicitly impose a selection.

TESTS OF SIGNIFICANCE—THEORY OF NEYMAN AND PEARSON

3.3. The foregoing methods were developed intuitively, and it is only in later years that their basis has been fully examined. We shall discuss this basis in terms of a simplification of the theory put forward by Neyman and E. S. Pearson, dealing in particular with tests of significance of the mean by way of illustration.

The method consists in rejecting the hypothesis concerning the population value of a mean if the sample mean falls in a certain *critical region*, and accepting it if it falls outside that region. In the usual convention the critical region is that beyond the limits situated at plus and minus twice, or more precisely 1·96 times, the standard error away from the mean. One of four possible situations may arise :

(1) we may wrongly reject a true hypothesis,
(2) we may wrongly accept a false one,
(3) we may rightly accept a true hypothesis, or
(4) we may rightly reject a false one.

Situation (1) gives rise to what are commonly called *errors of the first kind*, and situation (2) to *errors of the second kind*.

In the long run of statistical experience, the ratio of wrong inferences under (1) to total inferences under (1) and (3) when the hypothesis is true, is the probability corresponding to the chosen level of significance, usually 0·05, and can be made as low as we please. The reason for choosing a particular level must be discussed by considering what happens when the hypothesis is false, or in other words, what happens when some alternative hypothesis is true.

Let us assume a normal sampling distribution with a standard error of unity, and let the main hypothesis be that the population mean is $\bar{\xi} = 0$. Then, if this hypothesis is true the sampling distribution is that shown by the full line in the top part of Fig. 3.3 ; and if we adopt the 0·05 level of significance we reject the hypothesis whenever the sample mean is less than −1·96 or greater than +1·96. The probability of 0·05 of rejecting the hypothesis is the area under the tails of the curve outside these limits and is plotted against $\bar{\xi} = 0$ in the lower section of Fig. 3.3. Now let us suppose that in fact $\bar{\xi} = 1·5$ and that we apply the same rule for accepting or rejecting the main hypothesis. The sampling distribution is the broken line in the top part of Fig. 3.3 ; the area under this curve below $\bar{x} = −1.96$ is 0·000 3 (too small to show in Fig. 3.3) and above $\bar{x} = +1·96$ it is 0·322 8, the total probability of rejecting the main hypothesis being 0·323. This is the probability of establishing significance when $\bar{\xi} = 1.5$ and the test is based on a 5 per cent. significance level, and is plotted against $\bar{\xi} = 1\cdot5$ in the lower part of Fig. 3.3. Similarly, if $\bar{\xi} = 3\cdot0$, the sampling distribution is that shown by the dotted line in Fig. 3.3, and the probability of rejecting the main hypothesis, i.e. of inferring a significant deviation from $\bar{\xi} = 0$, is $0\cdot851$. Thus, for all possible values of $\bar{\xi}$, including negative values, can be determined probabilities of $\bar{x}$ falling within the critical region, and hence, according to our rule, of inferring significant deviations from the hypothesis that $\bar{\xi} = 0$. These may be plotted to form

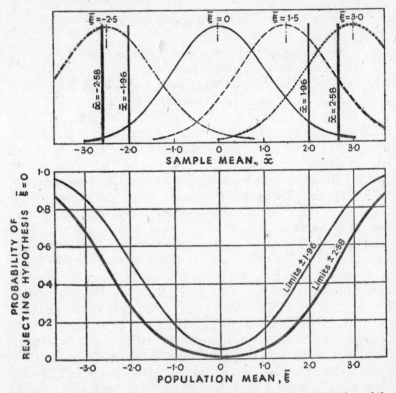

FIG. 3.3. The power function of the mean for two limits of rejection of the hypothesis.

the upper of the two curves in the lower section of Fig. 3.3. This is termed the *power function* of the test of significance. It shows the power of the test to cause a rejection of the main hypothesis when it is false and the various alternative hypotheses are true. The power function corresponding to certain inference would show a probability of zero at $\bar{\xi} = 0$ and of $1 \cdot 0$ for all other values of $\bar{\xi}$; the best test is one having a function that comes nearest to this.

Now let us consider the power function of a similar test, differing from the above test only in rejecting the hypothesis with a probability of $0 \cdot 01$ when $\bar{\xi} = 0$—a fairly commonly used level of significance. The critical region for sample means is outside the limits plus and minus $2 \cdot 58$ giving tail areas of $0 \cdot 005$ each when $\bar{\xi} = 0$, and is shown on the upper section of Fig. 3.3. The probabilities of rejection at $\bar{\xi} = 0$, $1 \cdot 5$, $3 \cdot 0$ and $-2 \cdot 5$ are respectively $0 \cdot 01$, $0 \cdot 140$, $0 \cdot 663$ and $0 \cdot 468$; and these together with all the other values are plotted to give the lower power function in the lower part of Fig. 3.3. By comparing the two power functions we see illustrated the general result that as the critical region is changed in extent to reduce the probability of errors of the first kind, so is the risk of errors of the second kind increased by reducing the probability of rejecting the hypothesis that $\bar{\xi} = 0$ when it is false. The choice of the level of significance involves making a compromise.

It may be that the power function will one day be used to calculate a suitable level of significance for a test in given circumstances, balancing the probabilities of the two kinds of error against some quantitative measure of the seriousness of their consequences. If, in our example, it were known that values of $\bar{\xi}$ between $-5 \cdot 0$ and $+5 \cdot 0$, say, could not occur except at $\bar{\xi} = 0$, and it were desired to make the probability of an error of the first kind when $\bar{\xi} = 0$ equal to that of the second kind when $\bar{\xi} = +5 \cdot 0$ or $-5 \cdot 0$, it is not difficult to calculate that the critical region should be beyond the limits $\pm 2 \cdot 625$, with a probability of rejection of $0 \cdot 008\ 7$ when $\bar{\xi} = 0$ and $0 \cdot 991\ 3$ when $\bar{\xi} = +5 \cdot 0$ or $-5 \cdot 0$. Calculations of this kind have not so far been made, and the level of significance is chosen on more vague considerations and general experience.

Single experiments are not usually done in isolation, and main hypotheses are not chosen haphazardly. We usually have a large body of knowledge and a scientific tradition to guide us. One of the strongest traditions is derived from Occam's Principle that entities should not be multiplied unnecessarily, and favours simple hypotheses involving few constants in preference to complex ones involving many constants. For example, in investigating a possible difference in height between Englishmen and Scotsmen as in section 3.21, it was in accordance with this tradition to prefer the hypothesis of a single mean height to one involving two heights, i.e. to hold to the so-called " null " hypothesis of no difference until the contrary was proved. There is a strong predisposition towards accepting the main hypothesis, and the level of significance is thus chosen at a low probability level. Moreover, by our habits of thought, acceptance of a hypothesis is never more than tentative : rejection is apt to be final ; and so errors of the second kind are less serious than those of the first. The effect of using a low probability level is to favour the *status quo* in scientific knowledge and to impede the admittance of new knowledge ; and if progress is to be maintained, the probability

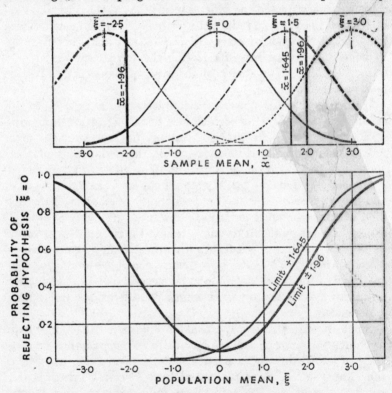

FIG. 3.3*a*. Power functions of the mean when the hypothesis is rejected, (*a*) if the sample value is greater than one limit or less than another, and (*b*) if the sample value is greater than one limit. The probability of rejection when the hypothesis is true ($\bar{\xi}=0$) is the same for (*a*) and (*b*).

level must not be too low. It should act as a kind of a brake of scepticism to control progress without obstructing it. Experience shows that a deviation greater than 0·05 level may be regarded as establishing a prima facie case for rejecting a hypothesis, perhaps strong enough to justify a change in some technical practice, but not to justify an important change in scientific theory : that would require a probability level of 0·01 or even lower. On the other hand, in a new field where there is little previous knowledge and the investigator is casting round for new lines of experiment, it may be worth while following up differences and effects that are on the 0·1 or even the 0·2 level of significance, especially if data are hard to come by, as are some clinical data in medicine.

Now let us return to the example of Fig. 3.3. For a given level of significance (we shall take the 0·05 level), the critical region of $\bar{x}$ below $-1·96$ and above $+1·96$ is not the only one that can be chosen ; there is an infinity of regions all of which enclose areas of 0·05 under the sampling distribution for $\bar{\xi} = 0$, and all of which therefore give the same control of errors of the first kind. One region of interest is that for $\bar{x}$ greater than 1·645, which cuts off a single tail of the distribution of area 0·05. The frequency distributions for $\bar{\xi} = 0$, 1·5, 3·0 and $-2·5$ are in Fig. 3.3a, the tails beyond the limits $\pm1·96$ being marked in thick lines or dots, and the extra part between 1·645 and 1·96 in medium ones. The corresponding power functions are plotted in the lower part of the figure.

The power curves cross at $\bar{\xi} = 0$ and at a probability of 0·05 ; we have arranged that this should be so. For positive values of $\bar{\xi}$, the test using one tail (reject for $\bar{x} > 1·645$) has the greater power of rejecting the false hypothesis that $\bar{\xi} = 0$. But for negative values of $\bar{\xi}$, the probability of rejection is very low—lower even than the probability of rejection when $\bar{\xi} = 0$. With this test, therefore, we are more likely to reject the main hypothesis when it is correct, than when it is wrong and an alternative hypothesis with a negative value of $\bar{\xi}$ is correct. A test having this unsatisfactory property is said to be *biased*. (A biased test and a biased sample are different things ; the adjective is used in two senses.) But if negative deviations of $\bar{\xi}$ from the hypothetical value are ruled out as being inadmissible alternatives, the test using one tail of the sampling distribution is preferable, and it can be shown that it is more powerful than a test involving $\bar{x}$ based on any other critical region. When positive and negative deviations in $\bar{\xi}$ are admitted as possibilities, the test using the single tail is unsatisfactory, and that using two equal tails is more powerful than any other symmetrical test. In such instances it seems natural to use a symmetrical test, giving a power function that is symmetrical about an ordinate drawn at $\bar{\xi}$ corresponding to the main hypothesis, but circumstances are conceivable in which a test may be preferred that gives a power curve below that of Fig. 3.3a for negative values of $\bar{\xi}$ and (correspondingly) between the two curves shown for positive values. Normally, however, the symmetrical test is used.

In testing the hypothesis that $\bar{\xi} = 0$ against alternatives that $\bar{\xi} \neq 0$, we have used the mean, $\bar{x}$, calculated from the sample, but

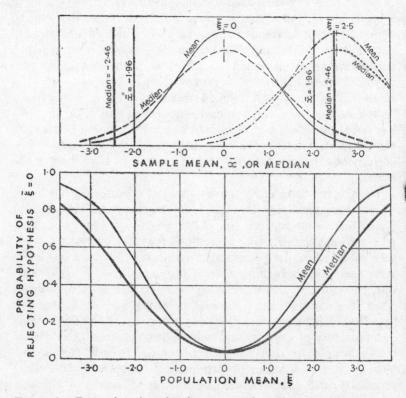

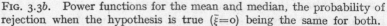

FIG. 3.3b. Power functions for the mean and median, the probability of rejection when the hypothesis is true ($\bar{\xi}=0$) being the same for both.

there are other quantities that could be used. The median, for example, is in large samples of N distributed normally about a mean value equal to $\bar{\xi}$ with a standard error of $1{\cdot}253\ \sigma/\sqrt{N}$, where σ is the standard deviation of individuals in the population. For our example of Fig. 3.3, therefore, the median would have a standard error of $1{\cdot}253$. For the sampling distribution of medians corresponding to $\bar{\xi} = 0$, the two tails beyond $\pm 1{\cdot}96 \times 1{\cdot}253 = \pm 2{\cdot}46$ cut off an area of $0{\cdot}05$, so the test for the $0{\cdot}05$ level of significance becomes : reject the hypothesis when the median is less than $-2{\cdot}46$ or greater than $2{\cdot}46$. Typical sampling distributions for this and the corresponding test of sample means are given in Fig. 3.3b, together with the power functions. Clearly, the test using means is more powerful for all values of $\bar{\xi}$, and hence preferable. This illustrates the general point that some statistical quantities calculated from samples provide more discriminative tests than others. If the sampling distributions are normal, the quantity with the lowest standard error is always best, just as a test becomes more discriminative as the sample size increases ; but if the sampling distributions of the tests to be compared are different in form, the full power function must be investigated.

The foregoing illustrates by a particular case the way in which many commonly used tests of significance have been justified *post hoc* on Neyman's and Pearson's theory, and new tests are investigated. The result is not always so unequivocal as those given above. The theory has been and is being developed along general lines, and readers who wish to follow the subject further will find a good survey and list of references in Neyman (1942).

Tests of Significance Based on Skew Sampling Distributions

3.31. When the sampling distribution is symmetrical, and positive and negative deviations from the population value are admissible, the " two-tailed " test is used and the limits bounding the critical region are symmetrically placed, so that for, say, the $0{\cdot}05$ level of significance, each tail corresponds to a probability of $0{\cdot}025$. When the sampling distribution is skew, there are several possible courses of action, and in any particular case the best can be chosen by constructing the power function. As a general rule, however, it seems reasonable to choose limits so that the areas in the two tails are equal (the limits will not be equidistant from the population value), and for practical purposes this rule suffices.

STATISTICAL AND TECHNICAL SIGNIFICANCE

3.4. The statistical significance gives no information about the magnitude or technical importance of any effect under investigation. A very large sample may make very small and unimportant differences overwhelmingly significant ; a small one may have random errors large enough to obscure large and important differences.

If a difference is judged to be statistically significant, the technical significance is a separate question to be dealt with subsequently by someone with technical knowledge. The difference may be due to the factor under investigation, to faulty sampling technique that invalidates the application of the theory of random sampling, or to the falseness in some other assumption.

If a difference is statistically insignificant, the technical man should remember that the verdict is more like the " not proven " of Scots law than " not guilty," and consider whether such a difference, if statistically significant, would have technical significance. If so, he should increase his information. Ideally, it should be possible to decide beforehand what difference is on the borderline of technical importance, and then to determine statistically the size of sample required to make that difference significant. The choice of the borderline difference is for the technician ; it is often difficult to make, but no statistical principles are involved. In principle, the statistical part of the procedure would be done by deriving power functions for samples of various sizes and choosing the size for which the probability of rejecting the main (null) hypothesis is at a sufficiently high level, say 0·95 or 0·99, when the alternative hypothesis corresponds to the previously decided borderline difference. The sampling distributions would be determined from preliminary samples or other experience. When the sampling distribution is normal this procedure reduces to finding the value of N (or N_1 and N_2 if there are two samples) necessary to make the standard error small enough—e.g. to one-third of the borderline difference if it is to be tested as a difference between two sample means and the 0·05 level of significance is used. By way of illustration, let us suppose that in 1943 it was desired to determine whether the average height of Englishmen had changed from the value given in Table 3.21 for 1883. How many men should be measured in 1943 ? Let us suppose that a difference of 0·2 inch or greater is of technical significance, having regard perhaps to differences in height that occur between other groups of men and to the errors of measurement, that the matter is important enough to justify the stringency of a 0·01 level of significance, and that to a first approximation the standard deviation of height is 2·5 inches, as it was in 1883. Then, since a difference of 2·58 times the standard error corresponds to the 0·01 level of significance (see Fig. 3.3), we have for N, the size of sample in 1943

$$2 \cdot 58 \times 2 \cdot 5 \sqrt{\left(\frac{1}{6\ 194} + \frac{1}{N}\right)} = 0 \cdot 2$$

whence $N = 1\ 250$.

Tests of Batch Quality

3.5. In commercial and industrial practice, the results of tests made on samples are used to determine whether batches of materials shall be accepted for use or rejected. In making decisions of this kind, there arise the same issues as in making tests of significance, but in slightly different guise. Such transactions based on samples vary in circumstance and detail, but we shall illustrate the principles by taking a simple, typical case in which a " producer " offers the batch to a " consumer."

Let us suppose that the producer offers articles in batches or lots of several thousands, that a sample of 75 is taken from each batch, that the articles in each sample are classified as defective or satisfactory, and that the batch is accepted if there are only 0, 1, 2, 3 or 4 defective articles in the sample or rejected if there are five or more. For such a scheme, 4 is termed the *acceptance number*. Then, if the sampling is random and we may regard each batch as infinite in size compared with the size of the sample, the probability of accepting a given batch is, by the binomial theory,

$$(1 - \pi)^{75} + 75\pi (1 - \pi)^{74} + \frac{75 \cdot 74}{2!} \pi^2 (1 - \pi)^{73} +$$

$$\frac{75 \cdot 74 \cdot 73}{3!} \pi^3 (1 - \pi)^{72} + \frac{75 \cdot 74 \cdot 73 \cdot 72}{4!} \pi^4 (1 - \pi)^{71}.$$

where π is the proportion of defective articles in the batch (here π is not 3·141 59 . .). This probability is plotted against π in the middle section of Fig. 3.5, where it is represented by the full curve. Such a curve is termed the *operating characteristic curve* of the sampling scheme, and corresponds closely to the power curve of a significance test.

In practice an operating characteristic curve is defined by two points chosen in the following way. The producer chooses a high probability level of acceptance which he regards as a safe level;

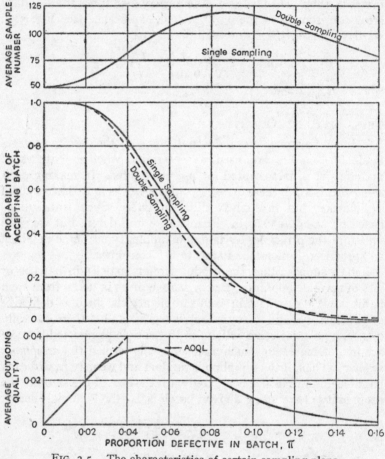

FIG. 3.5. The characteristics of certain sampling plans.

the corresponding value of π is termed the *producer's safe point* or the *acceptable quality level* at that probability level. For the scheme described, a probability of acceptance of 0·95 corresponds to $\pi = 0·027$ (Fig. 3.5), and this is the 0·95 (or 19 to 1) producer's safe point; the producer knows that any batch for which π is less than this is fairly " safe " to be accepted. He also chooses a low probability corresponding to a high risk of rejection ; the corresponding value of π is the *producer's risk point* at the chosen probability of rejection. Thus, for our sampling scheme, a probability of acceptance of 0·10 corresponds to $\pi = 0·104$ (Fig. 3.5), and this is the 0·90 (or 9 to 1) producer's risk point. The scheme may be looked at from the consumer's point of view, and then $\pi = 0·027$ becomes the 19 to 1 consumer's risk point and $\pi = 0·104$ the consumer's 9 to 1 safe point or, when multiplied by 100, the *lot tolerance per cent. defective*.

The two risks and the corresponding risk or safe points are the criteria whereby the technician can decide whether a given scheme is sufficiently discriminating.

A development of the above type of scheme is the *double sampling scheme*, of which the following is an example. A sample of say 50 is taken ; if it contains 0, 1 or 2 defective articles the batch is accepted, if 7 or more the batch is rejected, and if 3, 4, 5 or 6 a second sample of say 100 is taken ; then if in the two samples combined there are 6 or fewer defective articles the batch is accepted, if there are 7 or more it is rejected.

It is easy to see that, if $P (n, s)$ is the probability that a sample of n contains s defectives, calculated according to the binomial formula for a given value of π, the probability of accepting the batch is

$$[P(50, 0) + P(50, 1) + P(50, 2)]$$
$$+ P(50, 3) [P(100, 0) + P(100, 1) + P(100, 2) + P(100, 3)]$$
$$+ P(50, 4) [P(100, 0) + P(100, 1) + P(100, 2)]$$
$$+ P(50, 5) [P(100, 0) + P(100, 1)]$$
$$+ P(50, 6) P(100, 0).$$

For example, the second line of this expression arises because if the first sample contains 3 defectives and the second contains 0, 1, 2 or 3 defectives, the batch is accepted. The probability of acceptance has been calculated for different values of π and is shown as the broken line in the middle section of Fig. 3.5. This operating characteristic curve is close to that for the single sampling scheme with samples of 75. The two schemes do not have very different producer's and consumer's safe and risk points : they have almost equal power to discriminate between batches with high and low values of π.

Triple or higher multiple sampling schemes are clearly possible, and are known as *sequential sampling schemes*. In the limiting case a sequential scheme provides rules for deciding immediately after each individual article is examined whether to accept or reject the batch or to continue sampling, and sampling continues until ultimately the batch is accepted or rejected, the size of the sample thus varying according to the results. By such a scheme, the decision to accept or reject is taken at the earliest possible moment in the sampling process. Sequential sampling schemes have their operating characteristic curves obtained by a mathematical elaboration of the kind of formula used for the double sampling scheme.

So far we have imagined decisions being taken about each batch in isolation, but in industry batches are often produced in a stream, and the interest lies in what happens, less to any individual batch than in the long run. This attitude gives rise to two further quantities.

The first is the *average sample number*. According to our first scheme above, the sample number or size is always 75 ; according to our second it is either 50 or 150, the average sample number per batch for a large number of batches all having a given proportion π of defective articles being

$$50[P(50, 3) + P(50, 4) + P(50, 5) + P(50, 6)]$$
$$+ 150[1 - P(50, 3) + P(50, 4) + P(50, 5) + P(50, 6)].$$

This is plotted against π in the top part of Fig. 3.5. When π is very low most batches are accepted on the result of the first sample and the average sample number is little more than 50 ; as π increases, the number increases to a maximum of 118 at $\pi = 0.09$; for further increases of π the average sample number decreases as more and more batches are rejected as a result of tests on the first sample. Although these single and double sampling schemes have substantially the same powers of discrimination, they have not the same average sample number, and the more economical scheme depends on the range within which π may be expected to lie. Each double and sequential sampling scheme has its average sample number curve on the basis of which the more economical of alternative, equally discriminative, schemes can be chosen.

The second special quantity arises where the unacceptable

batches are not rejected but " rectified," every article in such a batch being examined and made satisfactory. Then if π is the proportion of defective articles in the incoming batches and A is the probability of acceptance, a proportion A of the batches are accepted without rectification and a proportion $(1 - A)$ are passed forward free from defective articles, the average proportion of defective articles in all the batches passed forward thus being $A\pi$; this is termed the *average outgoing quality*, and is plotted in the bottom section of Fig. 3.5 for the single sampling scheme. The curve is always below the line *incoming quality = outgoing quality*; it rises to a maximum of 0·034 defective articles when the proportion of defective incoming articles is 0·05; when π is large, there is much rectification and defective articles are largely eliminated. The maximum level of defectives is termed the *average outgoing quality limit*.

These measures of outgoing quality provide further criteria for assessing the technical or commercial value of a scheme.

There are two ways proposed for overcoming the practical difficulty of π varying from one batch to another and of being unknown. One is to treat the batches as belonging to a stable population of batches with a frequency distribution of values of π determined empirically from past experience. Then it is only a matter of calculation to substitute for all the curves of Fig. 3.5 single means of the probabilities, sample number and outgoing quality, applicable in the long run when the batches are from this population. The other is to design a sampling and rectification scheme to give a required level of the average outgoing quality limit.

Different sampling schemes, of course, have different operating characteristic, average sample number and outgoing quality curves, and the practical problem is to select a scheme that gives the required assurance of quality, be it an appropriate risk or safe level or average outgoing quality limit. Among all the schemes—single or double sampling schemes with various numbers of defective articles in the samples for acceptance or resampling, and sequential schemes—some are more economical than others, and it is obviously advisable to choose the most economical, after due regard is paid to questions of practicability, cost, and administrative convenience. Tables are available to assist in all this.

The whole subject is most highly developed for application

when the individuals are classified into two categories, but the same principles apply when the individuals are measured, and means and measures of variation are estimated from the samples.

Single and double sampling are well discussed, and tables and charts are given, by Dodge and Romig (1944). Sequential analysis is described by Barnard (1946) and Wald (1947), and tables are given by Anscombe (1949). The book by the Columbia University Statistical Research Group (1948) gives a comprehensive treatment of the whole subject, together with charts and tables.

DETERMINATION OF POPULATION VALUE FROM SAMPLE

3.6. There are three main approaches to the problem of estimating the population value of a parameter from the value given by a sample: these are outlined in the following three sections.

Confidence Limits

3.61. In making tests of significance, we make a hypothesis concerning the population independently of the sample result, and use the sample only to give the answer " probably yes " or " probably no " whether the hypothesis is acceptable. Sample values of statistical quantities are calculated only incidentally and do not appear in the final answer.

This approach has tended to dominate the application of statistical theory to experimental data because in most applications it has been easy to choose a main hypothesis—usually that there is no difference between two population values corresponding to two samples. Sometimes, however, we are not content with a verdict that two sample values are not significantly different; we ask what is the largest difference in population values that is consistent with the small difference in sample values. Or, having for example established that there is a significant difference in mean height between Englishmen and Scotsmen, we wish to know the precision with which we can estimate the magnitude of that difference in the two populations. Questions of these kinds can be answered if the sampling distribution is known, and we shall illustrate the kind of answer provided by referring to samples of 100 individuals taken to estimate the proportion in the population having a given character, i.e. the proportion of successes, or in the language of an industrial sampling scheme, the proportion of defectives.

The population value of this proportion may be denoted by π^* and any sample value by p. Then a diagram like that of Fig. 3.61 may be drawn (this is not drawn to scale), where for any population value π_1 the point B for which $p = \pi_1$ represents the mean of all the sample values, and the points A and C represent values of p

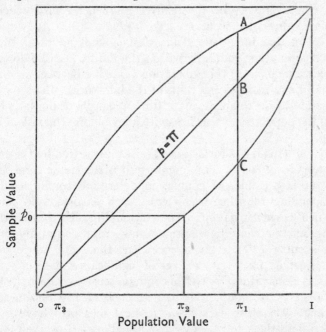

FIG. 3.61.   A diagram illustrating the derivation of confidence limits.

lying on the 5 per cent. level of significance. These points may be found from the sampling distribution of p, which is given by the terms of the binomial $(\pi_1 + \overline{1 - \pi_1})^{100}$, and if we may assume this to be approximately normal,

$$AB = BC = Twice\ the\ Standard\ Error = 2\sqrt{\{\pi_1(1 - \pi_1) \div 100\}}.$$

For example, if $\pi_1 = 0.8$, B is at $p = 0.8$, and the standard error is $\sqrt{(0.8 \times 0.2 \div 100)} = 0.04$; hence A is at $p = 0.8 + 0.08 = 0.88$ and C is at $p = 0.8 - 0.08 = 0.72$. In this way, points corresponding to A and C may be found for all possible values of π, and these lie on the curved lines shown diagrammatically in Fig. 3.61. The points corresponding to B lie on the line $p = \pi$.

* Again π is not 3·141 59. . . .

Then we know that for any one value of π, 95 per cent. of the sample values p lie within the limits represented by the points on the curved lines at which an ordinate drawn at π cuts them, and so by adding the experience for all populations, we know that 95 per cent. of the sample values lie within the limits of the curved lines, whatever may be the relative frequencies with which the different values of π occur.

If in making inferences from samples it is assumed that all sample-population points lie within the limits, i.e. that for every sample value p_0 (say) the population value lies between π_3 and π_2, we shall be right in 95 per cent. of the inferences. In this way, it is possible to make an estimate from a sample of limits between which the population value lies, with a given long-run risk of being wrong.

Neyman (1934) has termed the limits represented by the curved lines *confidence limits* corresponding to a *confidence coefficient* of 0·95. It is possible, of course, to determine confidence limits corresponding to other coefficients, such as 0·99, and for any statistical constant having a known sampling distribution that is continuous, or may be approximately represented by a continuous curve. For a given coefficient there are many sets of limits, just as for a given level of significance there are many critical regions ; it is a matter of common sense to choose the limits that are closest together, in the absence of any reason to the contrary. Also just as some statistical measures have greater power than others to reject a false hypothesis at a given level of significance (see Fig. 3.3*b*), so some estimates of the population value of a given measure have, for a given confidence coefficient, limits that on the average are narrower than the limits of other estimates, and these are naturally the best to use.

According to Neyman's procedure, no attempt is made to provide a basis for preferring any one population value to any other within the confidence limits, and if the limits contain the hypothetical value that would have been postulated in a test of significance, that value may be accepted. The theory of confidence limits thus provides an alternative approach to the testing of hypotheses, but it has not been much elaborated in this direction.

Fisher's Theory of Estimation

3.62. Fisher's theory of estimation (1922*a*, 1925*a* and 1925*c*) provides criteria for preferring some sample estimates to others and measures of the precision with which they estimate the population value. Here I give, as correctly as I can, a simplified summary of that theory.

So far, we have regarded statistical measures as convenient measures of various characteristics of samples and populations, and have assumed some mathematical form of distribution for the population more or less incidentally. In Fisher's theory of estimation it is necessary to assume or specify some mathematical form of distribution in the population as a starting point. The equation of this form has one or more constants or parameters that may vary from one population of that form to another, and the particular values of which define any given population. For example, if the assumed form of the population is the normal curve described by equation (2.5), the two parameters are m and σ, and given values of these define a particular normal population. On this view, m and σ are not thought of as the mean and standard deviation, i.e. as measures of position and dispersion ; they are thought of as mathematical parameters. Similarly, statistical measures (Fisher calls them *statistics**) calculated from samples are not descriptive averages ; they are estimates of the parameters in the equation, and it is as such that the relative suitability of equivalent statistics are judged. Fisher bases this judgment on three criteria : consistency, efficiency and sufficiency.

Consistency. A consistent estimate of a parameter must equal the parameter when it is derived from the whole distribution in the population. In a normal population, all the measures we have used are consistent estimates of m or σ. This criterion is an obvious one and is satisfied by all statistical estimates in common use.

Efficiency. This criterion applies to those statistical estimates from large samples for which the sampling distribution is known and is normal, so that it is completely described by the mean and standard error. As an approximation, the ideas and criteria may be applied where the sampling distribution is nearly normal, i.e. to all measures the standard errors of which are given in this and the next chapter, except β_2. The mean of the estimate in the

---

* Other writers refer to them as *estimators*, distinguishing them from the general rule or expression for obtaining an estimate from a particular value given by one sample (see Kendall, 1946a).

sampling distribution may differ from the parameter, but this difference may be calculated and allowed for as bias, akin to sampling bias. The standard error defines the inaccuracy of the estimate ; here it will be more convenient to deal with the square of the standard error, viz. with the sampling *variance* of the estimate.

For statistics of the class with which we are now dealing the variance in samples of N may be expressed in the form

$$\frac{1}{IN}$$

where I depends on the statistic and is called its *intrinsic accuracy*. For example, the intrinsic accuracy of the sample mean as an estimate of m in the normal population is $1/\sigma^2$ and that of the sample median is $1/(1\cdot253\sigma)^2 = 1/1\cdot570\sigma^2$.

For each parameter, there is a class of statistics that have the same intrinsic accuracy, that is greater than the intrinsic accuracy of all other estimates, and these Fisher terms *efficient* statistics ; Kendall (1943) less equivocally terms them *most efficient* statistics. The ratio of the intrinsic accuracy of any given statistic to that of a most efficient one is termed the *efficiency* of the given statistic. The mean as defined in section 1.22 is a most efficient estimate of m in the equation of the distribution for a normal population, and the efficiency of the median is 0·64 or 64 per cent. The standard deviation and variance calculated from the sample both provide most efficient estimates of σ. They are related functionally, so that for any one sample if one is known the other is determined exactly ; this kind of relation contrasts with that between statistics that are not both most efficient, such as the mean and median ; such a relationship is statistical and applies on the average to all samples, not to individual samples.

Sufficiency. The sampling distributions of most statistics are normal only in the limit when the sample is infinite in size, and in practice this is taken as being when the sample is large (the distinction between large and small samples is discussed more fully in the next two chapters). When the sample is small, the distribution may be non-normal, and different statistics may have the same sampling variance but different forms of distribution, so that the criterion of efficiency is not enough for discrimination. Fisher has shown mathematically that for many parameters there are statistics having the property that all other statistics that can be calculated from the sample give no additional information about the parameters estimated. These he terms *sufficient* statistics, and they are said to contain all the information contained in the sample about the parameters in the population. Sufficient statistics of the same parameter are exactly related. For example, the mean and standard deviation of finite samples are sufficient estimates of m and σ respectively in the normal population, and the standard deviation and variance are exactly related.

In large samples, for which the sampling distributions of alternative consistent estimates of a parameter are normal, we may regard the sample as containing a certain quantity of information concerning the parameter, measured on such a scale that the quantity increases in proportion with N, the size of the sample, and the statistic as giving a part or the whole of that quantity. The sampling variance specifies the precision of the sampling distribution, and since its inverse, NI, is proportional to N, this is an appropriate measure of the quantity of information given by the statistic. Following out this idea, Fisher in his later writings (1935) has referred to the intrinsic accuracy I as the *quantity of information given by a single observation* through the statistic. In these terms, the median may be said to give two-thirds of the quantity of information given by the mean concerning the parameter m.

Just as for a given estimate the number of individuals is additive in the sense that two independent samples of N_1 and N_2 give the same amount of information as one sample of $N_1 + N_2$, so for different estimates and samples, independent quantities of information are additive. When combining estimates of a parameter that have normal sampling distributions, the estimates being from different samples, we may take a weighted mean, using the quantities of information as weights. This is analogous to combining estimates of the mean, say, by using the numbers in the samples as weights. The sampling variance of the combined estimate is the inverse of the quantity of information. This result is used in sections 9.22 and 11.73.

To use a statistic that is not most efficient is equivalent to throwing away part of the data, and this is justified only if there is more than a counterbalancing saving in the labour of observation or computation. Moreover, the χ^2 tests described in the next chapter apply only when efficient estimates are used. It seems obvious, too, that a sufficient statistic (where one exists, which is not always so) is absolutely the best criterion to use in testing the significance of departures from some hypothesis concerning a parameter, since the sufficient statistic contains all the information concerning the parameter. This basis of choice differs from that of Neyman and Pearson (section 3.3), who make a choice by considering what alternative hypotheses are admissible. Fortunately, the two approaches lead to the same conclusions for all practical purposes. For example, both approaches will lead to the choice of the statistics with the smallest sampling variance, except possibly in some very rare or artificial circumstances.

Fiducial Probability

3.621. Fisher (1930b) has dealt with the problem of specifying the precision with which a parameter is estimated from a sample in a way that is superficially similar to Neyman's method of confidence limits. Indeed, for years some writers (including myself) wrongly thought that the two methods were the same.

The confidence limits π_2 and π_3 in Fig. 3.61 corresponding to a given sample value of p_0 are merely two limits in a continuous distribution of population values associated with different probability levels. This Fisher terms the *fiducial probability distribution*, and the various limits *fiducial limits* corresponding to various *fiducial probabilities*.

In the simple case, fiducial limits and probabilities are algebraically identical with confidence limits and coefficients, but there are conceptual differences that lead to different applications.

Fiducial probability is a special concept and a measure of confidence that is not given the statistical interpretation of a ratio of frequencies, as ordinary probability is ; although in the simple case of a single parameter it *can* be interpreted numerically in the same way as Neyman's confidence coefficient. Fisher also limits the term *fiducial* to distributions derived from sufficient statistics on the ground that only thus can a unique distribution be obtained for each parameter and sample. Fiducial distributions of more than one parameter can be combined, and when this is done, the possibility of giving even a limited frequency interpretation to fiducial probability disappears.

Fiducial probability may be used as a basis for tests of significance, for if a hypothetical value for the parameter falls in a region with low fiducial probability it is rejected, and otherwise it is accepted. For single parameters, a fiducial probability level of 0·05, say, would cause the same departures from hypothesis to be rejected as a probability level of 0·05 would in the ordinary tests of significance dealt with in sections 3.2 and 3.3. For these simple cases, the two approaches are numerically equivalent. When, however, there are two or more parameters in combination and the fiducial probability cannot be given a frequency interpretation, it still leads to a test of significance. This is true notably of the so-called Fisher-Behrens test for the significance of the difference between two means (see section 5.31). Statisticians who accept the concept of fiducial probability accept the validity of this test ; those who accept only concepts of probability that are susceptible to frequency interpretation and to experimental test by repeated sampling, reject the test.

Inverse Probability

3.63. This discussion would be incomplete without some reference to the methods associated with Bayes's Theorem and inverse probability (see notably the paper by K. Pearson, 1920*a*).

According to these methods, a probability distribution for the population value to be estimated is assumed *a priori*. When the quantity under discussion is the proportion π, the usual assumption is that all values between zero and unity are equally likely. Then, the product of the *a priori* probability of π being between say $\pi_0 - \frac{1}{2}d\pi$ and $\pi_0 + \frac{1}{2}d\pi$, multiplied by the probability that given $\pi = \pi_0$, a sample value of p, say, will be obtained is described as the *inverse probability* that, given a sample value of p, the population value is between $\pi_0 - \frac{1}{2}d\pi$ and $\pi_0 + \frac{1}{2}d\pi$. This inverse probability is used as a measure of the degree of confidence that π_0 may be accepted as the population value for a sample value of p. The argument can be extended to other quantities.

Inverse probability does not now find favour with many statisticians, who have difficulty in accepting the assumption of any *a priori* probability for the population value. It is, however, used by Jeffreys, and readers who are interested should refer to his book *The Theory of Probability* (1939).

3.64. The differences between the three approaches to the problem of estimating population values from a sample, which is a particular case of the general problem of arguing from the particular to the general, remain to be resolved. For me, there is no difficulty in accepting Neyman's confidence limits ; but I find Fisher's concept of fiducial probability without a frequency interpretation esoteric and hence unacceptable ; and the need to assume an *a priori* probability is a stumbling-block to the acceptance of inverse probability. However, the difficulties are not of great practical importance, for seldom is any practical investigation held up because of them.

Method of Maximum Likelihood

3.7. There are several general methods for arriving at estimates of the parameters of frequency distributions from samples, of which the most important is the *method of maximum likelihood*. An estimate obtained by this method has the properties that in large samples it is the most efficient estimate and has a normal sampling distribution, and that generally it is a sufficient statistic (where sufficient statistics exist).

We have already seen in section 2.72 how the probability of a given sample may be deduced when the population and its parameters are known. When the form of population is known the expression for that probability (without the differential terms) for any assumed values of the parameters is termed the *likelihood* of the assumed values. The particular values that make this likelihood a maximum are the *maximum likelihood* estimates. They are obtained by differentiating the logarithm of the likelihood with respect to the parameters, equating to zero, and solving the equations.

For the normal distribution with assumed parameters $\bar{\xi} = \hat{x}$ and $\sigma = \hat{s}^*$ and a sample of N, the logarithm of the likelihood (to the base e) is derived from equation 2.72 as

$$L = -\frac{N}{2}\log 2\pi - N \log \hat{s}$$

$$-\frac{1}{2}\left\{ \frac{(x_1 - \hat{x})^2}{\hat{s}^2} + \frac{(x_2 - \hat{x})^2}{\hat{s}^2} + \cdots \frac{(x_N - \hat{x})^2}{\hat{s}^2} \right\} \quad . \quad (3.7)$$

* The Latin letters denote estimates from the sample and the sign ^ denotes the particular kind of estimate dealt with in this section.

If this is differentiated with respect to $\hat{x}$ and the differential equated to zero, it is easily deduced that

$$\hat{x} = \frac{x_1 + x_2 + \ldots x_N}{N}.$$

Thus, the mean of the sample, as defined in section 1.22, is the maximum likelihood estimate of $\bar{\xi}$. Similarly, by differentiating L in (3.7) with respect to $\hat{s}$ and equating to zero, the maximum likelihood estimate of σ is found to be the standard deviation as defined in section 1.23.

When the data are in the form of a frequency distribution with frequencies of $n_1\, n_2 \ldots n_s \ldots$ in the groups, the logarithm of the likelihood is

$$L = S_s n_s \log \hat{n}_s \quad \ldots \ldots \quad (3.7a)$$

where S_s is the summation over all groups and $\hat{n}_s$ is the estimated frequency in the sth group, determined from the equation for the assumed population and expressed in terms of the unknown parameters.

For example, for the Poisson distribution the proportion of frequency with s successes is

$$\frac{\mu^s}{s\,!}e^{-u}.$$

If $\hat{m}$ is the maximum likelihood estimate of μ, and the total number in the sample is N,

$$L = S_s n_s \left\{ s \log \hat{m} - \hat{m} - \log \frac{s\,!}{N} \right\}.$$

By equating to zero the first differential of this with respect to $\hat{m}$ we have

$$\hat{m} = \frac{S_s s n_s}{S_s n_s} = \frac{S_s s n_s}{N}.$$

Thus, the efficient estimate of μ is the mean of the distribution. This result is not without interest, since we have seen in section 2.3 that the second moment of the distribution is also a possible estimate of μ, and hitherto no rational grounds have been advanced for regarding it as an inferior estimate.

The method of maximum likelihood may be used whenever a distribution can be expressed in terms of parameters that are required to be estimated from the sample. It is much used in genetical studies for estimating linkages, as in Fisher (1925c).

3.71. When an efficient statistic has a normal sampling distribution, the square of the standard error or variance in a large sample may be obtained from the second differential of the logarithm of the likelihood L. Generally, if κ is the parameter, $\hat{k}$ the maximum likelihood estimate, and $\sigma_{\hat{k}}$ is the standard error of $\hat{k}$,

$$-\frac{\mathrm{I}}{\sigma_{\hat{k}}{}^2} = \left[\frac{\partial^2 L}{\partial \hat{k}^2}\right] \quad . \quad . \quad . \quad . \quad . \quad (3.71)$$

where the square brackets [ ] signify " the mean for all possible sample values of the term contained therein."

For the normal distribution, on differentiating equation (3.7) twice we find that

$$\frac{\partial^2 L}{\partial \hat{x}^2} = -\frac{N}{\hat{s}^2},$$

and since the mean value of $\hat{s}^2$ for all possible samples is the population value σ^2,

$$\sigma_{\hat{x}}{}^2 = \frac{\sigma^2}{N}.$$

This is an alternative derivation of the square of the standard error of the mean.

CHAPTER IV

ERRORS IN LARGE SAMPLES

STANDARD ERRORS OF VARIOUS STATISTICAL MEASURES

4.1. In developing most of the sampling theories of the previous chapter we simplified the problem by assuming a normal sampling distribution and working out criteria in terms of the standard error. This assumption is very near the truth for the distribution of mean in samples more than 20, even when the frequency distribution of the individuals is markedly not normal, and for the distribution of various other measures it is fairly close to the truth in samples of more than 100. The standard error, and the normal sampling theory on which its use is based, thus has a very wide field of application. More exact methods for application to small samples are described in the next chapter, and it is usually more convenient as well as preferable to use them when they are appropriate. But sometimes a standard error can be determined where the full sampling distribution can not; and then the normal sampling theory may be used as a rough approximation even for samples containing as few as, say, ten individuals. After all, an investigator who, because of approximations, uses a significance level of, say, 0·04 or 0·06 when he purports to use one of 0·05, will not go far astray in assessing individual results. He should, however, be more careful when pooling many results each based on a small sample, as for example in using the results of routine daily tests in a factory.

In deducing standard errors we shall make much use of the result derived in section 1.311 that if h is a constant, the standard error of h times a quantity is h times the standard error of the quantity.

Means of Binomial and Poisson Distributions

4.11. When developing the binomial distribution in section 2.2 we regarded the sets of trials as individuals and the number of successes per set as the variate. If, however, we regard the trials as individuals for which the variate can take only one of two values, viz. success or failure, the set of n trials becomes a sample of n and the binomial distribution becomes a sampling distribution of the number of successes per sample. From this point of view the small n of the binomial is equivalent to the large N denoting the sample size. As stated in section 2.5, when the number in the sample is large, the binomial distribution approaches the normal and the normal sampling theory may be applied.

If the number of successes in a sample is l ($= np$ where p is the proportion of successes in the sample), and the corresponding population values are $\lambda = n\pi$, the standard error of l is, by equations (2.2a),

$$\sqrt{\{n\pi(\mathrm{I} - \pi)\}} = \sqrt{(\lambda - \lambda^2/n)} \;;$$

on dividing this by n we obtain :

Standard error of $p = \pm \sqrt{\{(\pi - \pi^2)/n\}}$.

Darbishire (1904), on crossing waltzing with normal mice, found in the F_2 generation 458 normals and 97 waltzers (total 555). The Mendelian expectation for λ is 416 normals with a standard error of $+\sqrt{\{4\mathrm{I}6 \quad 4\mathrm{I}6^2/555\}} = \pm\mathrm{IO} \cdot 2$. The difference between the actual and expected number of normal mice is 42, and being 4·1 times the standard error is significant ; it could arise from random sampling only four times in 100 000 samples.

TABLE 4.11

Diet	Males	Females	Total Young	Percentage Males
Vitamin B Deficient	123	153	276	44·57
Vitamin B Sufficient	145	150	295	49·15
Totals ...	268	303	571	—

Parkes and Drummond (1925) give the data of Table 4.11 showing the effect of vitamin B deficiency on the sex-ratio of the offspring of rats. In comparing the sex-ratios we are comparing not an experimental ratio with a theoretical one but two experimental ones. Hence we do not know the value of π in the infinite population, required for calculating the standard errors ; we shall use sample values as approximations. The standard errors of p are : $\pm \sqrt{\{(0 \cdot 445 \; 7 - 0 \cdot 198 \; 6)/276\}} = \pm 0 \cdot 029 \; 9$, and $\pm\sqrt{\{(0 \cdot 491 \; 5 - 0 \cdot 241 \; 6)/295\}} = \pm 0 \cdot 029 \; \mathrm{I}$, and that of the difference is $\pm 0.041\ 7$, or ± 4.17 per cent. The difference in sex-ratio is 4.58, and being only 1.1 times its standard error, is insignificant; it would arise from random errors about 27 times in 100 samples.

4.12. When the mean number of failures (μ) per set is large, the Poisson distribution also approaches the normal form. Then the standard error per set is $\sqrt{\mu}$, the standard error of the mean of N sets is $\sqrt{(\mu/N)}$, and that of the total number of failures in N sets, i.e. of μN, is $N\sqrt{(\mu/N)} = \sqrt{(\mu N)}$. Thus for the distribution of yeast cells of Table 2.4b, the total number of cells counted is 1 872. If, as an approximation, we equate this to μN, the standard error is $\pm\sqrt{1\ 872} = 43.3$; the mean number of cells per square is 4.68, and its standard error is $\pm\sqrt{(4.68/400)} = 0.108$.

We have shown that the Poisson and exponential distributions apply approximately to the data of warp breaks of Tables 2.4d and 2.4e; let us as an example assume this result to apply generally in weaving and calculate the necessary scale of an imaginary experiment. Suppose that the mean breakage rate is round about 2 per 10 000 picks and that differences between pairs of means of 20 per cent. are required to be on the 0.05 level of significance (these are technical data and decisions). Then, if each mean is determined from N 10 000-pick units of weaving, how large must N be? The total expected number of breaks in each series is $2N$, 20 per cent. of this is $0.4\ N$, and the standard error of a mean is $\sqrt{(2N)}$; we have it from section 3.21 that for the 0.05 level $3\sqrt{(2N)} = 0.4N$, whence $N = 112.5$. In practice the number should be greater than this to allow for the possibility that the standard error may be greater than the Poisson value; for the actual variance of 1.548 for Table 2.4d is somewhat greater than the expected value of 1.279.

Measures of Dispersion

4.13. The standard deviation estimated from the variance has a standard error of

$$\sigma/\sqrt{(2N)}$$

where σ is the standard deviation of the population and N is the size of the sample. Its distribution is not normal, but for large samples it approaches normality; e.g. at $N = 100$, $\beta_1 = 0.005\ 1$ and $\beta_2 = 3.000\ 0$. Let us see if the Scotsmen of Table 3.21 are really more regular in height, as well as being taller on the average, than the Englishmen. The standard error of a standard deviation is $1/\sqrt{2}$ times that of a mean, so for the difference of standard deviations of the table it is

$$0.075\,9 \times 1/\sqrt{2} = \pm 0.053\,7.$$

The difference $(2.548 - 2.480 = 0.068)$ being only 1.27 times its standard error is not significant; in fact, random sampling would give as big a difference in about one trial in five $(P = 0.2)$.

In view of the example of warp breaks in section 4.12, let us estimate the 90 per cent. confidence limits of standard deviation corresponding to the estimate of $\sqrt{1.548} = 1.244$ obtained from Table 2.4d. Let the lower one be σ_1 and the upper one σ_2. Then since $N = 147$, $\sigma_1 + 1.645\sigma_1/\sqrt{294} = 1.244$ and $\sigma_2 - 1.645\sigma_2/\sqrt{294} = 1.244$, whence $\sigma_1 = 1.14$ and $\sigma_2 = 1.38$. The expected value of $\sqrt{1.279} = 1.131$ is just outside this range, which is based on a fairly low confidence level. But a population standard deviation as high as 1.38 is quite likely, and this is 1.22 times the expected value. In so far as this ratio obtains generally (and considerable investigation would be required to determine this), the required number of 10 000-pick weaving units deduced in section 4.12 should be increased at least to $112.5 \times 1.22^2 = 167$.

Only when found from the second moment has the standard deviation the above standard error. We shall now deal with its standard error when estimated from the range. E. S. Pearson (1926 and 1932) has worked out the sampling distribution of the range fairly fully, and although for no size of sub-sample is it normal, it is only moderately skew for those of about 10; for sub-samples of 10, $\beta_1 = +0.156$ and $\beta_2 = 3.22$. In such circumstances we may use the standard error as an approximate description of the sampling errors; and if the estimate is made from a mean range in several sub-samples, the approximation is close. Pearson gives the standard error or deviation of the range for several sub-samples (values are in Table A at the end of this book), and for those of 10 it is 0.797σ, where σ is the true standard deviation. Suppose that the sample of N contains m sub-samples of 10, so that $N = 10m$, then from section 2.71 we find that the

$$\textit{Standard Error of Mean Range} = \frac{0.797\,\sigma}{\sqrt{m}}.$$

We also have from Table A,

$$Estimated\ Standard\ Deviation = \frac{Mean\ Range}{3 \cdot 078},$$

whence

Standard Error of Estimated Standard Deviation

$$= \frac{Standard\ Error\ of\ Mean\ Range}{3 \cdot 078} = \frac{0 \cdot 797\ \sigma}{3 \cdot 078 \sqrt{m}} = \frac{1 \cdot 158\ \sigma}{\sqrt{(2N)}}.$$

This may be compared with the standard error of the estimate obtained from the variance.

In large samples, the standard error of the mean deviation is

$$1 \cdot 068 \frac{\delta}{\sqrt{(2N)}} = 0 \cdot 852 \frac{\sigma}{\sqrt{(2N)}}$$

where δ is the population value of the mean deviation. It follows that the standard error of the standard deviation estimated from the mean deviation is

$$1 \cdot 253 \times 0 \cdot 852 \frac{\sigma}{\sqrt{(2N)}} = 1 \cdot 068 \frac{\sigma}{\sqrt{(2N)}}.$$

Of these measures of dispersion, that estimated from the second moment is (in Neyman's and Pearson's terms) most powerful and (in Fisher's terms) most efficient; it is absolutely *the* efficient statistic for estimating σ. For this purpose, the mean range in sub-samples of 10 has an efficiency of $100 \div 1 \cdot 158^2 = 75$ per cent. and the mean deviation one of $100 \div 1 \cdot 068^2 = 88$ per cent.

Measures of Shape

4.14. The β ratios are useful for testing the departure of any data from normality, but their distributions in samples drawn from an infinite normal population have not yet been worked out. The first four moments of the sampling distributions have been derived by Fisher (1930*a*), and from approximate values E. S. Pearson (1930) has determined appropriate empirical frequency curves of K. Pearson's system. Curves found in such a way usually give good approximations to the actual distributions.

To test asymmetry, $\gamma_1 = \sqrt{\beta_1}$ (with the same sign as μ_3) is used. For samples of N from the normal population, this has a standard error of $\sqrt{(6/N)}$ (to a first approximation), and the distribution itself is so nearly normal that a deviation of twice the standard error lies practically on the 0·05 level of significance.

The standard error of β_2 is $\sqrt{(24/n)}$ (to a first approximation), but the distribution is so skew, and this approximation is so poor, that it does not give a reliable test. E. S. Pearson's tables (1930) give for samples from the normal population, values of β_2 lying on each side of the population value (3·0) which cut off tails of 5 and 1 per cent. of the whole curve ; these tables should be used. From the discussion in section 3.3, it is suggested that the 0·05 level of significance should be taken as lying on the 2·5 per cent. value.

For the distribution of heights of Table 1.32, we have

$$\gamma_1 = -\,0\cdot116 \pm 0\cdot074\,6, \ \beta_2 = 2\cdot908 \text{ and } n = 1\,078.$$

γ_1 is less than twice its standard error, and so is insignificant, while from Pearson's table, when $n = 1\,000$, the lower value of β_2 with a " tail " of 0·05 is 2·76, and since the value above is nearer 3 than that, we may conclude that the data are, as far as we can tell, from a normal population.

It is not often, in my experience, that these tests have been needed, for marked departures from normality have been easily seen, and moderate departures have not mattered much.

Standard Errors of Functions of Statistical Measures

4.15. Sometimes it is desired to calculate the standard errors of functions of one or more statistical measures, the errors of the individual measures being known. We have already had an example in the difference between two means ; the ratio and product of two means, and the square of the standard deviation are other examples. We shall describe here an approximate method that is applicable to large samples. Where there are more than one measure we shall assume they are obtained from independent samples except in one instance.

Let the population values of the measures be α and β, let the function be

$$\lambda = f(\alpha, \beta)$$

and let the corresponding sample values for any one pair of samples be l, a and b, where

$$l = \lambda + \delta\lambda, \ a = \alpha + \delta\alpha \text{ and } b = \beta + \delta\beta,$$

δ being used as a sign meaning a deviation. Then for the pair of samples

$$l = f(\alpha + \delta\alpha, \beta + \delta\beta).$$

It can be shown that, for the purposes of deducing standard errors and variances, the relations between $\delta\lambda$, $\delta\alpha$ and $\delta\beta$ may be approximately derived by regarding them as mathematical differentials, so that

$$\delta\lambda = \frac{\partial f}{\partial \alpha}\, \delta\alpha + \frac{\partial f}{\partial \beta}\delta\beta.$$

The degree of approximation involves neglecting quantities of the order $1/N$ compared with unity, where N is the number in the sample.

The mean values of the squares of $\delta\lambda$, $\delta\alpha$ and $\delta\beta$ for all possible pairs of samples from the population are the squares of the corresponding standard errors or the sampling variances and may be written V_l, V_a and V_b. Hence, by squaring the terms of the above equation and finding the means for all pairs of samples, we obtain

$$V_l = \left(\frac{\partial f}{\partial \alpha}\right)^2 V_a + \left(\frac{\partial f}{\partial \beta}\right)^2 V_b + 2\frac{\partial f}{\partial \alpha}\frac{\partial f}{\partial \beta}[\delta\alpha\,\delta\beta] \quad . \quad (4.15)$$

where $[\delta\alpha\,\delta\beta]$ is the mean value of the product of the deviations $\delta\alpha$ and $\delta\beta$ for all pairs of samples. If the two samples in the pair are independent, this mean product is zero, as will be shown in Chapter VIII. Hence, for independent pairs of samples,

$$V_l = \left(\frac{\partial f}{\partial \alpha}\right)^2 V_a + \left(\frac{\partial f}{\partial \beta}\right)^2 V_b \quad . \quad . \quad . \quad (4.15a)$$

This equation may easily be extended to three or more statistical measures.

When the function is the difference between two means, equation (3.21) follows from (4.15a) directly.

By way of example, let us deduce the standard error of the variance v of a sample in terms of that of the standard deviation s, so that $l = v$, $a = s$ and there is no b. Let the population value of the standard deviation be σ; then

$$v = s^2$$

$$V_v = 4\sigma^2 V_s = \frac{2\sigma^4}{N}.$$

We can use this result to test the significance of the deviation of the variance of the distribution of warp breaks in Table 2.4d

of 1·548, from the Poisson expectation of 1·279. Since both estimates are from the same data we do not need to consider the sampling errors of both and may regard 1·279 as the population value. Then the standard error is $\sqrt{(2 \times 1·279^2 \div 147)} = 0·149$, and the deviation of $1·548 - 1·279 = 0·269$ is 1·8 times this. The corresponding test on the standard deviations gives a difference of 1·7 times the standard error, the discrepancy being due to the fact that only approximate sampling distributions are used. The difference is below the 0·05 level of significance, but in accordance with the result obtained in section 4.13 by calculating the confidence limits, is above the 0·10 level.

As another example, let l be the ratio between two means $\bar{x}$ and $\bar{y}$, with corresponding population values of λ, $\bar{\xi}$ and η. Then

$$l = \bar{x}/\bar{y} \text{ and } V_l = \lambda^2\{V_x/\bar{\xi}^2 + V_y/\bar{\eta}^2\}.$$

The standard errors of $\bar{x}$ and $\bar{y}$ have already been given in section 2.71.

It has been shown in section 2.72 that the mean and standard deviation estimated from the same sample are independent, and it follows from this that equation (4.15a) may be used to determine the standard error of the coefficient of variation. If 100 κ, $\bar{\xi}$ and σ are respectively the population values of the coefficient of variation, mean and standard deviation, corresponding to λ, α and β, and k is the sample estimate of κ, it is easy to see from equation (4.15a) and the standard errors given in sections 2.71 and 4.13 that the standard error of the coefficient of variation is

$$100\kappa\sqrt{\left(\frac{2\kappa^2 + 1}{2N}\right)}.$$

THE χ^2 TEST FOR GOODNESS OF FIT

4.2. So far we have been using as expressions of differences between distributions, such measures as the mean, the standard deviation, β_1 and β_2, which summarise their chief properties or are estimates of their parameters. Except for populations of particular forms, these do not express all the features of the distributions. It is desirable to have some index which measures the degrees of difference between the actual frequencies in the groups, and so compares all the essential features. Such is K. Pearson's

(1900) χ'^2,* which we shall first use to measure the deviations of an experimental distribution from the form of some hypothetical population. Both must be grouped in the same way, and the theoretical distribution must be adjusted to give the same total frequency; then if v_s is the number of observations in any one group in the theoretical distribution, and n_s is the corresponding number in the experimental one,

$$\chi'^2 = S_s \frac{(n_s - v_s)^2}{v_s} \quad . \quad . \quad . \quad . \quad . \quad (4.2)$$

where S_s is the summation over all groups. It will be appreciated that since $(n_s - v_s)$ is squared, all differences in frequency, whether positive or negative, add a positive amount to χ'^2, and further that the greater these differences are, the greater is χ'^2; if the two distributions are exactly alike, χ'^2 is zero.

In using χ'^2 to test whether one distribution differs from the other, we must remember that because of random errors, it will never (or hardly ever) be zero, and we need to know its sampling distribution so that we can tell the probability of an observed χ'^2 being equalled or exceeded by that for any random sample from the hypothetical population. As usual, if that probability (which is symbolised by P) is low enough, the χ'^2 is said to be significant, and it is unreasonable to suppose that such a significant value could be a result of sampling errors alone.

The exact distribution of χ'^2 as defined in equation (4.2) is to be derived from the binomial distribution; for the probability of an individual falling into the sth frequency group is v_s/N, where N is the total number in the sample, and consequently, in all samples the actual number (n_s) in the sth group will, from section 2.2, vary according to the terms in the binomial

$$[v_s/N + (1 - v_s)/N]^N.$$

However, it is assumed that v_s and N are large enough to justify approximating this binomial by a corresponding normal distribution, and then the distribution of χ'^2 as defined in equation (4.2) becomes that given in equation (2.73) for χ^2, and the corresponding probability tables may be used.

* It is perhaps unfortunate that χ^2 has come in the literature to denote both the quantity defined in section 2.73 and distributed exactly according to equation 2.73, and a quantity such as that defined in equation 4.2—calculated from finite frequencies and distributed only approximately according to equation 2.73. We have added the prime to make the distinction.

This assumption limits the application of the χ'^2 test, but not seriously. Cochran (1942) has examined the effect of using the approximation when the frequencies are small and finds that it depends somewhat on how many large and small frequency groups there are. For most practical purposes, the χ'^2 test described in this section may be used provided all but one or two groups contain expected frequencies greater than 10 and none contain frequencies fewer than 5. It is usual to combine groups, as necessary, to satisfy this condition.

In order to determine the probability corresponding to a given value of χ'^2 it is necessary to know g, the degrees of freedom (a term borrowed from geometry and arising because of a convention of representing a frequency distribution as a point in space with as many dimensions as there are frequency groups). This conception of *degrees of freedom* is not altogether easy to attain, and we cannot attempt a full justification of it here ; but we shall show its reasonableness and shall illustrate it, hoping that as a result of familiarity with its use the reader will appreciate it. Here the number of degrees of freedom is the number of groups, modified. Clearly, since the error in each group in the experimental distribution contributes a positive amount to χ'^2, the greater the number of groups the larger would χ'^2 be expected to be, as a result of random variations alone, and account of this is taken through the quantity g. Further, it is often the practice to fit the theoretical distribution to the observations by calculating constants from the sample, just as in the example of section 2.51 we fitted a normal curve by making its mean, standard deviation and total equal to those of the sample. If we wish to test the adequacy of the theoretical form, further account must be taken of the degree to which we have made it fit the observations by this method. Suppose, in an extreme case, there were g' groups and we fitted a curve involving g' constants which were calculated from the data ; then the two distributions would agree exactly and χ'^2 would be zero because sampling errors would have had no play. To take account of this second factor, we must subtract from the number of groups (say g') the number of constants that have been determined from the data in fitting, thus obtaining the degrees of freedom (g). Every constant so determined has the effect, from the point of view of χ'^2, of reducing the number of groups by one, and the number of degrees of freedom may be regarded effectively as the number of independent groups remaining to contribute to χ'^2. When only the totals have been made equal, $g = g' - 1$, but in a case like the fitting of a binomial to the number of germinating seeds in Table 2.4a, the theoretical distribution has been adjusted to make its mean and total both equal to the sample, and $g = g' - 2$. It should be noted that this procedure is strictly valid only if the fitted constants satisfy Fisher's criterion of efficiency (section 3.62).

Equation (2.73) approximately describes the distribution of χ'^2 only if the sample is truly random and the individuals are independent. Indeed, a large value of χ'^2 corresponding to a low probability may signify either that the population frequencies v_s are other than those postulated, or that the individuals are mutually dependent in the sense that the group into which one falls affects that into which others fall. This would occur, for example, if the distribution was of, say, height measured on a sample containing a fair proportion of identical twins.

In its sampling distribution, χ^2 (and χ'^2 approximately) may vary between zero and plus infinity, the population value corresponding to exact agreement between the actual and hypothetical distributions being, of course, $\chi^2 = 0$. There is no question of alternative hypothetical population values of χ^2 being negative, so, the appropriate critical region (in the language of section 3.3) for the ordinary test of significance is that containing values of χ^2 greater than that at which an ordinate cuts off a single tail of 0·05, or whatever other level is chosen. A value of P very near to 1·0 (say greater than 0·99) corresponds to no significant difference between experiment and hypothesis, but it indicates an agreement that is too close for an experience subject to random variations, and it usually results from some error in the application of the theory. Experienced statisticians do not often encounter such values nowadays, but they did before the correct evaluation of the degrees of freedom was properly understood.

The χ'^2 test is more universal in its application than most others in that there is no assumption made as to the normality of the distributions being compared.

First let us test the fit of the normal curve to the distribution of heights of men in Table 1.32 ; the arithmetical operations are set out in Table 4.2, and it will be noticed that the tail groups have been lumped together, giving 14 groups. Three constants have been fitted (total, mean and standard deviation), leaving 11 degrees of freedom, and we wish to see if the χ'^2 (8·59) resulting

TABLE 4.2

Stature in Inches	Frequencies		$(n_s - v_s)$	$\dfrac{(n_s - v_s)}{v_s}$	$\dfrac{(n_s - v_s)^2}{v_s}$
	Observed (n_s)	Expected (v_s)			
below 61·5	14·5	11·8	•2·7	0·229	0·62
61·5–	17	17·7	−0·7	−0·040	0·03
62·5–	33·5	35·5	−2·0	−0·056	0·11
63·5–	61·5	62·8	−1·3	−0·021	0·03
64·5–	95·5	96·7	−1·2	−0·012	0·01
65·5–	142	130·1	11·9	0·091	1·08
66·5–	137·5	153·0	−15·5	−0·101	1·57
67·5–	154	157·1	−3·1	−0·020	0·06
68·5–	141·5	141·0	0·5	0·004	0·00
69·5–	116	110·5	5·5	0·050	0·27
70·5–	78	75·7	2·3	0·030	0·07
71·5–	49	45·2	3·8	0·084	0·32
72·5–	28·5	23·7	4·8	0·203	0·97
over 73·5	9·5	17·2	−7·7	−0·448	3·45
Total ...	1 078·0	1 078·0	0·0	—	$\chi'^2 = 8·59$ $g = 11$ $P = 0·65$

from those 11 can be attributed to random variations. From Chart D we find that $P = 0·65$, and this is so large that we might reasonably suppose the deviations to have arisen from errors of random sampling ; we say that the normal curve gives a good fit. Indeed, 65 random samples in 100 would have given a χ^2 equal to or greater than 8·59. In computing χ'^2 the total of the fourth column (= 0) checks the accuracy of the subtractions ; and the terms in the sixth column are the products of those in the fourth and fifth.

The reader may test the agreement between experiment and expectation for all the distributions given in section 2.4. The corresponding distributions in Table 2.4 are made to agree only in their totals, and the degrees of freedom are one less than the number of frequency groups remaining after combining those with expected frequencies lower than 5. In Table 2.4a referring to

approximately normally with unit standard deviation, and none of the ten would be expected to exceed 2·0. Alternatively we may calculate ten values of χ'^2, and since there are two frequency groups, each plant contributes one degree of freedom. In this simple case, χ'^2 happens to be the square of the above ratio.

Table D gives the value of χ^2 lying on the 0·05 level of significance as 3·841 for one degree of freedom, and as none of those in Table 4.21 is as large as this no individual plant differs significantly from expectation. Further, for all plants combined, the proportion of round peas is 0·768 9, giving a χ'^2 of 0·96, which also is insignificant. It may be, however, that the variability in the proportion of round peas from plant to plant is greater than can be explained by random errors, when all are considered together. To make this clear, we may imagine an extreme case in which the values of χ'^2 for all the plants are near the level of significance, but the ratio n_s/N varies above and below expectation, so that the ratio for all plants combined is near expectation. Then,

TABLE 4.21

FREQUENCIES OF PEAS

Plant Number	Round n_s	Angular n_t	Total N	Ratio n_s/N	χ'^2
1	45	12	57	0·789 5	0·47
2	27	8	35	0·771 4	0·09
3	24	7	31	0·774 2	0·10
4	19	10	29	0·655 2	1·39
5	32	11	43	0·744 2	0·00
6	26	6	32	0·812 5	0·67
7	88	24	112	0·785 7	0·76
8	22	10	32	0·687 5	0·67
9	28	6	34	0·823 5	0·98
10	25	7	32	0·781 2	0·17
Total ...	336	101	437	—	—
Expected	327·75	109·25	437·00	—	—

although no *individual* plant appears to differ significantly from expectation, it is unlikely that all would be so near the level of significance if it were not that the deviations as a whole were real, but in different directions, so that when added they average out. To test such a point we may add the values of χ'^2, giving a total

5·30 for 10 degrees of freedom so that P is about 0·87, and we conclude from the data that the plants do not vary significantly, and they may be regarded as so many random samples of peas. Had there been enough plants, instead of adding the values of χ'^2 we could have formed a frequency distribution of them, and have compared it with the theoretical form for one degree of freedom.

The χ'^2 test is thus an extension of the method of using the standard error for testing the significance of the deviation of a single binomial mean from some expected value, and enables the information given by a number of tests of individual means to be combined.

It follows, of course, that if a number of values of χ'^2 and their degrees of freedom may be added and treated as one, a total χ'^2 may be split up into parts, and each part may be tested separately.

CONTINGENCY TABLES

4.3. The problem of the sex-ratio of rats (in Table 4.11) may be looked at in a different way. We are not concerned with the total numbers of males, of females, or of young resulting from the two diets, but with the distribution of young in the four cells giving the two sex-ratios. If diet has had no effect on the sex-ratio, the 571 observations would be expected to be distributed at random in the four cells, with the one restriction that they should add up to give the totals of the table. In the infinite population of tables with those totals, the probability of an observation falling in the " deficient " group is 276/571, and that of it falling in the male group is 268/571, so that the probability of it falling in the " deficient " male square is (by Rule II, section 2.11)

$$\frac{268}{571} \times \frac{276}{571},$$

and the expected number of individuals in that square is that probability multiplied by 571 = 129·54. Similarly, the other squares can be filled as in Table 4.3 ; they are the frequencies that would be expected if sex were independent of diet and the individuals were distributed at random. We may now test to see if Table 4.11 differs significantly from Table 4.3 by finding χ'^2 for the four cells, and then the P for one degree of freedom. There is only one degree of freedom, since only one cell can be filled independently ; the numbers in the others can be obtained from that one and the totals. In our example, $\chi'^2 = 1\cdot20$ and $P = 0\cdot28$ (from Chart D) ; the deviations are not greater than can be attributed to random errors. It will be noticed that this probability is practically the same as that obtained previously from the standard error of the ratios ($0\cdot27$) ; indeed, it should be, for both methods are equivalent, being based on the assumption that the

TABLE 4.3

EXPECTED FREQUENCIES

Diet	Males	Females	Total
Vitamin B deficient	129·54	146·46	276·00
Vitamin B sufficient	138·46	156·54	295·00
Total	268·00	303·00	571·00

number in a cell (or its ratio to the total) is distributed normally. It can be shown algebraically that the square of the difference between the two ratios divided by the square of their standard error is equal to χ'^2. The two ways of looking at a fourfold table do not yield quite the same results when the frequencies are small and the normal approximation is not used.

Table 4.11 is a fourfold or 2×2 *contingency table*. Contingency tables may also be manifold, as is that of Table 4.3a ; if in such a table there are n rows and m columns, there are $(n - 1)(m - 1)$ degrees of freedom.

Table 4.3a contains Brownlee's data of the severity of smallpox attack and degree of vaccination (quoted by K. Pearson, 1910) ; below the frequencies are given in brackets the expected frequencies obtained by Rule II of mathematical probabilities. As there are expected frequencies smaller than five and several smaller than ten in the first row and column, these have been combined with the second row and column to form a 4×4 table. Then, $\chi'^2 = 196\cdot33$, there are 9 degrees of freedom, and P is less than $0\cdot000\ 001$. The departure from expectation is overwhelmingly significant.

In this example we have calculated the expected frequencies by applying Rule II for calculating the probability of an individual being characterised by the composite " event " of a certain time since vaccination combined with a certain severity of attack, the probabilities of the separate events being given. This rule applies only if the incidence of the two component " events " is independent and the result of the χ'^2 test is that the incidence is not so. The probability of an individual suffering a given severity of attack

TABLE 4.3a

		SEVERITY OF ATTACK				
		Hæmor-rhagic	Con-fluent	Abun-dant	Sparse	Very Sparse	Totals
Years since vaccina-tion	0-10	— (0·87)	1 (5·13)	6 (9·02)	11 (8·60)	12 (6·38)	30
	10-25	5 (13·25)	37 (78·20)	114 (137·45)	165 (130·96)	136 (97·14)	457
	25-45	29 (27·04)	155 (159·47)	299 (280·32)	268 (267·07)	181 (198·10)	932
	over 45	11 (4·50)	35 (26·52)	48 (46·62)	33 (44·42)	28 (32·94)	155
Unvaccinated ...		4 (3·34)	61 (19·68)	41 (34·59)	7 (32·95)	2 (24·44)	115
Total		49	289	508	484	359	1 689

of smallpox depends on the time since vaccination. We say that the two characters are *associated*. This conception of association will be more fully discussed in Chapter VIII ; here we merely test its statistical significance.

Notes on the Fourfold Table

4.31. The computation of χ'^2 for a fourfold table may be simplified by using the following equation, which is easily proved algebraically :

$$\chi'^2 = \frac{(ad - cb)^2 (a + b + c + d)}{(a + c)(b + d)(a + b)(c + d)} \quad . \quad . \quad (4.31)$$

where a, b, c and d are the actual frequencies as set out in Table 4.31.

Part of the approximation involved in using the χ^2 distribution for testing the significances of differences between frequencies lies in the fact that actual frequencies can vary only in units and the χ'^2 calculated from them in discrete steps, whereas the theoretical χ^2 distribution is continuous. Where the cell frequencies are large, or the number of independent cells is more than two or three, the steps in the consecutive possible discrete values of the calculated χ'^2 are so small that errors resulting from this

TABLE 4.31

TYPICAL FOURFOLD TABLE

a	b	$a + b$
c	d	$c + d$
$a + c$	$b + d$	$a + b + c + d$

approximation are negligible. In Table 4.31*a* (the data are by M. Hellman and are taken from a paper by Yates, 1934) showing the relation between the type of feeding and the state of the teeth of children, the frequency corresponding to a in Table 4.31 can take only the values 0, 1, 2, 3, 4, 5, etc., giving values of χ'^2 of 2·43, 0·44, 0·05, 1·30, 4·11, 8·56, etc., respectively; and the

TABLE 4.31*a*

FREQUENCIES OF CHILDREN

	Normal Teeth	Maloccluded Teeth	Total
Breast-fed	4	16	20
Bottle- or bottle- and breast-fed	4	68	72
Total	8	84	92

discreteness of the steps cannot be ignored. Moreover, the dispersion on either side of the expected frequency of $20 \times 8 \div 92 = 1\cdot74$ is asymmetrical, and it is well to consider separately the deviations above and below 1·74. This is often done by taking the square root of χ'^2 and giving it a sign corresponding to the deviations, so that the values of χ' corresponding to the above values of χ'^2 would be $-1\cdot56$, $-0\cdot66$, $0\cdot22$, $1\cdot14$, $2\cdot03$, $2\cdot93$, etc. For large frequencies χ' is regarded as having a theoretical χ distribution that is symmetrical about $\chi = 0$ and extends from $-\infty$ to $+\infty$.

For positive values, the probability integrals are one-half of the probability integrals for the corresponding χ^2.

In attempting to approximate the distribution of the above discrete values of χ' by the continuous theoretical distribution it would be reasonable to regard $\chi' = 2\cdot03$ say as being the central value of a sub-range extending from $1\cdot585$ to $2\cdot48$, i.e. extending half-way towards the adjacent values of χ'. Then, in order to test whether the frequency 4 is significantly greater than the expected value of $1\cdot74$ we calculate the probability of χ exceeding $1\cdot585$. The corresponding value of χ^2 is $2\cdot51$ and from Chart D, $P = 0\cdot12$; the probability of χ (and of χ') exceeding $1\cdot585$ is thus about $0\cdot06$.

Another, less laborious and equally reasonable procedure is to regard the first frequency of 4 in Table 4.31a as being at the centre of a sub-range of frequencies extending from $3\cdot5$ to $4\cdot5$, and to regard the corresponding values of χ' as marking the boundaries of the sub-range of the continuous distribution. This leads to Yates's (1934) correction for continuity, which consists in increasing or decreasing the four cell frequencies by $\frac{1}{2}$ so as to leave the totals unchanged and to reduce the deviations from expectation, and calculating the corresponding χ' and the corresponding probability from the theoretical distribution.

For Table 4.31a, the adjusted frequencies are $3\frac{1}{2}$, $16\frac{1}{2}$, $4\frac{1}{2}$ and $67\frac{1}{2}$, and χ'^2, calculated from equation (4.31), is $2\cdot50$, giving $\chi' = 1\cdot58$, which is very near to the value previously obtained. The probability of the cell frequency a in Table 4.31a being equal to or greater than 4, the total frequencies remaining unchanged, can be calculated exactly [the formula is given by Yates (1934) and by Fisher (1925c) section 21.02] ; it is $0\cdot064$ 6, so that the approximation given by using Yates's correction and the theoretical distribution of χ is quite good, even though the expected frequency is as low as $1\cdot74$. When expected frequencies are very small the approximation is not so good for testing negative deviations.

In regarding $P = 0\cdot06$ as the level of significance of the deviations from expectation in Table 4.31a, we have used only one tail of the χ distribution and have not in our test considered the possibility that the frequency a might be less than the expected value of $1\cdot74$. We have entertained only the possibilities that breast-feeding has a good effect or no effect on the occlusion of teeth, not that it has a bad effect. It would be difficult to devise a good test of significance for the data of Table 4.31a if this last possibility were entertained, for its effect could only be to give an actual frequency of 0 or 1 corresponding to the expected frequency of 1·74, and these frequencies are highly probable from chance. The data are useless for discriminating between the hypotheses that breast-feeding has no effect on occlusion and that it has a bad effect.

It should be noted that Yates's correction for continuity can be used only when there is one degree of freedom. It is to be made, too, only in the final stage of using the continuous probability distribution of χ or χ^2 to obtain an approximation to the probability of the deviation from expectation. When combining values of χ^2 as in the example of Table 4.21, the correction is not used.

COMPARISON OF EXPERIMENTAL DISTRIBUTIONS

4.4. The test of Table 4.3a for association may be looked at in another way. The table consists effectively of a number of frequency distributions of years since vaccination, and χ'^2 is the measure of the deviations of these distributions from hypothetical ones deduced from the " totals " column and differing only in total frequencies. The independent " constants " of these hypothetical distributions are four of the proportionate frequencies in the totals column ; the fifth may be obtained from the others, since they all add up to unity. In addition to these, the five totals in the last row give the five totals of the hypothetical distributions, so that altogether nine " constants " have been fitted, leaving 16 degrees for a 5×5 table. Alternatively, the table may be regarded as a collection of five distributions in which the variate is the severity of attack.

The above argument demonstrates the application of the χ'^2 test to the comparison of a number of frequency distributions, e.g. for the purpose of checking sampling technique. The separate distributions may be regarded as rows in a contingency table, and if the χ'^2 is large enough, they are significantly different. As a special case of this, when there are two distributions and g' groups in each, there are $g' - 1$ degrees of freedom, and the expression for χ^2 becomes

$$\chi'^2 = S_s \frac{N_1 N_2 \, (_1 n_s / N_1 - _2 n_s / N_2)^2}{_1 n_s + _2 n_s} \qquad . \quad . \quad . \quad (4.4)$$

where N_1 and N_2 are the two totals (they need not be equal),

$_1n_s$ and $_2n_s$ are frequencies in one corresponding group in the two distributions, and

S_s is the summation over all groups.

The grouping must, of course, be the same for both distributions under comparison. These tests are alternative to those involving only the means and standard deviations. They are more complete, since they compare the distributions in all respects, but they are not necessarily as powerful if the two distributions do not differ much in form.

CHAPTER V

SMALL SAMPLES

THE investigator often has to draw conclusions from single small samples, or from collections of small samples, and then the methods of the last two chapters become invalid. The theory of errors has been developed to give more exact methods suitable for use in such circumstances. There have been developments in the theories of testing significance and of estimation mentioned in Chapter III, which are elaborations and do not alter the general principles ; we shall not deal with them further. Another line of development has been the elimination of various approximations that have been mentioned as limiting the application of the previous methods.

The limitation of sample size has been largely removed, but that of population form has not, and we shall continue to assume that the individuals in the population are distributed normally. Fortunately, the effect on these methods of fairly large departures from normality is unimportant, and the limitation is not very serious.

VARIANCE ESTIMATED FROM SMALL SAMPLES

5.1. With a few observations, it is futile to form a frequency distribution, but the usual frequency constants may be calculated, and regarded as estimates, obtained from the sample, of the constants of the infinite population. For the normal population, the mean is found in exactly the same way as for large samples, but the best estimate of the variance (σ^2) is obtained by dividing the sum of the squares of the deviations from the mean, *not* by the number of observations, but by the number of *degrees of freedom*. Here the number of degrees of freedom is the number of deviations minus the number of constants determined from the sample and used to fix the points from which those deviations are measured ; in the simple case, when the mean only is found from the sample, the degrees of freedom are one less than the number of observations. The justification for using this estimate is given in section 2.72. We shall illustrate this by the data of Table 1.1, which are the 100 random observations from an artificially constructed population, divided into groups of 5. We may find the variance either from the squares of the deviations from the grand mean or, regarding each group of five as a small sample, from the squares of the deviations from the sample means. For the latter process, instead of finding the variance for each sample separately, we may sum the squares of all the deviations and divide by the total degrees of freedom contributed by the ten samples. The sum of squared deviations from the grand mean is 8 864·75, and on dividing this by 99 we obtain the variance, viz. 89·5. The sum of squares from the sample means is 7 056·4, and since each sample contributes four degrees of freedom, there are 80 degrees altogether and the variance is 88·2. There is quite a fair agreement between the two estimates.* If we had used the old method for large samples we should have obtained values 8 864·75/100 = 88·6 and 7 056·4/100 = 70·6, with a much poorer agreement. In a large sample, the difference between dividing by N and $(N - 1)$ is quite unimportant.

As a special case, it may be determined that the mean variance for a number of pairs is

$$\frac{S(x_1 - x_2)^2}{2M}$$

where x_1 and x_2 are the individuals of any pair, M is the number of pairs and S is the summation over all pairs. In this way, the variance of any character between brothers from the same parents can be obtained as accurately from pairs of brothers from a hundred families as from a single family of one hundred and one brothers.

In testing cottons for " effective length," a special measure of location of the frequency distribution of fibre lengths, it is common as a routine to take two independent samples from each delivery of cotton and to test them independently, so that the differences between the duplicate results disclose the combined errors of sampling and testing. Table 5.1 (unpublished data supplied by E. Lord) gives pairs of results for 48 Egyptian cottons, so that $M = 48$, and it is calculated that S $(x_1 - x_2)^2 = 144$. The estimate of the variance between pairs is thus 144 ÷ 96 = 1·50, and

---

* We have not tested the agreement by the ordinary sampling theory, using the standard errors of the values, since the values are not independent ; they have been taken from the same data.

the standard error of the mean of the two results for any one delivery of cotton is $\sqrt{1\cdot50} \div \sqrt{2} = 0\cdot87$ thirty-seconds of an inch. In using such an estimate it is assumed that the standard error is the same for all cottons. In fact, many more than 48 sets of results are available for each type of cotton, so that subject to the assumption, the standard error of the determination is known with considerable precision.

TABLE 5·1

EFFECTIVE LENGTH, IN THIRTY-SECONDS OF AN INCH, OF EGYPTIAN COTTONS

48	46	49	46	52	45	43	47	47	46	47	50
47	46	49	48	48	44	45	48	49	44	48	47
48	46	46	46	46	48	50	48	47	50	46	45
45	46	48	46	44	51	48	48	45	51	47	44
50	49	51	45	49	46	49	48	49	45	48	50
49	48	51	48	51	48	49	47	51	48	49	47
49	45	51	46	50	48	49	48	48	48	49	49
47	48	52	46	51	48	49	48	49	49	50	48

SAMPLING ERRORS OF THE MEAN : THE t TEST

5.2. The sampling distribution of the mean is normal, with a standard error of $\sigma/\sqrt{N}$, even when N is small, provided the standard deviation in the population, σ, is known. In the example of the previous paragraph, although each result is obtained from what is known to the cotton technician as a " sample," it is statistically an individual, and the mean result for each cotton is based on a statistical sample of two individuals. The standard error of such a mean, deduced in the way described above, with σ determined from very many pairs of results, may be accurately interpreted in terms of a normal sampling distribution even though the statistical sample for each cotton mean contains only two individuals.

When only a single small sample is available to estimate the mean and the standard deviation, the normal sampling theory does not apply. If d is the deviation of a sample mean from the population value $\bar{\xi}$, σ is the population value of the standard deviation and N is the size of the sample, the ratio

$$\frac{d}{\sigma/\sqrt{N}},$$

corresponding to w of equation 2.51, is distributed normally with unit standard deviation, and this fact is used in testing significances in large samples, the error involved in using the sample estimate s in place of σ being negligible. " Student " (1908) made the famous and important discovery (in slightly different terms) which Fisher (1925b) proved, that the ratio

$$t = \frac{d}{s/\sqrt{N}}$$

is distributed according to the equation

$$df = \frac{\left(\frac{\nu - 1}{2}\right)!}{\left(\frac{\nu - 2}{2}\right)! \sqrt{(\nu\pi)}} (1 - t^2/\nu)^{-(\nu+1)/2} \, dt \quad . \quad (5.2)$$

where ν is the number of degrees of freedom on which s is estimated, and in the simple case of one sample, is $N - 1$. Every term in equation 5.2 can be computed from the sample ; the distribution is independent of σ and depends only on the degrees of freedom, ν ; it therefore provides an exact test of significance for use with small samples.

The distribution of t is symmetrical and can be shown to approach the normal form as the degrees of freedom approach infinity. Full tables of value of t lying on various levels of significance are given by Fisher (1925c) and Fisher and Yates (1943), and an excerpt is in Table E at the end of this book. Full tables of the probability at the two " tails " for various values of t are given by " Student " (1925), and Hartley and Pearson (1950). From the latter, Chart C, given at the end of this book, has been constructed. For large samples ($\nu = \infty$), $t = 1{\cdot}96$ lies on the 0·05 level of significance ; other values lying on the same level are : $t = 12{\cdot}7$ for samples of 2 ($\nu = 1$), $t = 4{\cdot}3$ for samples of 3 ($\nu = 2$), $t = 3{\cdot}2$ for samples of 4 ($\nu = 3$), $t = 2{\cdot}3$ for samples of 10 ($\nu = 9$) and $t = 2{\cdot}09$ for samples of 20 ($\nu = 19$). Only for samples smaller than 20 is it usually important to use the exact distribution of t

instead of the normal sampling distribution assumed in large sample theory. Chart C is drawn on the equivalent of probability paper, so that the probability integral of a normal distribution becomes a straight line, as for the distribution of t when $v = \infty$. The approach to normality for other values of v can be seen by the approach of the probability integrals to this straight line.

When computing t, s must be calculated from the variance estimated according to section 5.1, so that if $\bar{\xi}$ is the population mean

$$\left. \begin{array}{l} d = \dfrac{Sx}{N} - \bar{\xi} = \bar{x} - \bar{\xi} \\[3mm] s = \sqrt{\left(\dfrac{S(x - \bar{x})^2}{N - 1)} \right)} \end{array} \right\} \quad \dots \quad (5.2a)$$

Table 5.2 shows the effect of a small electric current on the growth of maize seedlings, giving the difference between the elongation of the treated and untreated in parallel pairs of boxes (data from Collins, Flint and McLane, 1929), a positive difference showing that the electrical treatment increased the rate of growth. The mean is 4·29 mm. ; is this significantly different from zero ? The sum of squares of deviations from the mean is 937·189, and since on our hypothesis $\bar{\xi} = 0$, $t = 4 \cdot 29 \sqrt{(90/937 \cdot 189)} = 1 \cdot 33$, and $v = 9$; according to Chart C, $P = 0 \cdot 2$, and there is thus no evidence from the sample that the treatment has made any difference to growth. The mean elongation is not large enough compared with the variations between those of the separate boxes to be significant.

TABLE 5.2

ELONGATION IN MM. (TREATED AND UNTREATED)

6·0	1·3	10·2	23·9	3·1	6·8	—1·5	—14·7	—3·3	11·1

Mean 4·29

The t distribution may be used for determining confidence limits or fiducial levels for $\bar{\xi}$. Thus, we see from Chart C for $v = 9$, the probability of t coming within the limits $\pm 2 \cdot 26$ is 0·05, and the

95 per cent. confidence limits for the mean elongation corresponding to the results of Table 5.2 are thus

$$4 \cdot 29 \pm 2 \cdot 26 \sqrt{(937 \cdot 189/90)} = -3 \cdot 01 \text{ and } 11 \cdot 59 \text{ mm.}$$

SIGNIFICANCE OF DIFFERENCE BETWEEN MEANS

5.3. The quantity t may be used for testing the significance of the difference between two sample means. In this section we shall deal with the situation in which the hypothesis includes the postulate that the samples are from populations having a common standard deviation σ as well as a common mean, and since they are assumed to be normal, this is equivalent to testing the hypothesis that the samples are from the same population. Then, if N_1 and N_2 are the numbers in the two samples, and $\bar{x}_1$ and $\bar{x}_2$ are the sample means, $(\bar{x}_1 - \bar{x}_2)$ is distributed normally about zero and an estimate of its standard deviation (or error) is

$$s\sqrt{(1/N_1 + 1/N_2)},$$

where s is obtained by summing the squares of the deviations from the two sample means, dividing by the total degrees of freedom and finding the square root. Thus

$$s^2 = \frac{S_1(x_1 - \bar{x}_1)^2 + S_2(x_2 - \bar{x}_2)^2}{(N_1 - 1) + (N_2 - 1)} \quad \cdot \quad \cdot \quad \cdot \quad (5.3)$$

where S_1 and S_2 are the summations over the two samples and x_1 and x_2 are individuals in the two samples. Then

$$t = \frac{(\bar{x}_1 - \bar{x}_2)}{s\sqrt{(1/N_1 + 1/N_2)}}, \quad \cdot \quad \cdot \quad \cdot \quad \cdot \quad (5.3a)$$

which in large samples is distributed normally with unit standard deviation, is in small samples distributed as Fisher's t, the degrees of freedom being

$$\nu = (N_1 - 1) + (N_2 - 1).$$

Our example is from data provided by Corkill (1930) showing the effect of insulin on rabbits ; the results for separate animals are given in Table 5.3. The difference in means is not large compared with the variations within each sample, and a statistical test of significance is necessary. The sums of squares of the deviations are 0·253 0 and 0·071 5, and thus $s^2 = 0 \cdot 324\ 5/19 = 0 \cdot 017\ 08$ and

$s = 0.130\ 7$; there are ten and eleven rabbits in the two samples, so that $\sqrt{(1/N_1 + 1/N_2)} = 0.436\ 9$ and

$$t = \frac{0.138}{0.130\ 7 \times 0.436\ 9} = 2.42.$$

By interpolation in Chart C we see that for $\nu = 19$ and $t = 2.42$, $P = 0.027$, approximately, and the departure from the hypothesis is probably real.

The technical difference between this and the earlier example of the effect of electrical treatment on growth is that here there is no reason for taking the controls and treated animals in pairs, they are independent ; in the former instance, boxes were treated in

TABLE 5.3

Muscle Glycogen (per cent.)	
Controls	After Insulin
0·19	0·15
0·18	0·13
0·21	Trace*
0·30	0·07
0·66	0·27
0·42	0·24
0·08	0·19
0·12	0·04
0·30	0·08
0·27	0·20
—	0·12
Means 0·273	0·135

parallel pairs, and there was reason for expecting that the members of each pair would be subject to some of the same disturbing factors, which would not affect the differences.

One statistical result of this difference has been that according to the test we have used, the effect of insulin may be on the mean or the variability or both. Here, the separate estimates of variance from the two samples are $0.253\ 0/9 = 0.028\ 11$ and $0.071\ 5/10 = 0.007\ 15$, and it will be shown in section 5.41 that this difference, which can be tested independently of any difference there may be

* Assumed to be 0·00.

between the means, is probably significant. So far, the statistical analysis thus has not shown that insulin has affected the mean—although the technician may incline to the view that if insulin affects the variability it probably also affects the mean.

However, Welch (1938) has shown that when $N_1 = N_2$, the t test of significance is not sensitive to differences in the population variances, and as in our example the two sample sizes are nearly equal, we may take it that there is probably a real difference between the two means.

Again, if we may assume the t distribution to apply, we may determine confidence levels or fiducial limits for the true difference between the means, $\bar{\xi}_1 - \bar{\xi}_2$. The 0·05 level for significance of t (using two tails) when $\nu = 19$ is 2·093, and the 95 per cent confidence limits are

$$0·138 \pm 2·093 \times 0·130\,7 \times 0·436\,9 = 0·018 \text{ and } 0·258.$$

Significance of Difference Between Means when Variances are Unequal

5.31. The problem of testing the significance of the difference between two sample means when the variances in the two populations are, or may be, unequal, has received a degree of attention in the literature that reflects perhaps its theoretical interest and difficulty rather than its practical importance.

If the two population variances are known, the distribution of the difference between two sample means is accurately normal, with the standard error given in equation 3.21a, however small the samples.

When the only data are those given by the samples and the possibility of the variances being unequal is entertained, the best estimate of the standard error of the difference is

$$\sqrt{(s_1^2/N_1 + s_2^2/N_2)}$$

and the analogue of t is

$$d' \text{ (say)} = \frac{\bar{x}_1 - \bar{x}_2}{\sqrt{(s_1^2/N_1 + s_2^2/N_2)}}.$$

For a given $\nu_1 (= N_1 - 1)$ and $\nu_2 (= N_2 - 1)$, and a given value of the ratio of variances σ_1^2/σ_2^2, the sampling distribution of d' can be deduced, and thus, sampling distributions are determined for all possible values of σ_1^2/σ_2^2. Further, for a given s_1^2/s_2^2 the fiducial probability distribution of σ_1^2/σ_2^2 can be determined in a way indicated in the next section ; and hence the distributions of d' for the different values of σ_1^2/σ_2^2 may be combined with weights given by the fiducial probabilities to give a mean distribution of d' from which the fiducial distribution of $\bar{\xi}_1 - \bar{\xi}_2$ corresponding to a given d' and s_1^2/s_2^2 can be determined. This distribution is used in the so-called Fisher-Behren's test. The composite fiducial distribution has no corresponding set of confidence limits, and the fiducial probabilities have no frequency interpretation ; the test is therefore not acceptable to many statisticians. It is somewhat laborious to apply since it depends on four quantities : d', ν_1, ν_2 and s_1^2/s_2^2. Some tables are given by Fisher and Yates (1943) ; readers who are interested in the controversy may refer to Fisher (1941) and to papers listed there. Kendall (1946a) also gives a good account of the matter.

More recently Welch (1947) has proposed another solution to the problem which uses ordinary probabilities ; tables are given by Aspin (1949).

SAMPLING DISTRIBUTION OF ESTIMATES OF VARIANCE

5.4. The exact sampling distribution of the variance is given in equation 2.72b, and as shown in section 2.73, the distribution of an estimate s^2 of a population variance σ^2, based on ν degrees of freedom is the same as that of $\chi^2 = \nu s^2/\sigma^2$ for $g = \nu$ degrees of freedom, given in equation 2.73.

As an example, we shall use this result to test the assumption that the within-pair variance is the same for all the cottons of Table 5.1. Table 5.4 gives in columns (1) and (2) a frequency distribution of the 48 differences between the means. Each difference provides a separate estimate, s^2, of the within-pair variance, σ^2, based on one degree of freedom ($\nu = 1$), where s^2 is the square of the difference. If the variations in variance between cottons are random, the frequency distribution should be the same as that of χ^2 (s^2/σ^2) for $g = 1$ degree of freedom. In order to test this, we convert the distribution of Table 5.4 into a continuous one by assuming each difference to be at the centre of a sub-range with boundaries shown in column (3). The corresponding values of $\chi^2 = s^2/1\cdot50$ (taking the estimate of σ^2 obtained in section 5.1 as the population value), are in column (4) and values of P, the probability integral, read from Chart D, are in column (5) ; from these the expected frequencies in column (6) are then readily calculated. The frequencies for the groups with differences of 0 and 1 have been combined, because P changes considerably for small changes in χ^2 in that neighbourhood, and there is no fundamental reason for fixing the boundary exactly at any particular point. Moreover, Chart D is not very accurate in that neighbourhood. The discrepancies between the frequencies of columns (2) and (6) suggest that the true within-pair variance varies from one cotton to another, and probably (since several testers were employed) from one tester to another, although the discrepancies are not large. Thus, it must be remembered that for particular

TABLE 5.4

Difference (1)	Frequency (2)	Boundary Difference (3)	χ^2 (4)	P (5)	Expected Frequency (6)
± 4	1		8·17	·00	0
		3·5			
± 3	7				2
		2·5	4·17	·04	
± 2	12				9
		1·5	1·50	·22	
± 1	17				37
0	11				
Total	48				48

cottons the standard error may be slightly more or less than the estimate of section 5.1. If the matter were of importance, it would be necessary to investigate more than 48 cottons, to use more accurate values for χ^2 than are given by Chart D, and to investigate the effect of placing the boundaries of column (3) at other plausible places.

A similar test could be applied to data like those of Table 1.1 to test whether the variances within sub-samples of five are homogeneous in the sense that differences in variance are no greater than such differences as can be attributed to random errors. The computation of many variances is, however, laborious, and when there are many sub-samples it is appropriate to use the range, the probability integrals of which have been given by E. S. Pearson (1942).

Cotton yarns are commonly tested for " count," the inverse

of the weight per unit length, by weighing specimens of 120 yards, called "leas," and the variation is commonly measured as the mean range in groups of four leas taken from different bobbins. In testing a certain yarn, 109 such sets of four were taken at different times and from different parts of the bulk, and gave a mean range of weight of 25·688 grams, leading to an estimate of standard deviation of 25·688 ÷ 2·059 = 12·48 grams. The 109 ranges were then grouped to form the frequency distribution shown in the first two columns of Table 5.4a. The expected frequencies of Table 5.4a have been obtained from Pearson's tables with a view to testing the significance of the variations in the ranges. Pearson gives for different values of the range divided by the standard deviation in the population, which ratio he terms W, the probability integral between the limits 0 and W. In default of anything better we use the above estimate of the

TABLE 5.4a

Range of Count grams	Frequency of Sets of Four Leas	
	Actual	Expected
Under 10·5	6	7·2
10·5–15·5	17	12·8
15·5–20·5	24	18·0
20·5–25·5	16	19·7
25·5–30·5	10	17·7
30·5–35·5	12	13·6
35·5–40·5	10	9·2
40·5–45·5	5	5·5
Above 45·5	9	5·3
Total ...	109	109·0

standard deviation, so that W corresponding to a range of 10·5 grams is 10·5 ÷ 12·48 = 0·841. For $W = 0·80$ and sets of four Pearson gives as the probability integrals the values 0·057 8 and 0·068 2, and linear interpolation gives a value of 0·066 5 for $W = 0·842$. This value multiplied by 109 gives the first expected frequency of Table 5.4a. We may use the χ'^2 test in the way of section 4.2 in order to test the significance of differences between the actual and expected frequencies, and in doing so find that $\chi'^2 = 10·50$, $g = 9 - 2 = 7$ (allowing that the two distributions have been made to agree in total frequency and mean range), and from Chart D, that $P = 0.16$. There is no evidence of lack of homogeneity in the ranges.

If the distributions of Table 5.4a are plotted, there is a slight suggestion to the practised eye of a systematic difference which gives somewhat greater importance to the discrepancies than the χ'^2 test has done, and we may carry the test further. From the original data we find that the variance of ranges is 242.6 grams^2, so that the standard deviation is 15.58, and the ratio

standard deviation of ranges/mean range $= 15.58/25.688 = 0.607$.

According to Table A at the end of this book this ratio would be $0.880/2.059 = 0.427$ if the ranges were homogeneous. If, without knowing that it is true, we assume that the standard deviation and the mean of ranges are independent, the standard error of this ratio in a sample of 109 ranges is, by a straightforward application of equation 4.15a, 0.034. The difference $0.606 - 0.427 = 0.179$ is 5.3 times its standard error, and even though we realise that the normal sampling theory is an approximation approximately applied, we cannot resist the conclusion that the ranges are more variable than they should be if the conditions under which they were obtained were statistically uniform. Here, the χ'^2 test for goodness of fit applied to frequencies is the less sensitive of two tests.

Significance of Difference Between Two Estimates of Variance

5.41. When testing the difference between variabilities for large samples in section 4.13, we assumed $(s_1 - s_2)$, the difference in standard deviations of the samples, to be distributed normally with a standard error of

$$\sqrt{(\sigma^2/2N_1 + \sigma^2/2N_2)}$$

where σ is the standard deviation in the population from which the samples are presumed to be taken ; and not knowing σ, we substituted s_1 and s_2 in the expression. Errors arising from this approximation are again important in small samples, but Fisher (1924a and 1925c) has suggested as an index :

$$z = \tfrac{1}{2} (\log_e s_1{}^2 - \log_e s_2{}^2) = \log_e (s_1/s_2) \quad . \quad . \quad (5.41)$$

where $s_1{}^2$ and $s_2{}^2$ are the two variances calculated on the degrees of freedom. For samples of N_1 and N_2 drawn from the same population, z is distributed in the form

$$df = k\, \frac{e^{v_1 z}}{(v_1 e^{2z} + v_2)^{\frac{1}{2}(v_1 + v_2)}} dz,$$

where v_1 and v_2 are the degrees of freedom ($= N_1 - 1$ and $N_2 - 1$) and k is a constant involving v_1 and v_2. This distribution, containing as variables only z, v_1 and v_2, is independent of the standard deviation of the population, σ, and since it involves no approximating assumptions, is applicable to small samples. It is related to the distribution of s and hence to that of χ^2 (see Fisher, 1924a). The quantity z may vary between plus and minus infinity, being negative when s_1/s_2 is less and positive when s_1/s_2 is greater than unity, and unless $v_1 = v_2$, is skew. The positive part of the curve of z corresponding to s_1/s_2, however, is the same as the negative part of z corresponding to s_2/s_1, and so the probability integrals for positive deviations only are sufficient for any combination of degrees of freedom, the others can be obtained by interchanging v_1 and v_2. It is simpler, however, not to deal with negative values of z, but always to take the difference of logarithms so that it is positive, and hence to choose v_1 to be the degrees of freedom on which the *larger* variance is measured.

For some years z was used for testing significances, but the publication of equivalent tables of the probabilities of the ratio of the variances, usually designated F ($= s_1{}^2/s_2{}^2$), obviated the necessity for the somewhat troublesome logarithmic transformation necessary to compute z. The distribution of F is given by the equation

$$df = k'\, \frac{F^{\frac{1}{2}v_1 - 1}}{(v_1 F + v_2)^{\frac{1}{2}(v_1 + v_2)}}\, dF$$

and is asymmetrical except when $v_1 = v_2$, extending from $F = 0$ to $F = \infty$. The " right-hand " tails of F corresponding to $s_1{}^2/s_2{}^2$ are the same as the " left-hand " tails of F corresponding to $F = s_2{}^2/s_1{}^2$, so that analogously with z, tables of F are necessary only for values of F greater than unity, and v_1 is conventionally taken to be the degrees of freedom on which the larger estimate is made. The method of obtaining values of F for the " left-hand " tail may be expressed by the following equation :

$$F\{P = x, v_1 = i, v_2 = j\} = \frac{1}{F\{P = 1 - x, v_1 = j, v_2 = i\}} \qquad . \quad . \ (5.41a)$$

where the terms in curly brackets specify the values of F.

There are now available several tables of z and F. The original tables of z were given by Fisher (1925c), and have been extended in the later editions of the book. They give values of z that cut off tails of 5, 1 and 0·1 per cent. of the total distribution for various values of v_1 and v_2. Mahalanobis (1932) calculated corresponding tables of F and $\sqrt{F}$. More extensive tables of z and F are given by Fisher and Yates (1943), and Merrington and Thompson (1943) give very full tables of F cutting off tails of 50, 25, 10, 5, 2·5, 1 and 0·5 per cent. of the total distribution. At the end of this book are given in Charts E1, E2 and E3 the full probability integral of F for various degrees of freedom and probabilities up to 0·5, and these for many practical purposes will serve better than the tables, since they will enable the actual probability level to be determined, albeit only approximately.

Some years ago it was an advantage for z that for any one probability level it was nearly linearly related to $1/v_1$ and $1/v_2$, and interpolation for untabulated values of the degrees of freedom was thereby facilitated. Now, however, the tables are so full that interpolation into tables of F is easy, and F will usually be found most convenient to use.

In testing the significance of the difference between two estimates of variance, when the alternative hypothesis is that either may correspond to a greater population variance, the 0·05 level of significance corresponds roughly to a single tail of 0·025, just as, by analogy, the difference between two means lying on the 0·05 level cuts off a tail of 0·025, the two tails being added to provide the level of significance. Often, however, as will be exemplified in later chapters, the hypotheses are either that the population variances are equal, or that one population variance specified *a priori* is greater than the other. Then the test would only be applied if the sample estimates differed correspondingly, and the 0·05 tail corresponds to the 0·05 level of significance.

We may now test whether the two variances of muscle glycogen calculated from the data of Table 5.3 differ significantly. They are 0·028 11 and 0·007 15, and $F = 3\cdot93$. The degrees of freedom corresponding to the larger estimate is 9, so that $v_1 = 9$ and $v_2 = 10$. From Chart E2 we find that for this value of F, $v_1 = 8$ and $v_2 = 10$, $P = 0\cdot023$; and from Chart E3 that for $v_1 = 12$ and $v_2 = 10$, $P = 0\cdot019$; and we may take it that for $v_1 = 9$ and $v_2 = 10$, $P = 0\cdot022$ (approximately). In the absence of any *a priori* reason for supposing that the variance for the controls should be greater than that for the insulin-treated rabbits, the value of F is just above the 0·05 level of significance.

We can use the distributions of z and F to determine confidence or fiducial limits (the two are the same in this instance) for population values of the ratio of two variances corresponding to sample values of that ratio. Suppose that the population values of the variances are σ_1^2 and σ_2^2 where $\sigma_2^2 = \Phi\sigma_1^2$, Φ thus being the population value of the ratio. Then if the variances are

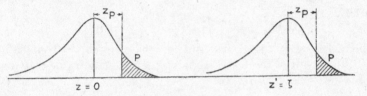

FIG. 5.41.

independently estimated by the sample values s_1^2 and s_2^2 respectively, the quantity $z' = \frac{1}{2} \log_e (s_1^2/s_2^2)$ has the same shape and scale as that of z for $\sigma_1^2 = \sigma_2^2$, but (in graphical terms) the distribution is moved along the z axis so that the ordinate which is located at $z = 0$ in the z distribution is located at $z' = \zeta$ in the z' distribution, where $\zeta = \frac{1}{2} \log_e \Phi$. This is represented graphically in Fig. 5.41, where the limit of z that is exceeded with a probability P is represented by the symbol z_P; z_P is the quantity in the standard tables. Then if we represent the confidence limit of ζ corresponding to the probability P and samples value z' by ζ_P, we see from Fig. 5.41 that

$$\zeta_P = z' - z_P$$

and on transforming this to the corresponding ratio of variances we have

$$\Phi_P = F'/F_P \quad \ldots \quad \ldots \quad (5.41b)$$

where Φ_P is the required confidence limit of ratio of variances, $F' = s_1^2/s_2^2$ and F_P is obtained from the standard F tables or from Chart E. Fig. 5.41 has been drawn for a small tail to the " right "; for the other tail it is best to take P large, i.e. $P = (1 - \text{area in tail})$, when z_P is negative and F_P is less than unity, and equation (5.41b) still applies.

We shall illustrate the procedure by finding 0·95 confidence limits (with two tails of 0·025 each) for the ratio of variances of muscle glycogen, estimated from Table 5.3. The sample data give $\nu_1 = 9$, $\nu_2 = 10$ and $F' = 3.93$. If we use the F tables of Merrington and Thompson (readers can check the results roughly with the aid of Charts E1 and E2), we have for one limit

$$P = 0.025, \; F_{0.025} = 3.779 \, 0 \; \text{and}$$

$$\Phi_{0.025} = 3.93 \div 3.779 \, 0 = 1.04.$$

For the other limit we have $P = 0.975$ and in order to evaluate $F_{0.975}$ we apply equation (5.41a). For $\nu_1 = 10$ and $\nu_2 = 9$, $F_{0.025} = 3.963 \, 9$, so that for $\nu_1 = 9$ and $\nu_2 = 10$, $F_{0.975} = 1/3.963 \, 9$, and

$$\Phi_{0.975} = 3.93 \times 3.963 \, 9 = 15.6.$$

The value of $\Phi = 1$ is just outside these limits, in conformity with the result of the test of significance ; the true value of Φ may easily be as large as 15.

Significance of Differences Between Several Samples

5.5. We have given several examples of testing the significance of the differences between more than two samples when there are so many that a theoretical sampling distribution may be compared with an actual one. In this section we deal with the intermediate case in which there are more than two samples, but not enough to form a frequency distribution.

The extension of the t test to testing the differences between several sample means when a common population standard deviation may be assumed is dealt with in the next chapter ; it constitutes an application of the analysis of variance.

The problem of testing the significance of the difference between several sample variances was first dealt with by Neyman and E. S. Pearson (1931). Since 1931, several approximations have been made to the necessary sampling distributions, and these are referred to in a note by Hartley and E. S. Pearson prefacing tables by Thompson and Merrington (1946).

In its final form, the test involves computing

$$M = (n_1 + \ldots n_k) \log_e \frac{n_1 s_1{}^2 + \ldots n_k s_k{}^2}{n_1 + \ldots n_k}$$

$$- (n_1 \log_e s_1{}^2 + \ldots n_k \log_e s_k{}^2) \quad \ldots \quad (5.5)$$

where there are k samples, $n_1 \ldots n_k$ are the respective degrees of freedom and $s_1{}^2 \ldots s_k{}^2$ the respective estimates of variance.

The sampling distribution of M is complicated, depending partly on the variations in degrees from sample to sample. The most convenient approximation is that of Bartlett (1937) which involves the quantity

$$C = 1 + \frac{1}{3(k-1)} \left\{ \frac{1}{n_1} + \ldots \frac{1}{n_k} - \frac{1}{n_1 + \ldots n_k} \right\} \quad . \quad (5.5a)$$

Bartlett showed that the quantity M/C is approximately distributed as χ^2 for $g = k - 1$ degrees of freedom, and the approximation is satisfactory provided none of the individual sample degrees of freedom is less than 4. If this condition is not satisfied or the probability is near a critical level, use should be made of the tables of Thompson and Merrington.

In a series of six experiments (Tippett, 1934), the following six variances of yarn breakages were obtained : 0·205 6, 0·557 8, 0·648 9, 0·337 8, 0·619 4 and 0·431 1 ; each was based on 9 degrees of freedom. Before combining the results of these experiments it was considered necessary to test the variances for homogeneity. We have it that $n_1 = \ldots n_k = 9$, $k = 6$, $M = 3\cdot89$, $C = 1\cdot043$ and $M/C = 3\cdot73$. From Chart D we see that for $\chi^2 = 3\cdot73$ and $g = 5$, $P = 0\cdot6$, and we infer that the differences between the estimates of variance are not significant.

COMBINATION OF RESULTS FROM SEVERAL SMALL SAMPLES

5.6. It often happens that separate investigations have given separate results based on small samples, and that a combined result is required. The following sub-sections deal with several types of combination.

Combination when Variances are Homogeneous

5.61. When the variances of the separate samples differ by no more than they would if they were estimates of a common population variance, combination of results is often relatively easy.

A combined estimate of variance is obtained by adding the separate sums of squares of deviations from the respective means, adding the degrees of freedom, and dividing the two sums. This has already been exemplified in section 5.1, and in the t test for the difference between two means (section 5.3).

If the investigations lead to several sets of deviations from some population mean, such as the differences of Table 5.2 showing growth in maize seedlings, they may be combined into one set before applying the *t* test in the usual way.

An interesting case arises when there are several sets of results like those of Table 5.3. An experiment may have been repeated at different times with different controls, and changed conditions may have affected the controls and the " treated " individuals in the same way, without affecting the variability in results at any one time. We shall here deal with the case when there are two such sets, and shall denote the various quantities for one set by the notation of section 5.3, without primes, and those for corresponding quantities for the other set by corresponding symbols with primes. It is easy to extend the results to more sets.

The two mean differences are

$$\bar{x}_1 - \bar{x}_2 \text{ and } \bar{x}'_1 - \bar{x}'_2,$$

and their respective standard errors are

$$\sigma\sqrt{(1/N_1 + 1/N_2)} \text{ and } \sigma\sqrt{(1/N'_1 + 1/N'_2)}.$$

We combine the two mean differences by weighting them according to the inverse of the square of the standard errors, i.e. according to their quantities of information (see section 3.62), so that if we use square brackets [ ] to signify " combined estimate " we have

$$[\bar{x}_1 - \bar{x}_2] =$$

$$\frac{(\bar{x}_1 - \bar{x}_2) \, N_1 N_2/(N_1 + N_2) + (\bar{x}'_1 - \bar{x}'_2) \, N'_1 N'_2/(N'_1 + N'_2)}{N_1 N_2/(N_1 + N_2) + N'_1 N'_2/(N'_1 + N'_2)}$$

$$. \quad . \quad . \quad (5.61)$$

The standard error of this combined estimate is

$$\sigma\sqrt{\left(\frac{1}{N_1 N_2/(N_1 + N_2) + N'_1 N'_2/(N'_1 + N'_2)}\right)}$$

The combined estimate of the variance within samples is obtained in the way described above and is based on

$$v = (N_1 - 1 + N_2 - 1 + N'_1 - 1 + N'_2 - 1)$$

degrees of freedom ; let the square root of this estimate be [*s*]. Then the *t* test for significance is applied to

$$[t] = \frac{[\bar{x}_1 - \bar{x}_2]}{[s]\sqrt{\left(\frac{1}{N_1 N_2/(N_1 + N_2) + N'_1 N'_2/(N'_1 + N'_2)}\right)}} \quad (5.61a)$$

Combination of Several Probabilities of Significance

5.62. When there is no justification for assuming a common population variance for the several samples, the only common measure that can form a basis of combination is the probability used in the significance test.

It is easy to deduce that if tests of significance are made when there are no real deviations from hypothesis, all values of the probability P between 0 and 1 are equally likely; and this is expressed by describing the frequency distribution of P as rectangular, and represented by the equation

$$df = dP \qquad \dots \dots \dots \quad (5.62)$$

If now we write

$$U = -2 \log_e P$$

and substitute in equation 5.62, we find that

$$df = \tfrac{1}{2} e^{-\frac{1}{2}U} dU$$

and on comparing this with equation (2.73), we see that U is distributed as χ^2 with $g = 2$ degrees of freedom. Moreover, since several values of χ^2 and their degrees of freedom may be added and treated as one value of χ^2 with one value of g, several values of U may be added, and their combined significance be tested by entering tables of χ^2 or Chart D with g equal to twice the number of values of U.

The following example is provided by a correspondent of the *American Statistician* and is treated by Fisher (1948). Four experiments were done to investigate the difference in mean between two sets of scores, and as there was no justification for combining the results according to section 5.61, conclusions had to be based on the four values of t and ν given in Table 5.62.

We must suppose that in each experiment set 1 and set 2 (say) could be defined and that the mean for set 1 was greater than that for set 2 in experiments 2 to 4 and less in experiment 1, giving three positive values and one negative value for t. In order to have a scale of P that distinguishes between positive and negative values we must use only one tail of the t distribution, letting $P = 0.5$ for $t = 0$. Then for experiment 2 we find from Chart C that the sum of the two tails is 0.144 so that the single tail P is 0.072. Similarly the values of P in Table 5.62 for experiments 3 and 4 are obtained from Chart C. The two-tail probability for

$t = +0.68$ and $\nu = 6$ is from Chart C 0.53, the one-tail probability is 0.265 and that for $t = -0.68$ is thus 0.73. The values of U are entered in Table 5.62, and their sum 20.15 is near the 0.01 level of χ^2 for 8 degrees of freedom (see Chart D). Now we must

TABLE 5.62

Experiment No.	t	ν	P (single tail)	U
1	-0.68	6	0.73	0.63
2	1.53	18	0.072	5.26
3	2.21	22	0.020	7.82
4	1.85	25	0.040	6.44
				20.15

get back to the equivalent of the ordinary two-tail t test. Presumably, had the mean for set 2 been greater than that for set 1 in the three experiments and less for the one, and the subtractions had been done to give the same values of t as those in Table 5.62, the significance would have been tested in the same way with U lying near the 0.01 level. The probability level for one or other set of differences being significant corresponding to the two-tail t test is thus near to 0.02.

Common sense tells us to test the hypothesis that the real difference is zero against the alternative that it is positive, and to use the values of P given in Table 5.62 instead of their complements 0.27, 0.928, 0.980 and 0.960; the positive values of t predominate and that is our guide. Had there been two positive and two negative differences, common sense would have been puzzled—but then the difference would hardly have been worth testing for significance.

In the foregoing we have tested the hypothesis that the difference between the means is zero against the alternative that the mean for set 1 is greater than that for set 2, and have used the single-tail P in Table 5.62 so as to take account of changes in sign in t, making the adjustment for the two-tail equivalent at the end. In the unusual event that the alternative hypothesis is merely that the mean for set 1 is different from that for set 2, the difference possibly changing sign from experiment to experiment (for example, we may have lost the labels identifying the sets), all values of t would be positive, and P would be computed for two tails so that the range of possible values of t from zero to plus infinity would give the corresponding range of values of P from unity to zero. Then the values of P for Table 5.62 would be 0·53, 0·144, 0·040 and 0·080 ; the values of U would be 1·27, 3·88, 6·44 and 5·05 ; their sum would be 16·6, which is near the 0·04 level of χ^2 for 8 degrees of freedom. This test must lower the apparent significance of a real difference that always goes the same way for the two sets, as compared with the previous test, because it makes no use of the information provided by the signs of t.

When only one tail is used to determine the level of significance P, as in the χ'^2 test for the goodness of fit of a theoretical to an actual frequency distribution, the dilemma of the last two paragraphs does not arise. The following example, which is artificial, is instructive and perhaps somewhat puzzling. Table 5.62a gives in the first three columns the results of four goodness of fit tests made according to section 4.2, the probabilities P having been obtained from Chart D (the other details of the test do not concern us). The total χ'^2 for 24 degrees of freedom is slightly above the 0·01 level of significance. Now, as an alternative, we may test the total value of U (19·5) for significance on 8 degrees of freedom —it happens to come just below the 0·01 level. The two methods of combination would not be expected always to give results so

TABLE 5.62a

χ'^2	g	P	U
8·8	4	0·065	5·47
11·5	8	0·17	3·54
11·5	5	0·045	6·20
11·4	7	0·12	4·24
43·2	24	0·01	19·45

close, and the method employing U should be adopted only where no other is available. Readers may for further exercise break up any series of results for which a single t test is appropriate into several smaller series each yielding a separate value of t, and compare the combined significance obtained with the aid of the U test with that given by the single t test.

A fuller discussion of this method of combining probabilities is given by E. S. Pearson (1938).

Small Samples from the Binomial and Poisson Distributions

5.63. In section 2.4 we used the binomial and Poisson series to test the randomness in the variations of a large number counts of dots, cabbage seeds, accidents and so on. For each count the conditions were, by hypothesis, uniform, so that the actual frequency distribution could be compared with one calculated from the appropriate binomial or Poisson series. In these distributions the individuals are not the things counted, but the counts, the number of things counted being the variate. Sometimes, however, we have a small sample of counts from each of a number of populations, and then the experiences can be reduced to a common measure and combined.

For example, Table 4.21 may be regarded as the result of one sample providing 10 counts of a quantity, the number of round peas, that is distributed binomially. The frequency test cannot be applied on such a small sample, and randomness may be tested by calculating χ'^2 as for a 2×10 contingency table, and if the expectations are calculated from the totals rather than from the Mendelian ratios, there are 9 degrees of freedom. If there are several such tables obtained (say) from different varieties of peas, with different numbers and ratios, separate values of χ'^2 and their degrees of freedom may be added, and the sum tested in the usual way. Further, there may be enough tables each with the same number of degrees of freedom to form a frequency distribution of χ'^2 for comparison with the theoretical form for χ^2. The quantity χ'^2 is thus the common measure to which a variety of experiences may be reduced.

Table 5.63 gives the counts of cotton fibres that, under a certain test, are mature (M) and abnormal (A). Three cotton samples were taken from each of 20 growths, and each was divided into two sub-samples (a) and (b). We expect the population proportion of mature fibres to differ with the growth, and for the present also entertain the possibility of it differing for samples from the same growth. We ask whether the variations in observed proportions between the sub-samples (a) and (b) are random in the sense of conforming to the binomial distribution. Each pair of sub-samples yields a fourfold table for which χ'^2 can be calculated, and the whole table yields 60 values of χ'^2 each based on one degree of freedom. The sum of these is 82·86, for $g = 60$ degrees of freedom, and in order to test its significance we may use the result

TABLE 5·63

NUMBERS OF MATURE (M) AND ABNORMAL (A) COTTON FIBRES IN TWENTY GROWTHS OF COTTON

Cotton Growth	Sample 1		Sample 2		Sample 3		Cotton Growth	Sample 1		Sample 2		Sample 3	
	(a)	(b)	(a)	(b)	(a)	(b)		(a)	(b)	(a)	(b)	(a)	(b)
1 M	56	47	47	31	64	53	11 M	26	62	28	23	40	32
A	28	17	20	19	34	26	A	32	58	38	38	34	39
2 M	47	45	60	42	40	66	12 M	17	34	24	20	30	24
A	16	25	34	28	13	24	A	74	66	26	46	38	39
3 M	64	48	66	64	53	52	13 M	42	48	26	25	27	24
A	38	32	30	40	18	44	A	21	34	27	29	38	39
4 M	52	59	40	33	29	22	14 M	60	37	40	45	41	54
A	33	25	34	39	23	31	A	30	32	36	21	17	18
5 M	40	45	55	62	71	76	15 M	45	40	44	34	42	45
A	15	17	14	42	36	19	A	21	32	22	28	38	34
6 M	26	31	30	39	31	26	16 M	39	43	39	56	32	32
A	43	42	57	54	36	29	A	17	17	17	15	47	46
7 M	37	38	42	31	42	44	17 M	54	71	38	42	45	32
A	27	39	21	23	42	34	A	41	36	40	42	47	52
8 M	24	27	21	12	38	45	18 M	67	58	59	65	39	39
A	48	59	68	66	62	68	A	43	38	37	44	54	31
9 M	27	29	54	37	28	49	19 M	60	64	50	51	65	57
A	43	34	46	52	37	43	A	16	16	19	21	22	31
10 M	35	24	28	25	13	19	20 M	40	50	50	53	44	60
A	44	58	37	45	47	36	A	16	16	14	7	16	20

stated in section 2.73 that for large values of g, $\sqrt{(2\chi^2)}$ is approximately distributed normally about a mean of $\sqrt{(2g-1)}$ with unit standard deviation. Here, $\sqrt{(2\chi'^2)} - \sqrt{(2g-1)} = \sqrt{165\cdot72}$ $- \sqrt{119} = 1\cdot96$, and from Chart B we see that the probability of this deviation being exceeded (using one tail of the distribution) is 0·025. Even between sub-samples the variations are more than random.

The actual and expected distributions of χ'^2 are compared in Table 5.63a, where unequal sub-ranges are used so as to give equal expected frequencies in the groups. They are obtained from the positive half of the normal distribution, according to equation (2.73a). The deviation of the actual from the expected distribution may be tested after the manner of section 4.2, by calculating a χ'^2 (we shall write it χ''^2 here, in order to distinguish it from the values of χ'^2 tabulated in Table 5.63a). We have $\chi''^2 = (6-4)^2/6$ $+ \ldots = 13\cdot7$, $g = 9$, and from Chart D, $P = 0\cdot14$. The

TABLE 5.63a

χ'^2	Frequencies	
	Expected	Observed
0–0·016	6	4
0·016–0·064	6	6
0·064–0·148	6	6
0·148–0·275	6	2
0·275–0·455	6	5
0·455–0·708	6	2
0·708–1·074	6	10
1·074–1·642	6	6
1·642–2·706	6	11
over 2·706	6	8
Total ...	60	60

expected frequencies of 6 are perhaps rather small for the test; if we combine them in consecutive pairs, $\chi''^2 = 9\cdot2$, $g = 4$, and $P = 0\cdot06$. This test is not as sensitive as that given by summing the values of χ'^2 for 60 degrees of freedom. It is worth while making a table like Table 5.63a if the first test shows no significant departure from randomness in case an excess of large values of χ'^2 should be balanced by an excess of small values. When a significant departure from randomness is established, a distribution like Table 5.63a may give a clue as to its nature, or may be used to investigate various possibilities. It would be convenient if, for example, any non-random were related to the random variations in such a way as to enhance χ'^2 in a constant ratio (say $82{\cdot}86/60 = 1{\cdot}38$ in this instance), so that the standard error of a result would be proportional to the value calculated from binomial theory. Such a possibility could be tested by dividing the individual values of χ'^2 by $1{\cdot}38$ and testing if these adjusted values fit the expected distribution any better than the unadjusted values. Here, since the differences between the distributions of Table 5.63a are barely significant, such a course would be profitless. Useful investigations of this kind require much more data, and usually the total numbers in the successive counts should be substantially constant.

Had there been no significant differences between the sub-samples, we could profitably have carried the investigation a stage further and tested the differences between the samples ; and the reader is recommended to do this as a statistical exercise. If we combine the results of the sub-samples, each cotton growth yields a 3×2 contingency table and a value of χ'^2 based on 2 degrees of freedom. For growth 1, $\chi'^2 = 0{\cdot}489$, and the sum of the 20 values is $149{\cdot}520$, which for 40 degrees of freedom is very highly significant. It may not be inferred from this that the non-random variations between samples are greater than those between sub-samples. The degrees of freedom are not the same, and the numbers of fibres in the samples are greater than those in the sub-samples. The full investigation of the variations would require much more data, and would carry us beyond the scope of this book.

When the total number in each of a set of parallel counts is constant, the expression for χ'^2 becomes simple. If there are g' parallel counts, each of n trials, with $m_1 \ldots m_s \ldots m_g$, successes respectively, and a mean of $\overline{m}$ successes, then

$$\chi'^2 = \frac{S\,(m_s - \overline{m})^2}{(\overline{m} - \overline{m}^2/n)} \quad \cdot \quad \cdot \quad \cdot \quad \cdot \quad (5.63)$$

where S is the summation over the g' parallel counts ; there are $(g' - 1)$ degrees of freedom for the set.

5.64. For the Poisson distribution, the index corresponding to that of equation (5.63) is

$$\chi'^2 = \frac{S(m_s - \overline{m})^2}{\overline{m}}$$

165

where m_s is any individual count, $\overline{m}$ is the mean, and S is the summation over all counts. Fisher, Thornton and Mackenzie (1922) first used this to test the accuracy of bacterial counts and found significant deviations from expectation. A little later, Smith and Prentice (1929) used it to check their technique of cyst counts in soil. They had 73 sets of 10 counts from different samples of soil, and calculated the 73 values of χ'^2. The distribution of this is compared with the theoretical one for 9 degrees of freedom in Table 5.64, and the expectations, being obtained from Fisher's book (1925c), are for unequal intervals of χ^2 (readers may obtain reasonably accurate values from Chart D).

TABLE 5.64

χ'^2	Frequencies	
	Expected (ν_s)	Observed (n_s)
0– 4·168	7·3	7
4·168– 5·380	7·3	7
5·380– 6·393	7·3	6
6·393– 8·343	14·6	22
8·343–10·656	14·6	18
10·656–12·242	7·3	2
12·242–14·684	7·3	5
over 14·684	7·3	6
Total ...	73·0	73

The agreement is quite fair ; it is tested in the usual manner by calculating another

$$\chi''^2 = S_s \frac{(n_s - \nu_s)^2}{\nu_s} = 9\cdot604,$$

which for seven degrees of freedom gives P greater than 0·2.

CHAPTER VI

THE SIMPLE ANALYSIS OF VARIANCE

PREVIOUS chapters are based on the presentation of collections of data in the form of frequency distributions and on the description of a few features, particularly the extent and form of the variation, by frequency characteristics. This is a process of summarisation in which some detail is inevitably lost. We shall now reverse the process a little way and deal with statistical methods designed to recover some of the detail, starting from the frequency distribution and its constants as bases. Comparatively little has been done in this direction with the *form* of variation, but the *amount* of variation can be split up into parts associated with different causes or sources. The method for analysing variation is introduced in its simplest form in this chapter; most of the remainder of the book is based on an elaboration of the method and its applications. As a first step, we shall in the next section prove a fundamental mathematical property of variance.

VARIANCE AN ADDITIVE QUANTITY

6.1. According to the simple statistical view, variability is considered to arise from a complex of causes producing small deviations, and forming an homogeneous system for which no attempt at analysis is made. Often, however, several relatively important causes or groups of causes can be discerned, as for example in Table 1.1*a* (vi), where we tentatively attributed the bi-modal character of the distribution of rays of chrysanthemums to the mixing of two strains, thus recognising the operation of two groups of causes, those causing differences between strains and those causing variations between flowers of the same strain. It is a fundamental property of that measure of the degree of variability, the variance, that it is additive, i.e. if a quantity is subject to the operation of several independent causes each of which contributes a certain variance, then the final variance of the quantity is the sum of those due to the several causes. Let it be assumed, for example, that a quantity x is subject to random variations, and to others associated with two factors A and B; then the value of any one observation of x is

$$x = \bar{\xi} + \alpha + \beta + \xi',$$

where $\bar{\xi}$ is the mean, α and β are the deviations arising from A and B, and ξ' is the random deviation. The square of the deviation of x from its mean is

$$(x - \bar{\xi})^2 = \alpha^2 + \beta^2 + \xi'^2 + 2\alpha\beta + 2\alpha\xi' + 2\beta\xi',$$

and this may be summed for a sample of N individuals, and divided by the degrees of freedom (N in this case, since we have not found the mean $\bar{\xi}$ from the sample, but have assumed it). Thus we obtain

$$\frac{S(x - \bar{\xi})^2}{N} = \frac{S\alpha^2}{N} + \frac{S\beta^2}{N} + \frac{S\xi'^2}{N} + \frac{2S\alpha\beta}{N} + \frac{2S\alpha\xi'}{N} + \frac{2S\beta\xi'}{N}$$

and as N becomes indefinitely large, the last three terms of this equation tend to zero if α, β and ξ' are independent ; the other terms are the squares of the standard deviations or variances, so that finally

$$\sigma_x{}^2 = \sigma_\alpha{}^2 + \sigma_\beta{}^2 + \sigma_{\xi'}{}^2 \quad . \quad . \quad . \quad . \quad (6.1)$$

Hence the variance of x is the sum of the random variance and of variances due to A and B. We used this property in Chapter III to find the standard error of a difference in terms of those of the two means ; since the variance is the square of the standard error, the above equation leads directly to equation (3.21).* We shall use it now to analyse the variability of quantities into parts.

ANALYSIS OF VARIANCE

6.2. Consider Table 6.2 in which the data (Harris, 1910) are frequency distributions of ovaries containing different numbers of ovules, and are for ten separate shrubs of the American Bladder Nut. The separate columns are called *arrays*. It is obvious that there are considerable differences between the shrubs, for while shrub 11 has ovaries with 22-30 ovules, shrub 13 has ovaries with between 17 and 24 ovules, and the other shrubs show similar differences. The variations between ovaries on any one shrub are less than those between all taken together, and the whole table suggests that we may legitimately divide the total variability into two parts : one associated with differences between ovaries

---

* α and β may be positive or negative.

from the same shrub, and another with differences between shrubs. We say that there is an association between the shrubs and ovules per ovary, and as evidence adduce the fact that the mean variance of deviations from the shrub means as found by the method of section 5.1, which is 3·057, is very much less than variance of the " totals " column (5·385).

Indeed, Table 6.2 is really a manifold contingency table, but the association is expressed differently because one variate is quantitative ; a treatment by the method of the contingency table would the be very laborious with so many squares.

We may present the analysis of the variability into the two parts

TABLE 6.2

Frequencies of Ovaries (Series O, 1908 C)

		Serial Number of Shrub										Totals
		11	12	13	15	16	18	19	20	21	22	
	17	—	—	1	—	—	—	—	—	—	—	1
	18	—	2	23	—	1	6	1	—	—	1	34
	19	—	5	13	—	1	4	5	5	—	1	34
	20	—	8	27	—	1	4	1	5	2	2	50
	21	—	10	4	1	1	5	2	7	1	1	32
Ovules per Ovary	22	4	21	18	—	7	13	9	12	6	2	92
	23	5	17	7	3	9	16	15	25	8	15	120
	24	41	35	7	16	42	48	44	39	61	68	401
	25	21	2	—	25	14	3	18	6	10	8	107
	26	9	—	—	21	9	1	4	1	4	2	51
	27	9	—	—	8	5	—	1	—	3	—	26
	28	4	—	—	8	3	—	—	—	2	—	17
	29	3	—	—	12	3	—	—	—	2	—	20
	30	4	—	—	5	4	—	—	—	1	—	14
	31	—	—	—	1	—	—	—	—	—	—	1
Totals ...		100	100	100	100	100	100	100	100	100	100	1 000

in a systematic manner. Let x be any individual reading, $\bar{x}_1\,\bar{x}_2 \ldots \bar{x}_s \ldots \bar{x}_m$ the m shrub means, $\bar{x}$ the grand mean, and n the number of readings per shrub, so that there are $nm = N$ readings altogether. Then, for any ovary on any one shrub, the deviation

SIMPLE ANALYSIS OF VARIANCE [6.2

from the grand mean is the deviation from the shrub mean plus that of the shrub mean from the grand mean :

$$(x - \bar{x}) = (x - \bar{x}_s) + (\bar{x}_s - \bar{x}).$$

We shall square these deviations, and sum for all observations from the one shrub ; denoting this summation by S' and applying the rules in section 1.311 we obtain

$$S'(x - \bar{x})^2 = S'(x - \bar{x}_s)^2 + n(\bar{x}_s - \bar{x})^2 + 2(\bar{x}_s - \bar{x})S'(x - \bar{x}_s).$$

The term $(\bar{x}_s - \bar{x})^2$ is constant for the one shrub and its sum for the n observations is n times the single value (the second term in the above equation) ; the third term above is zero, since the sum of the deviations from the mean, $S'(x - \bar{x}_s)$, is necessarily zero. To obtain the total sum of squares, we now sum the terms of this equation again for all shrubs (using the sign S_s) and finally obtain

$$S_sS'(x - \bar{x})^2 = S_sS'(x - \bar{x}_s)^2 + nS_s(\bar{x}_s - \bar{x})^2 \quad . \quad . \quad (6.2)$$

The sign S_sS' is equivalent to S, the simple summation over all observations in the sample. For the data of Table 6.2, equation (6.2) is

$$5\ 379{\cdot}775 = 3\ 026{\cdot}350 + 2\ 353{\cdot}425,$$

and each of these terms is given an appropriate place in Table 6.2a of the Analysis of Variance. The terms are the sums of squares of deviations, (a) of individual observations from the grand mean, (b) of individual observations from the shrub means, and (c) of the shrub means from the grand mean (the sum being multiplied by n in this case). The degrees of freedom are given in the table ; for the total, one mean has been found and there are thus 999 degrees ; for the deviations from the shrub means, each shrub contributes 99 degrees, giving a total of 990 ; and for the shrub means, 10 deviations are measured from the grand mean, leaving 9 degrees of freedom. The sums of squares and degrees of freedom of the parts should add up to give the " total," and the sums of squares, divided by the degrees of freedom, give estimates of the variances. That for the " total " is the ordinary variance of all the observations in the sample, and that for " within a shrub " is the variance of the intra-shrub deviations found by using the method of section 5.1, and is an estimate, based on 990 degrees of freedom, of the true variance, $\sigma_r{}^2$ (say). The variance " between shrubs " is n times the square of the standard deviation of shrub means. To investigate this more fully, let us suppose we have an indefinitely large number of ovaries from each of an indefinitely large number of shrubs, and let the variance of these shrub means be σ_s^2; this is the true value for the infinite population. If now we have only n ovaries from each shrub, the means are subject to random errors due to the intra-shrub variation, and their standard error is $\sigma_r/\sqrt{n}$. These errors increase the variability of the shrub means, and the resulting variance may be obtained by adding the two components, as shown in equation (6.1), giving $(\sigma_s^2 + \sigma_r^2/n)$; the variance of Table 6.2a is an estimate based on 9 degrees of freedom of n times this. If v_s is the variance between shrubs, and v_r the variance within a shrub, as found from the sample

$$\left. \begin{array}{l} v_s \rightarrow n\sigma_s^2 + \sigma_r^2 \\ v_r \rightarrow \sigma_r^{2*} \end{array} \right\} \quad . \quad . \quad . \quad . \quad . \quad (6.2a)$$

These two relations are the basis of the expression of association. If the variation between shrubs is relatively important, σ_s^2 is large

TABLE 6.2a

ANALYSIS OF VARIANCE

Source of Variation	Sum of Squares	Degrees of Freedom	Variance
Between shrubs ... ... Within a shrub	2 353·425 3 026·350	9 990	261·492 3·057
Total	5 379·775	999	5·385

compared with σ_r^2, and the two estimates v_s and v_r are very different. If the shrub variation is zero, $\sigma_s^2 = 0$ and v_s tends to equal v_r. In such a case, for normally distributed variates, v_s and v_r are two independent estimates of the same variance, σ_r^2. They are subject to the same random errors as are all estimates of variance, and the significance of any difference should be tested by the methods of section 5.41. For Table 6.2a, the one (261·492) is so much greater than the other (3·057) that the reality of the association needs no test.

Table 6.2b summarises the above relations and sets out the analysis of variance for the general case of n observations on each of m arrays. The variance within an array is often called the residual or remainder; having performed the analysis, we are not

---

* The sign → denotes that the quantity on the left is an estimate of that on the right, and that the former approaches the latter as the degrees of freedom increase.

very interested in the variance of the " total " row, since the two parts contain all the useful information.

If v_s is less than v_r, but not significantly so, the inference is that $\sigma_s{}^2 = 0$; v_s is only rarely significantly less than v_r, and when this

TABLE 6.2*b*

ANALYSIS OF VARIANCE

Source of Variation	Sum of Squares	Degrees of Freedom	Variance
Between arrays Within an array	$nS_s(\bar{x}_s - \bar{x})^2$ $S_sS'(x - \bar{x}_s)^2$	$m - 1$ $m(n - 1) = N - m$	$v_s \to n\sigma_s{}^2 + \sigma_r{}^2$ $v_r \to \sigma_r{}^2$
Total ...	$S(x - \bar{x})^2$	$mn - 1 = N - 1$	—

happens a new interpretation must be arrived at ; this will be dealt with in section 6.7.

It will be noted that since we are not often willing to entertain it as an alternative hypothesis that the population value corresponding to v_s is less than that corresponding to v_r, a single tail of the F or z distribution is appropriate in testing significances.

Substantive Variances

6.21. As it stands, a table of analysis of variance is useful only for establishing whether there are significant differences between arrays—whether individuals taken from different arrays vary more than individuals taken from the same array. Equations (6.2*a*) show that the value of v_s depends not only on the component variances, $\sigma_r{}^2$ and $\sigma_s{}^2$, but also on n, the number of individuals per array, which is not a fundamental characteristic of the population but a more or less arbitrary feature of the sample. In order to arrive at the characteristics of the population we must use equations (6.2*a*) to obtain estimates of $\sigma_r{}^2$ and $\sigma_s{}^2$; we may call these estimates of *substantive variances*.

For the shrubs we have :
$$261 \cdot 492 \to 100\,\sigma_s{}^2 + \sigma_r{}^2 \text{ and}$$
$$3 \cdot 057 \to \sigma_r{}^2,$$
$$\text{whence } 2 \cdot 584 \to \sigma_s{}^2.$$

If a sample of ovaries were taken at random from these shrubs, the number from each shrub being left to chance, the variance would be $\sigma_s{}^2 + \sigma_r{}^2$, of which an estimate is $5 \cdot 641$. This differs slightly from the variance in the "total" row of Table 6.2*a* because the sample to which the latter refers is not entirely random ; it has been arranged so that 100 ovaries come from each shrub. The measure of the importance of the shrub variations is that if ovaries are taken from different shrubs, the standard deviation of the variate is $\sqrt{5\cdot641} = 2\cdot38$; if they are from the same shrub, or alternatively, if shrub variations are eliminated, the standard deviation is reduced to $\sqrt{3\cdot057} = 1\cdot75$. The appreciation of an analysis of variance thus reduces to an appreciation of standard deviations.

The following is an example of a practical use of substantive variances. It is required to estimate the variance of the "count" (a measure of fineness, being the inverse of the weight per unit length) of a number of bobbins of cotton yarn, each bobbin being characterised by the mean of tests on all the yarn of the bobbin. There are about 12 "leas" (a test length of 120 yards) per bobbin, and since the test is destructive it is necessary as well as economical to make the estimate from only a part of the yarn on each bobbin. We may reasonably assume the leas on a bobbin to be a random sample of the within-bobbin variation. Four consecutive leas were tested from each of 90 bobbins, and the mean range of count was 5·5 per cent. of the mean count, leading to an estimate of standard deviation of $5\cdot5/2\cdot059 = 2\cdot67$ per cent., and a corresponding within-bobbin variance, $\sigma_r^2 = 7\cdot13$. Further, one lea was tested from each of 180 bobbins (including the 90), and the mean range in groups of four was 9·0 per cent., giving an estimate of standard deviation of $9\cdot0/2\cdot059 = 4\cdot37$ per cent., and a variance of 19·10. If σ_s^2 is the substantive variance between bobbins, 19·10 is the estimate of $\sigma_s^2 + \sigma_r^2$, whence the estimate of σ_s^2 is 11·97. The required variance of the means of 12 leas per bobbin is $\sigma_s^2 + \sigma_r^2/12$, which is estimated by $11\cdot97 + 0\cdot59 = 12\cdot56$, giving a standard deviation of 3·54 per cent. of the grand mean count.

The sampling errors of the estimates of the substantive variance σ_s^2 have not, as far as I am aware, been fully investigated, and no tables are available. Clearly no estimate can have much practical value unless the degrees of freedom on which $V_r = \sigma_r^2$ and $V_s = n\sigma_s^2 + \sigma_r^2$* are estimated are both large. Then, as an

---

* In the absence of an obvious Greek equivalent to *v*, we use V for the population value corresponding to the sample value *v*.

approximation, the large sample theory can be used ; the estimates v_r and v_s can be taken to be normally distributed and their standard errors of v_r and v_s can be used to estimate that of their difference.

For the example of the previous paragraph, the standard error of the estimate 2·67 is, by the method of section 4.13 and Table A,

$$\frac{0 \cdot 880 \times 2 \cdot 67}{2 \cdot 059 \times \sqrt{90}} = 0 \cdot 120\ 3,$$

and by section 4.15 that of 7·13 is $2 \times 2 \cdot 67 \times 0 \cdot 120\ 3 = 0 \cdot 642$. Likewise, the standard error of the estimate 4·37 is 0·278 4 and that of 19·10 is 2·433. The estimate 12·56 is $19 \cdot 10 - 7 \cdot 13 \times 11/12$, and its standard error is

$$\sqrt{[2 \cdot 433^2 + (0 \cdot 642 \times 11/12)^2]} = 2 \cdot 50.$$

By application of section 4.15, the standard error of the estimated standard deviation of 3·54 per cent. is deduced as $2 \cdot 50/(2 \times 3 \cdot 54)$ = 0·35.

Obviously, for estimating the substantive variance an arrangement with many arrays and few individuals per array is better than one like Table 6.2 with few arrays and many individuals per array. Readers may refer to a paper by Bross (1950).

COMPUTATION

6.3. When computing the sums of squares for Table 6.2b, the various deviations may be found explicitly, and squared and added. If the arithmetic is correct, the sums of squares between and within arrays should add up to give the total ; this provides a check. Usually, however, this process is laborious and it is convenient to apply a modification of equations (1.31a). If the original units are used so that $h = 1$, the appropriate part of equation (1.31a) may be written

$$S(x - \bar{x})^2 = Sx^2 - N\bar{x}^2 = Sx^2 - T^2/N, \quad . \quad . \quad (6.3)$$

where S, $\bar{x}$ and N have their usual meanings and T is the total value of the variate for the N observations, i.e. $T = Sx = N\bar{x}$.

Applying this to equation (6.2) and writing $T = S_s S' x$ and $T_s = S' x$ for the sth shrub,[*] we have

$$\left. \begin{array}{l} S_s S'(x - \bar{x})^2 = S_s S' x^2 - T^2/N, \\ S_s S'(x - \bar{x}_s)^2 = S_s S' x^2 - S_s T_s^2/n, \\ \text{and } n S_s (\bar{x}_s - \bar{x})^2 = S_s T_s^2/n - T^2/N, \end{array} \right\} \quad . \quad . \quad (6.3a)$$

* These values of T are not the total numbers of individuals but are the total amounts of variate in the several arrays. In Table 6.2, T_s is the total number of ovules in the 100 ovaries from the sth shrub.

The process of computation may be written in words :

(1) square the individual values and add,

(2) find the total value of the variate for the arrays, square, add, and divide the result by the number of individuals per array, and

(3) find the total value of the variate for all individuals, square, and divide by the grand total number of individuals.

Then if (1), (2) and (3) represent the results of the above operations, equation (6.2) becomes

$$[(1) - (3)] = [(1) - (2)] + [(2) - (3)].$$

When the data are grouped, readers should have no difficulty in applying equation (1.32). In such instances, it is better not to use Sheppard's corrections, but to keep the grouping fairly fine so that they are unimportant. The precise effect of these corrections is not certain ; but they increase the apparent association by reducing the residual variance, so to neglect them in testing significances is to be on the safe side.

It may be convenient to measure the values of the variate as deviations from some arbitrary origin and to divide them by an arbitrary constant h before summing and squaring. Then after applying equations (6.3a) it is only necessary to multiply the resultant sums of squares by h^2. The process of computation based on equations (6.3a) may easily be performed exactly, with the aid of a table of squares, down to the last stages of dividing by the numbers of individuals, and since there are only two such divisions, these may be performed with ample accuracy without much labour.

Tables with Non-uniform Array Totals

6.4. The analysis of variance may be performed on tables in which the numbers of individuals in the arrays are not equal. If the numbers in the arrays are $n_1 n_2 \dots n_s \dots n_m$, equation (6.2) becomes

$$S_s S'(x - \bar{x})^2 = S_s S'(x - \bar{x}_s)^2 + S_s n_s(\bar{x}_s - \bar{x})^2 \quad . \quad (6.4)$$

and $S_s(T_s^2/n_s)$ is written for $S_s T_s^2/n$ in equations (6.3a).

In such instances, the relations of equations (6.2a) do not hold, for in summing the squares of the deviations of the group means from the grand mean, each group has been given a different weight, n_s. If the true variance between groups (σ_s^2) is zero, however, $v_s \to v_r$, and the test for the existence of association is that v_s and v_r are significantly different.

Table 6.4 gives distributions of the lengths of cuckoos' eggs

TABLE 6.4

		Nest Type						Totals
		Meadow Pipit	Tree Pipit	Hedge Sparrow	Robin	Pied Wagtail	Wren	
Length of Cuckoos' Eggs in mm. (Central values)	19·65	I	—	—	—	—	—	I
	19·85	—	—	—	—	—	I	I
	20·05	I	—	—	—	—	I	2
	20·25	—	—	—	—	—	I	I
	20·45	—	—	—	—	—	—	—
	20·65	I	—	—	—	—	—	I
	20·85	I	—	I	—	—	3	5
	21·05	—	I	—	I	I	3	6
	21·25	—	—	—	—	—	I	I
	21·45	—	—	—	—	—	I	I
	21·65	3	—	I	—	—	—	4
	21·85	3	I	—	I	3	—	8
	22·05	10	I	I	3	I	3	19
	22·25	8	—	—	I	—	I	10
	22·45	3	I	—	2	I	—	7
	22·65	2	I	—	I	I	—	5
	22·85	4	—	I	—	—	—	5
	23·05	I	—	4	5	2	—	12
	23·25	2	3	—	I	I	—	7
	23·45	I	2	I	—	I	—	5
	23·65	I	I	—	—	—	—	2
	23·85	I	I	3	I	—	—	6
	24·05	—	3	I	—	3	—	7
	24·25	I	—	—	—	—	—	I
	24·45	I	—	—	—	—	—	I
	24·65	—	—	—	—	—	—	—
	24·85	—	—	—	—	I	—	I
	25·05	—	—	I	—	—	—	I
Totals n_s		45	15	14	16	15	15	120
T_s ...		56	78	75	42	64	−69	246
$\dfrac{T_s^2}{n_s}$ ...		69·69	405·60	401·79	110·25	273·07	317·40	504·30

⌐ in the nests of a variety of other birds (Latter, 1902). The ⌐l frequencies for the kinds of nest vary, and since the observa-⌐ns are fewer, the association is not quite so obvious as in the previous example. The grouping is rather fine for such a small sample, but has been adopted because Sheppard's corrections will not be applied. The values have been measured as deviations from the length 22·05 mm. in terms of the unit of grouping 0·2 mm. The quantities T_s and T_s^2/n_s are given in these units at the foot of the table, and we may calculate that

$$S_s S' x^2 = 3\ 934,\ S_s(T_s^2/n_s) = 1\ 577\text{·}80 \text{ and } T^2/N = 504\text{·}30.$$

From these, the terms of equation (6.4) are found and inserted in Table 6.4a. The variance between nest types is greater than the

TABLE 6.4a

ANALYSIS OF VARIANCE (LENGTHS OF CUCKOOS' EGGS)

Source of Variation	Sum of Squares	Degrees of Freedom	Variance
Between nest types ...	1 073·50	5	214·7
Within a nest type ...	2 356·21	114	20·7
Total	3 429·71	119	—

residual, and we will test it for significance. We find that $F = 10\text{·}4$ and it is clear from Chart E2 that P is less than 0·005. These variances are in terms of the arbitrary units (0·2 mm.), and if they are required in mm.² they must be multiplied by 0·04.

DIFFERENCES BETWEEN SAMPLES : CONTROL CHARTS

6.5. We have so far regarded the arrays as parts of a single, heterogeneous population, but equally we may regard them as separate samples, and the analysis of variance as a means of testing the significance of the differences between the sample means as a whole. We have already seen in section 3.22 the difficulties that arise when the theory of errors appropriate to single samples or pairs is applied to groups, and have used the range to determine whether the difference between the highest and lowest of a group of means is significant. The analysis of variance provides an efficient test for use in these circumstances,

M

provided the variances within the samples are the same (v
the limits of random errors) and the distributions are normal

Table 1.1 gives results for 20 groups or samples of 5 which
know to be taken from the same population. The analysis of
variance is in Table 6.5, and since the between sample (or between
group) variance is not significantly greater than that within
samples (P is between 0·4 and 0·5), we confirm that the differences between the sample means are not greater than would
be expected for samples from the same population.

TABLE 6.5

ANALYSIS OF VARIANCE (DATA TABLE 1.1)

Source of Variation	Sum of Squares	Degrees of Freedom	Variance
Between groups	1 808·35	19	95·18
Within a group	7 056·40	80	88·20
Total	8 864·75	99	—

In the application of statistics to quality control in engineering
and industrial production, it is convenient to express these results
in another form, on *control charts*. The upper part of Fig. 6.5 is
the control chart for the means of Table 1.1. The sample means
are represented serially by points, and abscissæ are drawn representing the grand mean of the sampling distribution of means,
and chosen probability levels of that distribution—the latter
being termed *control levels*. If *a priori* data are available, these are
used for determining the levels ; otherwise the limits are estimated
approximately from the given data. Here, the grand mean is
50·35, and the standard deviation within samples estimated from
the mean range (as would, for convenience, be done in practice)
has been calculated in section 1.23 as 9·6. The standard error of
means of 5 is $9·6/\sqrt{5} = 4·29$, and limits cutting off tails of 0·025
of the sampling distribution are $50·35 \pm 1·96 \times 4·29 = 41·94$
and 58·76. These are drawn in the upper part of Fig. 6.5. If the
variations between sample means are insignificant, nineteen out
of twenty of the points, on the average, should lie within these
limits ; all of the particular twenty points lie within.

The control chart is not as good, statistically, as the analysis of sampling distribution as the variance in effect does, and it makes no allowance for the approximation involved in estimating the mean and standard deviation from the data. Control charts are variance. It provides no estimate of substantive variances, it cannot be readily extended to cover the more complicated situations we shall discuss in the next chapter, it is inefficient in that it uses only one or two sets of probability levels instead of the whole

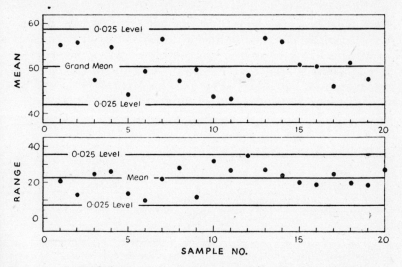

FIG. 6.5. Control charts of the mean and range for the data of Table 1.1.

normally used where long series of results are available, however, and the last two objections have no practical weight. An advantage is that after the chart has been set up, further points can be added immediately, as samples are taken from the factory production, and early indications thus be obtained of departures from the control level. For this purpose, 0·01 probability levels, or levels even more remote from the mean, are often used. A control chart also shows up trends, if any exist.

A control chart of the range is often used to determine whether the variations within samples are substantially uniform, or " in control." The ranges of Table 1.1 are plotted in the lower part of Fig. 6.5. Control limits may be determined from the distributions given by E. S. Pearson (1942), or, more conveniently, from tables in a pamphlet by Dudding and Jennett (1942). Here, the mean range is 22·3 and from the constants in Dudding and Jennett's tables we calculate the 0·025 limits in samples of 5 to be at 7·3 and 35·8. The control chart for ranges is an approximate equivalent to the test of section 5.5 for homogeneity of variances.

RELATION BETWEEN z OR F AND t TESTS

6.6. Since the analysis of variance with the associated z or F test does for several sample means what the t test does for two, there must be a relation between the two tests. Indeed, the case of two samples may be regarded as a special case of the analysis of variance. If there are two groups with n_1' and n_2' observations in each group, $\bar{x}_1$ and $\bar{x}_2$ are the means, and $\bar{x}$ is the grand mean, the analysis of variance is as set out in Table 6.6. S′ and S″ are

TABLE 6.6

ANALYSIS OF VARIANCE (TWO GROUPS)

Source of Variation	Sum of Squares	Degrees of Freedom	Variance
Between samples	$n_1'(\bar{x}_1-\bar{x})^2+n_2'(\bar{x}_2-\bar{x})^2$ $=\dfrac{(\bar{x}_1-\bar{x}_2)^2}{(1/n_1'+1/n_2')}$	1	v_s
Within a sample	$S'(x-\bar{x}_1)^2+S''(x-\bar{x}_2)^2$	$n_1'+n_2'-2$	v_r
Total	$S(x-\bar{x}^2)$	$n_1'+n_2'-1$	—

the summations within samples 1 and 2 respectively, S is the summation over the whole, and the degrees of freedom are $v_1 = 1$ and $v_2 = n_1' + n_2' - 2$.

The square root of the ratio of variances is the t of equation (5.3a), which was used in testing the difference between two means. Thus, if we make the transformation

$$z = \tfrac{1}{2}\log_e t^2 \text{ or } t = e^z,$$
$$\text{or } F = t^2$$

the distributions of t for v degrees of freedom, say, and of z or F for $v_1 = 1$ and $v_2 = v$ are equivalent. This is because z or F and t are mathematically related ; for any value of t there is only one value of z or F.

In using the z or F and t tests as equivalents, we use a single tail of the former and the two tails of the latter distribution. The alternative hypothesis to $\zeta = 0$ or $\Phi = 0$ is a positive value of ζ or Φ, and a test using one tail is appropriate ; the equivalent alternative to τ (say) $= 0$ (τ is the population value corresponding to t), is a positive or negative value of τ, and a test using two tails is appropriate. We can number our two groups so that t is always positive, and then the positive half of the t distribution corresponds exactly to the whole z or F distribution ; and one tail is the same fraction of the half of the t distribution as two tails are of the whole.

Assumptions and Interpretations

6.7. As an aid to the appreciation of the assumptions underlying the methods of this chapter, we may substitute for the mathematical analysis of section 6.2 an experimental model. Let us imagine two urns, the first containing tickets (not necessarily a large number) each labelled with a group number and a true group mean, and the second containing an infinite population of tickets each labelled with the value of a random deviation, the distribution of the deviations being normal, with a mean of zero. Each observation in the sample is the result of drawing a ticket from each urn and adding the two values, the selection from the second urn being random, and no restriction being placed on the selection from the first. The analysis of variance applies only where the causal system behind the results corresponds to this model. Experimenters may know enough of the causal system to justify them in applying the analysis appropriate to the model, at least as an approximation ; or they may test the data for evidences of departure from the assumption (the tests can only be indicative : they cannot be exhaustive) ; or they may justify the analysis on both grounds. We shall discuss some of the effects of departures from the assumptions.

The assumption of an infinite population of tickets in the second urn does not often give trouble ; it is the same as the general assumption of an infinite population in random sampling theory, and will be discussed in section 12.25. Work by E. S. Pearson and others indicates, too, that moderate departures from normality in the distribution of values in the second urn have little effect on the analysis of variance.

The use of *one* second urn, and the random selection of tickets from it are, however, important assumptions, as we may see if we consider some imaginary alternative systems. For example, we could have many " second " urns, one for each ticket in the first urn, and each containing a different distribution of random deviations. Then, each result would be the value on the ticket from the first urn plus that on a ticket drawn at random from the appropriate second urn. The effect of such a system is to give different within-group variances for the different groups, and this can be tested on the data by the methods of section 5.5. Sometimes a plotting of the within-group variance (or range) discloses a rough relationship which can be used in the analysis. The within-group variations may also differ in *form* from one group to another, but very seldom will such differences be important enough to be apparent.

In another system we may imagine two urns as in the assumed system, but with a non-random selection from the second. For example, the operator might successively draw the same ticket say twenty times from the first urn, and at each draw a handful from the second, choosing the highest value from the first handful, the lowest from the second, the highest from the third, and so on. The effect would be to enhance the within-group variance, possibly to the extent of making it significantly larger than the between-group variance.

Another type of non-random selection would occur if the tickets in the second urn were roughly stratified, perhaps with large positive deviations tending to be towards the top, small deviations towards the middle, and large negative deviations towards the bottom, and if the operator in making successive draws worked downwards from the top. In such a system also the within-group variance would be enhanced and its effect on the between-group variations reduced, relatively. Indeed, any non-random pattern of variation or selection within the second urn will have this effect, and a significant excess of within-group over between-group variance is evidence of such a pattern, although the absence of such excess is not proof that there is no pattern.

An example is in Table 6.7 from a paper by Warren (1909), showing the mean head breadths of termites taken from five nests during five months. Here, the 25 means are the individuals ; the frequency distribution of individual head breadths is not under consideration. If, now, we regard the five nests as providing the tickets in the first urn, and the monthly deviations from the nest means as those in the second, we can discern a monthly pattern, for the November and August values are in all nests lower than the March value ; but even so, when the variance is analysed as

TABLE 6.7

MEAN HEAD BREADTHS OF TERMITES (SMALL SOLDIERS) IN MM.

Nest Number	668	670	672	674	675	Means
November ...	2·273	2·479	2·404	2·447	2·456	2·411 8
January ...	2·332	2·603	2·457	2·388	2·626	2·481 2
March ...	2·375	2·613	2·452	2·515	2·633	2·517 6
May ...	2·373	2·557	2·396	2·445	2·487	2·451 6
August ...	2·318	2·377	2·279	2·312	2·410	2·339 2
Means ...	2·334 2	2·525 8	2·397 6	2·421 4	2·522 4	2·440 3

in the upper part of Table 6.7a the variance between nests is greater than that within a nest. Table 6.7 may be looked at in another way, the months providing the tickets in the first urn, and the variance be analysed into between- and within-month

TABLE 6.7a

ANALYSIS OF VARIANCE (HEAD BREADTHS OF TERMITES)

Source of Variation	Sum of Squares	Degrees of Freedom	Variance
Between nests	0·137 442	4	0·034 36
Within a nest	0·130 967	20	0·006 55
Between months	0·094 046	4	0·023 51
Within a month	0·174 363	20	0·008 72
Total	0·268 409	24	—

parts. This is done in the second section of Table 6.7a ; the variance between months is greater than that within a month, but the difference is of doubtful significance ($P = 0·06$). In these circumstances, the simple analysis of variance is invalid, but when the possible pattern of variation within a group is as defined as in Table 6.7, the analysis can be extended to deal with it, as shown in the next chapter.

We have so far placed no restrictions on the composition of the first urn. When the relations (6.2a) are used to estimate the substantive group variance σ_s^2, the first urn is usually regarded as containing an infinite population of tickets, and when σ_s is interpreted in the ordinary way, the frequency distribution of true group means in the first urn is tacitly assumed to be normal. These assumptions are not necessary for testing the significance of the between-group effect.

Daniels (1939) has dealt with the case where the number of groups is finite. Then, in the notation of section 6.21 the m arrays are not a random sample from an infinite population but are the whole population, and it is better for some purposes to allow for this by multiplying the estimate of σ_s^2 deduced from relations (6.2a) by $(m - 1)/m$. This will be referred to in section 12.24.

The question remains whether, when the between-group variance is not significantly different from the within-group variance, as in Table 6.5, an improved estimate of variance may be made by combining the two sums of squares and the two degrees of freedom. Such a procedure is likely to lead to bias, for sometimes one will combine estimates that are really (although insignificantly) different, and occasionally one will fail to combine apparently different estimates of what is really the same variance; the relative effects of the two types of error will depend partly on the level of significance adopted. The question is complicated and the answer is not clear. Where only a few degrees of freedom are available and combination would increase the number considerably, common sense suggests that combination should be made except for differences below say the 0·05 level of significance. In other circumstances combination is inadvisable, for if the two estimates do not differ much, the " improved " estimate is little different from the within-group variance and therefore little better ; and if the two estimates differ substantially, the risk of bias may outweigh the probability of the combined estimate being nearer the population value. The problem of " pooling " is further treated by Paull (1950).

CHAPTER VII

THE FURTHER ANALYSIS OF VARIANCE

THE data that have been subjected to a simple analysis of variance are all classified with respect to one factor : the shrub number in Table 6.2, the nest type in Table 6.4, and so on, the classification within each array being according not to any factor but to sub-ranges of the variate. The number of representatives of the factor, e.g. the number of shrubs or nest types, we term generally the number of *levels* of that factor included in the sample. When there are more than one factor the combination may take several forms ; but there is a series of forms the members of which are distinct from each other, and from which all other forms are built up. These we term *basic forms*, and the data of the previous chapter are all treated by the analysis suitable for the *one-factor basic form*. The next four sections will deal with the higher basic forms, and later sections with composite forms.

TWO-FACTOR BASIC FORM

7.1. Table 6.7 is of the typical two-factor basic form, the two factors being nests and months, random deviations being superimposed on deviations associated with these factors.

The experimental model giving rise to Table 6.7 requires three urns, the first for nests, with tickets each labelled with a nest number and the corresponding true nest mean expressed as a deviation from a grand mean, the second for months of the year with tickets labelled accordingly, and the third for random deviations. Five tickets are drawn from the first, one for each level of the first factor, and five from the second, one for each level of the second factor, and the two sets are combined in pairs giving 25 combinations. Twenty-five tickets are drawn at random from the third urn, and one is associated with each combination. Then the twenty-five results in Table 6.7 are formed by adding to the grand mean the deviations on the three tickets associated with each of the 25 combinations.

We do not in fact know the true nest and month means, and so use as estimates means calculated from the data, allowing for the effect on the estimates of variance by adjusting the degrees of freedom. Since each month is represented equally in the results for each nest, the month-to-month deviations contribute nothing to the variations between the nest means, and so we may eliminate the effect of the variations between nests by expressing the head breadths as deviations from their nest means as in Table 7.1.

TABLE 7.1

MEAN HEAD BREADTHS OF TERMITES (SMALL SOLDIERS)

(Deviations in mm. from nest means)

Nest Number	668	670	672	674	675	Means
November ...	− 0·061 2	− 0·046 8	+ 0·006 4	+ 0·025 6	− 0·066 4	− 0·028 48
January ...	− 0·002 2	+ 0·077 2	+ 0·059 4	− 0·033 4	+ 0·103 6	+ 0·040 92
March ...	+ 0·040 8	+ 0·087 2	+ 0·054 4	+ 0·093 6	+ 0·110 6	+ 0·077 32
May ...	+ 0·038 8	+ 0·031 2	− 0·001 6	+ 0·023 6	− 0·035 4	+ 0·011 32
August ...	− 0·016 2	− 0·148 8	− 0·118 6	− 0·109 4	− 0·112 4	− 0·101 08

We may now perform a one-factor analysis of variance on Table 7.1, giving the result shown in Table 7.1a.

The " total " sum of squares is, of course, the " within a nest " sum of Table 6.7a, and arises from 20 degrees of freedom. The " between months " sum is the same as before, since the elimination of the differences between the nest means has had no effect on the differences between months, and the degrees of freedom are

TABLE 7.1a

ANALYSIS OF VARIANCE

(Deviations of Head Breadths of Termites)

Source of Variation	Sum of Squares	Degrees of Freedom	Variance
Between months	0·094 046	4	0·023 51
Within a month	0·036 921	16	0·002 31
Total (within a nest) ...	0·130 967	20	—

still 4 ; the final residual within a month (and nest), based on 16 degrees of freedom, is very small. The ratio of variances in Table 7.1a is $F = 10·2$; and for $v_1 = 4$ and $v_2 = 16$ this lies well beyond the 0·005 level. Thus, by taking account of and eliminating the nest variations, we have established the month-of-year effect which, on the earlier incomplete analysis, seemed to be of doubtful significance.

There is no reason why we should not start with the deviations from the monthly means, and analyse the variance into two parts, between and within nests. Such a process would give the same between-nest variance as in Table 6.7a, and the same residual within a nest as is shown in Table 7.1a for within a month. This residual is common, and estimates the random deviations corresponding to the third urn. The significance of the nest variance then becomes even greater than before. The analysis is symmetrical with respect to nests and months, and the results can be assembled into a single table with four rows. In presenting such an analysis formally we shall generalise the terminology by referring to rows and columns instead of months and nests.

The algebraic relations may be expressed by the equation

$$(x - \bar{x}) = (\bar{x}_s - \bar{x}) + (\bar{x}_t - \bar{x}) + d, \quad . \quad . \quad (7.1)$$

where x is an individual reading for the sth row and the tth column,

$\bar{x}_s$ is the mean for the sth row,
$\bar{x}_t$ is the mean for the tth column,
$\bar{x}$ is the grand mean, and
$d = x - \bar{x}_s - \bar{x}_t + \bar{x}$ is the residual deviation.

Then squaring, and summing for all rows (S_s) and columns (S_t), we have

$$S_s S_t (x - \bar{x})^2 = S_s S_t (\bar{x}_s - \bar{x})^2 + S_s S_t (\bar{x}_t - \bar{x})^2 + S_s S_t d^2,$$

since the sums of the product terms come to zero. These are the sums of squares that go into the analysis table. If there are n_t rows and n_s columns (i.e. n_s observations in each row and n_t in each column, total $N = n_s n_t$), the above equation becomes

$$S_s S_t (x - \bar{x})^2 = n_s S_s (\bar{x}_s - \bar{x})^2 + n_t S_t (\bar{x}_t - \bar{x})^2 + S_s S_t d^2 \quad . (7.1a)$$

Expressed in words, this equation states that the sum of squares of deviations of individual observations from the grand mean equals the sum of squares of deviations of row means multiplied by the number of readings in each row, plus the sum of squares of deviations of column means multiplied by the number of readings in each column, plus the sum of squares of residual deviations.

These are entered in Table 7.1b, and symbols are written for the variances. If $\sigma_s{}^2$, $\sigma_t{}^2$ and $\sigma_r{}^2$ are the squares of standard deviations of row, column and residual variations in the infinite population, we obtain as in equations (6.2a)

$$\left. \begin{array}{l} v_s \longrightarrow n_s\sigma_s{}^2 + \sigma_r{}^2, \\ v_t \longrightarrow n_t\sigma_t{}^2 + \sigma_r{}^2, \\ v_r \longrightarrow \sigma_r{}^2. \end{array} \right\} \qquad \ldots \ldots \quad (7.1b)$$

In computing the residual sum of squares for Table 7.1b, it is troublesome to find the actual residual deviations, d, as we have done above, and provided the arithmetic is carefully checked, it is

TABLE 7.1b

ANALYSIS OF VARIANCE

Source of Variations	Sum of Squares	Degrees of Freedom	Variance
Rows	$n_s S_s (\bar{x}_s - x)^2$	$n_t - 1$	v_s
Columns	$n_t S_t (\bar{x}_t - \bar{x})^2$	$n_s - 1$	v_t
Residual	$S_s S_t d^2$	$N - n_s - n_t + 1$	v_r
Total	$S_s S_t (x - \bar{x})^2$	$N - 1$	—

sufficient to find the sums of squares for the rows, columns and total, and to obtain the residual by subtraction. The procedure is facilitated by extending the methods of section 6.3, performing the following operations :

(1) sum the squares of the individual observations,
(2) sum the squares of the row totals and divide the sum by the number of individuals in each row,
(3) sum the squares of the column totals and divide the sum by the number of individuals in each column,
(4) square the grand total and divide by the grand total number of observations.

Then it may easily be shown that the sums of squares required for Table 7.1b are :

for rows ... the result of operation (2) minus that of (4),
for columns ... (3) — (4),
for the total ... (1) — (4).

The observations may all be measured from some arbitrary origin, e.g. 2·200 mm. for the head breadths of termites, so that the quantities to be squared have only three or four significant figures,

and the computations may all be performed easily with the aid
only of a table of squares.

Assumptions and Interpretations

7.11. The same general remarks concerning assumptions and
interpretations apply to the analysis of the two-factor as to that
of the one-factor basic form, but a few special points need
mention.

After the statistical significance of the row or column effect has
been established, the practical significance is often adequately
assessed by comparing means. The biologist may, for example, be
content to note that the head breadth of termites in March is, on
the average, about 0·1 mm. greater than in November and nearly
0·2 mm. greater than in August. This kind of use of the two-factor
basic analysis has very frequently occurred in connection with
agricultural field trials. The columns represent blocks of trial
plots of ground and the rows experimentally controlled manurial
or other treatments (or vice versa) so arranged that each treatment
occurs once in each block. There may be significant differences
between blocks, which are of no importance, and significant differences between treatments, the investigation of which is the
object of the experiment. Such is termed a *randomised block*
arrangement, and the residual the *error variance*, so called because
it estimates the error with which the treatment effects are
measured. For comparing any pair of, say, row means (and this
may be necessary after the significance of the variations as a
whole has been established), the standard error of the difference
is estimated on $(N - n_s - n_t + 1)$ degrees of freedom by
$\sqrt{(2v_r/n_s)}$. For the monthly means of head breadths of termites,
this comes to $\sqrt{(0·004\ 62/5)} = 0·030$; since for 16 degrees of
freedom $t = 2·12$ lies on the 0·05 level of significance, only differences greater than 0·064 mm. would be judged as statistically
significant. Hence, the difference between January and March in
Table 6.7 would not be considered significant, did it not accord
with the significant rising trend from November to March. In
applying the standard error in this way to several means, due
regard must be paid to the fact that individual differences that are
tested are usually in some way selected. The standard error may
also be used to estimate confidence or fiducial limits for any
difference. It should be noted that the precision with which the

differences are estimated depends on the smallness of v_r as well as
the largeness of n_s, and that if v_r is small enough, n_s need not be
large.

This interpretation of a two-factor basic analysis does not
require an infinite population of tickets in the first two urns (in
the terms of our experimental model), nor a random selection ;
those conditions apply necessarily to the third urn only. But the
interpretation assumes the use of only three urns, with the
consequence of uniform residual variance for all rows and
columns. As an alternative interpretation we may imagine for
the termites, instead of the first two urns, twenty-five tickets (the
two urns can be dispensed with), each for a different nest-month,
with the true mean value for the nest-month on it. The results of
Table 6.7 would then be arrived at by combining with each of
these tickets one drawn at random from the original third urn.
If the two-factor basic analysis were applied to such a set-up,
equation (7.1) would become :

$$(x - \bar{x}) + (\bar{x}_s - \bar{x}) + (\bar{x}_t - \bar{x}) + \bar{x}'_{st} + d \quad . \quad . \quad (7.11)$$

where the values $(\bar{x}_s - \bar{x})$ measure the row effect common to all
columns, $(\bar{x}_t - \bar{x})$ measure the column effect common to all rows,
and x'_{st} measures the extent to which the true value for any row-
column (nest-month in the particular case) departs from the value
$\bar{x} + (\bar{x}_s - \bar{x}) + (\bar{x}_t - \bar{x})$. The common row and column effects
may or may not have technical significance ; they have been
invented by the analysis, and are termed the *main* row and column
effects. The deviation x'_{st} is termed the *interaction* between the
row and column effects. In the analysis it cannot be separated
from the error d, so that where this model applies the residual
variance in Table 7.1b measures the interaction plus the error.
We shall see later how by some arrangements the separation
can be made.

One can imagine that the particular monthly mean values in
Table 6.7 may have some biological significance, but that the nest
means have none. It matters nothing that nest 675 has a higher
mean than nest 668, say ; the nests are presumably a random
sample from a large population of nests and their numbering is
presumably arbitrary. The nest means can only be regarded as
showing the variation in the population of nests, and this can only
be expressed by a variance or standard deviation. In these

circumstances, relations (7.1b) may be used to estimate substantive variances. For the termites we have

$$\sigma_r^2 \rightarrow \qquad\qquad\qquad 0.002\ 31 \text{ (residual)},$$

$$\sigma_s^2 \rightarrow \frac{0.023\ 51 - 0.002\ 31}{5} = 0.004\ 24 \text{ (months)},$$

$$\sigma_t^2 \rightarrow \frac{0.034\ 36 - 0.002\ 31}{5} = 0.006\ 41 \text{ (nests)}.$$

It is not reasonable to assume an infinite population of months, and if we wish to bring σ_s^2 into our calculations, we must follow methods dealt with by Daniels (1939). But we may say that if, for the same month in the year, termites are taken from many nests, the variance of nest means will tend to equal $\sigma_t^2 + \sigma_r^2 = 0.008\ 72$, whereas if the nest variation can be eliminated the variance is reduced to $\sigma_r^2 = 0.002\ 31$. The corresponding standard deviations are 0.093 and 0.048, and these may be interpreted in terms of normal frequencies according to section 2.52. Such estimates of variance and standard deviation are of little value unless based on many degrees of freedom (see section 6.21), and this usually involves combining the results of several tables, in the way described in section 7.4. This application of substantive variances is specially useful for investigating the qualities of mass-produced industrial articles, where the measures of variability have a recognised practical significance.

THREE-FACTOR BASIC FORM

7.2. The experimental model lying behind the three-factor basic form of data requires four urns, the first containing a numbered ticket for each row, the second a numbered ticket for each column, the third a numbered ticket for each level of a third factor which we shall arbitrarily term a " treatment," and the fourth with tickets for random deviations. On all tickets are written deviations from the grand mean in the values of the quantity measured. The number of tickets in the first three urns may be finite or infinite, but the number in the fourth is infinite. A certain number of tickets, n, is taken from each of the first three urns. There are n^3 possible combinations of which we choose at random a set of n^2 subject to the restriction that each row occurs once with each column and treatment, each column once with each row and treatment, and (consequently) each treatment once with each column and row. The deviations on the three tickets in each combination are then added to the grand mean and to a random deviation drawn from the fourth urn.

An example of such an arrangement is in the upper part of Table 7.2, where the rows are labelled with period numbers, the

TABLE 7.2

Warp Breaks per 10 000 Picks and Treatments

Loom ...	7	8	9	10
Period		Yarn X		
1	1·4 (iv)	5·3 (i)	7·4 (ii)	3·2 (iii)
2	2·2 (iii)	4·1 (ii)	8·8 (i)	1·6 (iv)
3	2·1 (ii)	2·2 (iv)	4·8 (iii)	4·7 (i)
4	2·4 (i)	2·3 (iii)	2·6 (iv)	4·3 (ii)
Loom ...	15	16	17	18
Period		Yarn Y		
5	2·8 (iii)	1·5 (i)	1·9 (ii)	2·0 (iv)
6	1·5 (iv)	1·2 (ii)	2·0 (i)	1·8 (iii)
7	2·5 (ii)	1·4 (iv)	2·4 (iii)	2·0 (i)
8	5·8 (i)	1·9 (iii)	1·7 (iv)	3·2 (ii)

columns with loom numbers and the treatments with the Roman numerals in brackets ; the Arabic numerals are the values of the variate under investigation. The data originated in a weaving experiment in which there were four warps, each of which had been subject to a different sizing treatment. For the first weaving period of about one week, warp (iv) was woven in loom 7, warp (i) in loom 8, and so on. Then for the second period the warps were interchanged between the looms so that the warp (iii) was woven in loom 7, and so on.

The three-factor basic form is called a *Latin square* because in the original discussion of " magic squares " by Euler in 1782 the " treatments " were denoted by Latin letters. The introduction of this arrangement into statistics is due to Fisher (1925c), who used it for agricultural experiments where the rows and columns formed a layout of trial plots of ground, and the treatments were experimentally controlled manurial or other variations, disposed at random over the plots with the restriction that each treatment occurs once in each row and column. It will be noted that the number of observations in a Latin square must be a square.

Since each column and treatment is associated equally with each row, the differences between the row means are affected only by the random deviations, and the deviations $(\bar{x}_s - \bar{x})$ are good estimates of the row effect (we are using the notation of section 7.1). Similarly, the deviations $(\bar{x}_t - \bar{x})$ estimate the column effect free from the row and treatment effects, and $(\bar{x}_u - \bar{x})$ measure the pure treatment effect, the suffix u being used to denote the treatment. Corresponding to equation (7.1) we have

$$(x - \bar{x}) = (\bar{x}_s - \bar{x}) + (\bar{x}_t - \bar{x}) + (\bar{x}_u - \bar{x}) + d \quad . \quad . \quad (7.2)$$

and corresponding to equation (7.1a) we have

$$S_s S_t (x - \bar{x})^2 = n S_s (\bar{x}_s - \bar{x})^2 + n S_t (\bar{x}_t - \bar{x})^2 + n S_u (\bar{x}_u - \bar{x})^2$$
$$+ S_s S_t d^2, \quad . \quad . \quad . \quad . \quad . \quad . \quad (7.2a)$$

the double summation $S_s S_t$ necessarily including the triple summation $S_s S_t S_u$. The terms on the right-hand side of equation (7.2a) may be entered in a table of analysis of variance. The relations between the resulting estimates of variance and the substantive variances are

$$\left. \begin{array}{l} v_s \rightarrow n\sigma_s^2 + \sigma_r^2 \\ v_t \rightarrow n\sigma_t^2 + \sigma_r^2 \\ v_u \rightarrow n\sigma_u^2 + \sigma_r^2 \\ v_r \rightarrow \sigma_r^2. \end{array} \right\} \quad . \quad . \quad . \quad (7.2b)$$

The scheme for computation given in section 7.1 may be extended as follows :

(1) square every individual value and sum,
(2) find the total of the values for each row, square the totals, sum these squares, and divide the result by n,
(3) repeat (2) for the column totals,
(4) repeat (3) for the treatment totals, and
(5) square the grand total and divide by n^2.

The terms in the following equation correspond to those in equation (7.2a)

$$[(1) - (5)] = [(2) - (5)] + [(3) - (5)] + [(4) - (5)] + S_s S_t d^2.$$

All these terms except the last may be easily computed with the aid of a table of squares, particularly if the values are measured from an arbitrary origin, and the last may be obtained by difference.

N   193

The degrees of freedom are $n - 1$ each for rows, columns and treatments, $n^2 - 1$ for the total, and $n^2 - 3n + 2 = (n - 1)(n - 2)$ for the residual.

TABLE 7.2a

ANALYSIS OF VARIANCE (WARP BREAKAGE RATES)

Source of Variation	Sums of Squares	Degrees of Freedom	Variance	F	P
Periods ...	5·273	3	1·76	2·4	0·16
Looms ...	31·033	3	10·34	14	< ·005
Treatments ...	26·213	3	8·74	12	·006
Residual ...	4·339	6	0·72	—	—
Total ...	66·858	15	—		

The analysis for the upper part of Table 7.2 is in Table 7.2a, the ratios of the variance to the residual and the corresponding probabilities from Chart E1 being in the last two columns. The period effect is not significant, but the loom and treatment effects are overwhelmingly so, even allowing for the possibility that the residual variance may not be homogeneous.

When an analysis is done on data in a three-factor basic form the residual is usually regarded as estimating a homogeneous error variance, but there is the same possibility of interactions as mentioned in section 7.11 for the two-factor basic analysis, except that the possibilities are more complicated than are shown in equation (7.11). The average period effect could be different for the different looms : perhaps a tendency to an increasing breakage rate with period number on loom 7, a tendency to a decreasing rate on loom 8, and a tendency to rise and then fall on loom 10. Likewise, the average period effect could be different for different treatments, and the average loom effect could be different for different treatments ; these are termed *first-order interactions*. In addition there is the possibility of the treatment effect being different for each loom and period, giving a *second-order interaction*. The data are not sufficient to permit of a separation of these interactions—a complete separation could be made only if results for the n^3 combinations were available—and they cannot be separated from the error. It is not often, however, that the separation is necessary, but the possibility of interactions should not be overlooked.

As for the two-factor analysis, we may in suitable circumstances interpret any of the row, column or treatment variations as estimating the variation in an infinite population, using the relations $(7.2b)$ to estimate substantive variances.

MULTI-FACTOR BASIC FORMS

7.3. The three-factor basic form may be extended almost indefinitely to include almost any number of factors. If there are four factors in addition to the random deviations, the resulting four-factor basic form is termed a *Græco-Latin square*, so called because Euler in his treatment denoted the levels of two of the factors by Greek and Latin letters respectively, the levels of the other two being denoted by row and column numbers. All these arrangements have the same number of levels of each factor, and each level of each factor is associated once with each level of every other factor. There are severe limitations as to the numbers of possible arrangements of these more complex types.

The extension of the analysis to these types is obvious, and the same points arise in the interpretation, except that the question of interactions is even more complicated than for the three-factor analysis.

TABLE 7.3

WEIGHTS OF ROVING, GRAMS PER 180 YARDS, AND INTERMEDIATE-FLYER COMBINATIONS

Spindle	1	2	3	4	5
Doffing					
1	$16 \cdot 15 \ (i_1 f_1)$	$16 \cdot 50 \ (i_2 f_2)$	$15 \cdot 99 \ (i_3 f_3)$	$16 \cdot 79 \ (i_4 f_4)$	$16 \cdot 19 \ (i_5 f_5)$
2	$16 \cdot 46 \ (i_5 f_2)$	$16 \cdot 08 \ (i_1 f_3)$	$16 \cdot 24 \ (i_2 f_4)$	$15 \cdot 70 \ (i_3 f_5)$	$16 \cdot 30 \ (i_4 f_1)$
3	$15 \cdot 99 \ (i_4 f_3)$	$16 \cdot 14 \ (i_5 f_4)$	$16 \cdot 16 \ (i_1 f_5)$	$16 \cdot 19 \ (i_2 f_1)$	$16 \cdot 33 \ (i_3 f_2)$
4	$16 \cdot 25 \ (i_3 f_4)$	$16 \cdot 18 \ (i_4 f_5)$	$16 \cdot 55 \ (i_5 f_1)$	$16 \cdot 81 \ (i_1 f_2)$	$16 \cdot 42 \ (i_2 f_3)$
5	$16 \cdot 17 \ (i_2 f_5)$	$15 \cdot 84 \ (i_3 f_1)$	$16 \cdot 28 \ (i_4 f_2)$	$16 \cdot 29 \ (i_5 f_3)$	$16 \cdot 27 \ (i_1 f_4)$

Table 7.3 gives the results of an experiment in the spinning of a cotton roving, a product not unlike yarn but coarser and less highly twisted. Each bobbin of roving is spun on one spindle, from a particular bobbin of " intermediate " (the raw material of the process) and with each spindle is associated a part of the mechanism called a " flyer." The bobbins spun on the spindles of a frame at the same time constitute a " doffing." For the experiment

of Table 7.3 five spindles were chosen on a frame, there were five intermediates (i_1 to i_5) and five flyers (f_1 to f_5), and five doffings were spun. For the first doffing, i_1 and f_1 were associated with spindle 1, i_2 and f_2 with spindle 2, and so on as shown in the first row of the table. For the second doffing, i_1 was moved to spindle 2 and f_1 to spindle 5, and so on, the combinations being as shown in the second row of the table. Similarly, by interchanging the intermediates and flyers between the spindles for the later doffings the arrangement of Table 7.3, a Græco-Latin square, was completed, yielding 25 bobbins of roving altogether. It can easily be seen that each spindle is associated once and once only with each intermediate, flyer and doffing, each intermediate once with each spindle, flyer and doffing, and so on. Each bobbin was tested for the weight of roving per 180 yards, and the results are the figures in the table.

The analysis of variance which has been computed on closely parallel lines to the method described for the Latin square is in the first four columns of Table 7.3a ; the weights of Table 7.3 have been multiplied by 100 for convenience. The variance for spindles

TABLE 7.3a

ANALYSIS OF VARIANCE OF ROVING WEIGHTS

(Units of weight, grams × 100)

Source of Variation	Data of Table 7.3			Six Squares Combined		
	Sum of Squares	Degrees of Freedom	Variance	Sum of Squares	Degrees of Freedom	Variance
Spindles ...	1 324	4	331	13 060	24	544
Doffings ...	3 266	4	816	24 580	24	1 024
Intermediates	3 299	4	825	13 028	24	543
Flyers ...	4 943	4	1 236	17 166	24	715
Residual ...	2 428	8	303	15 346	48	320
Total ...	15 260	24	—	83 180	144	—

is not significantly greater than the residual, that for doffings and intermediates is on the 0·11 level, and so is insignificant, and that for flyers is on the 0·04 level.

The experiment was repeated for five further such Græco-Latin squares and the combined results for the six squares are in the last three columns of Table 7.3a. The doffing effect is now highly significant above the 0·005 level, and the effect of flyer variations is significant near the 0·01 level (see Chart E3).

The doffings and flyers have no individuality that makes it technically interesting to know that this or that doffing or flyer gives a higher mean roving weight than another, but the effect on the general variability is of interest. Accordingly we calculate the following estimates of substantive variances (all in grams squared) :

$$\text{doffings :} \quad (1\ 024 - 320)10^{-4}/5 = 0\cdot014\ 1$$
$$\text{flyers :} \quad (715 - 320)10^{-4}/5 = 0\cdot007\ 9$$
$$\text{residual :} \quad 320 \times 10^{-4} = 0\cdot032\ 0$$

There may or may not be real spindle and intermediate effects, but in any event they are relatively small and the data are not sufficient to give useful information about them.

COMPOSITE FORMS

7.4. Data are often in a form made up of several of the basic forms superimposed, and it is convenient to recognise the basic forms and analyse the whole in terms of these. If the values are expressed in terms of means, deviations of means from some composite means, and deviations of individual values from means, as in equations (7.1) and (7.2), the deviations of the various means must be summed over all the original observations, and computationally this is generally equivalent to squaring and summing the various totals, and dividing the sum of squares by the number of original observations per total. This is best described by working a few examples.

7.41. Table 7.41 is reprinted from page 81 of *Statistical Methods in Research and Production, with special reference to the Chemical Industry*, by permission of the editor, Dr. O. L. Davies, and the publishers, Messrs. Oliver & Boyd Ltd. Pieces of four fabrics were subjected to a test for waterproofness, the four pieces in each group being put into the testing machine and tested together, with the results shown.

If the classification according to fabrics is ignored the data are in the single-factor basic form and the variance may be analysed into two parts : between and within groups. This has been done in the left-hand parts of the columns of Table 7.41a. The sums of squares, obtained by using 60·0 as a working origin, are :

$$296 \cdot 86 = (21 \cdot 8^2 + 25 \cdot 7^2 + \ldots 41 \cdot 0^2)/4 - 365 \cdot 1^2/48$$
$$271 \cdot 43 = (3 \cdot 9^2 + 5 \cdot 3^2 + \ldots 12 \cdot 8^2)$$
$$- (21 \cdot 8^2 + 25 \cdot 7^2 + \ldots 41 \cdot 0^2)/4$$
$$568 \cdot 29 = (3 \cdot 9^2 + 5 \cdot 3^2 + \ldots 12 \cdot 8^2) - 365 \cdot 1^2/48.$$

The between-group variance is significantly greater than the residual or within-group variance.

The group totals and fabric totals in Table 7.41 are themselves in the single-factor basic form and the variance may be analysed

TABLE 7.41

PERCENTAGE WATER ABSORPTION OF PROOFED FABRIC

Fabric	Group of Tests	Individual Results				Group Totals*	Fabric Totals*
A	1	63·9	65·3	65·6	67·0	21·8	
	2	63·4	63·9	67·2	71·2	25·7	83·2
	3	69·4	67·1	69·2	70·0	35·7	
B	4	67·2	66·3	67·8	67·8	29·1	
	5	70·7	69·0	69·0	69·3	38·0	83·7
	6	67·5	62·7	64·0	62·4	16·6	
C	7	62·2	60·6	66·1	65·9	14·8	
	8	64·9	62·7	69·5	66·9	24·0	85·2
	9	71·6	70·8	73·6	70·4	46·4	
D	10	79·1	66·6	66·2	71·1	43·0	
	11	65·9	64·9	66·2	72·0	29·0	113·0
	12	68·9	68·8	70·5	72·8	41·0	

* The totals are of the original values measured as deviations from 60·0.

into two parts : between fabrics (3 degrees of freedom) and within fabrics but between groups (8 degrees). The results of the analysis are in the right-hand half of the columns of Table 7.41a, the sums of squares being

$$52 \cdot 62 = (83 \cdot 2^2 + \ldots 113 \cdot 0^2)/12 - 265 \cdot 1^2/48 \text{ and}$$
$$244 \cdot 24 = (21 \cdot 8^2 + 25 \cdot 7^2 + \ldots 41 \cdot 0^2)/4 - (83 \cdot 2^2 + \ldots$$
$$113 \cdot 0^2)/12.$$

The " total " sum of squares for this analysis is 296·86, and the divisors 12 and 4 are the number of tests per fabric and group respectively.

In order to interpret the variances of Table 7.41a we need to recognise three substantive variances :

$\sigma_r{}^2$, the within-group variance,

$\sigma_g{}^2$, the variance between group means that would be estimated if many groups of tests were made on one fabric and either $\sigma_r{}^2 = 0$ or there could be an infinite number of tests per group, and

$\sigma_f{}^2$, the variance between fabric means that would be obtained if either $\sigma_r{}^2 = \sigma_g{}^2 = 0$, or there could be an infinite number of groups per fabric.

It is easy to see qualitatively that the variance in Table 7.41a

TABLE 7.41a

ANALYSIS OF VARIANCE (PERCENTAGE WATER ABSORPTION)

Source of Variation		Sums of Squares	Degrees of Freedom	Variance
Between groups	Between fabrics	296·86 { 52·62	11 { 3	26·99 { 17·54
	Within fabrics	244·24	8	30·53
Within groups ...		271·43	36	7·54
Total ...		568·29	47	—

between groups within fabrics is affected by $\sigma_r{}^2$ and $\sigma_g{}^2$, and that the variance between fabrics is affected by $\sigma_f{}^2$, $\sigma_g{}^2$ and $\sigma_r{}^2$. An extension of the results of section 6.21 leads to the following :

$$17\cdot54 \rightarrow \sigma_r{}^2 + 4\sigma_g{}^2 + 12\sigma_f{}^2$$
$$30\cdot53 \rightarrow \sigma_r{}^2 + 4\sigma_g{}^2$$
$$7\cdot54 \rightarrow \sigma_r{}^2.$$

In order to test the significance of the variations between fabrics, 17·54 must be tested against 30·53 and not 7·54. There is no apparent fabric effect (17·54 is *less* than 30·53), but the group effect is highly significant. The substantive variances can be estimated by making the obvious subtractions.

7.42. The whole of the data of Table 7.2 consists of two Latin squares, and may be subjected to a combined analysis. The weaving experiment was performed on two warp yarns, X and Y, the four treatments being the same for both. First we may analyse each Latin square separately, and add the two sets of sums of squares to give the results in rows (2), (3), (4) and (5) of Table 7.42. If we square the two totals for yarns X and Y, add, divide by 16 (the number of observations per total), and subtract the grand total squared and divided by 32 [i.e. $(59\cdot4^2 + 35\cdot6^2)/16 - 95\cdot0^2/32$], we have the sum of squares in row (1) of Table 7.42 measuring the mean yarn effect on one degree of freedom.

TABLE 7.42

ANALYSIS OF VARIANCE OF WARP BREAKAGE RATES

Source of Variation	Sums of Squares	Degrees of Freedom	Variance
(1) Yarns	17·701	1	17·701
(2) Periods	10·348	6	1·725
(3) Looms	36·763	6	6·127
(4) Treatments	28·978	6	4·830
(5) Residual	8·539	12	0·712
(6) Total	102·329	31	—
Main Effects			
(7) Quantity	5·120	1	5·120
(8) Ingredient	17·111	1	17·111
Interactions			
(9) Quantity—Ingredient ...	0·046	1	0·046
(10) Quantity—Yarn	0·320	1	0·320
(11) Ingredient—Yarn	6·302	1	6·302
(12) Quantity—Ingredient—Yarn	0·079	1	0·079

If we discount the possibility of interactions between periods, looms and treatments, we may test the significance of each of these effects by comparing its variance with the residual, 0·712. The treatment effect, in which we are interested, is significant. The difference between the yarns is affected by loom and period variations as well as random errors, and so the variance in row (1) may not be compared with the residual in row (5). The arrangement does not readily lend itself to an investigation of the main yarn effect. We shall now investigate the treatment effect further.

The experiment was intended to investigate the effect of two sizing ingredients A and B, each being used in two concentrations : 1 and 2 units, so that the treatments were :

(i) 1 unit of ingredient A
(ii) 2 units of ingredient A
(iii) 1 unit of ingredient B
(iv) 2 units of ingredient B.

The yarn effect may be eliminated from the treatment comparisons by totalling over both yarns the warp breakage rates for the treatments. These totals are as follows :

		Ingredient	
		A	B
1 unit	...	32·5	21·4
2 units	...	26·7	14·4

This is a two-factor basic form, each factor being at two levels, and the sum of squares may be analysed into parts associated respectively with quantity, ingredient, and a residual, each having one degree of freedom. The quantity sum of squares is $[(53\cdot9^2 + 41\cdot1^2)/16 - 95\cdot0^2/32]$, the divisor in each instance being the number of original observations per total ; this sum is in row (7) of Table 7.42. The ingredient sum of squares in row (8) is obtained similarly. The corresponding variances measure the main quantity and ingredient effects. The residual of the above 2×2 table measures the interaction between quantity and ingredient (plus, of course, error), and is entered in row (9) of Table 7.42. It is $[(32\cdot5^2 + 26\cdot7^2 + 21\cdot4^2 + 14\cdot4^2)/8 - 95\cdot0^2/32 - 5\cdot120 - 17\cdot111]$.

Now we may eliminate the main ingredient effect by obtaining the following totals of the warp breakage rates

		Yarn	
		X	Y
1 unit	...	33·7	20·2
2 units	...	25·7	15·4

This is another 2×2, two-factor basic form, that may be analysed in the same way as the previous one to measure a main yarn effect [row (1) of Table 7.42], a main quantity effect [row (7)] and a quantity-yarn interaction [row (10)].

Similarly, the ingredient-yarn interaction in row (11) may be obtained from the following table of warp breakage rate totals :

		Ingredient	
		A	B
Yarn X	...	39·1	20·3
Yarn Y	...	20·1	15·5

The five sums of squares in rows (7) to (11) of Table 7.42 account for 5 of the 6 degrees of freedom associated with treatments in row (4). The remaining degree is associated with the so-called second order interaction that would arise if the quantity effect were different for each ingredient on each yarn. The sum of squares is best obtained as [28·978 − 5·120 − 17·111 − 0·046 − 0·320 − 6·302] and is entered in row (12).

Since we are regarding the residual variance in row (5) as measuring the errors with which the treatment effects are measured, we may compare with it each of the variances in rows (7) to (12). The variances in rows (9), (10) and (12) are less than that in row (5), although not significantly so, and the corresponding interactions are not statistically significant. The main effects of quantity and ingredient, and the interaction between ingredient and yarn are significant, and we may express the final results by the following mean values of the breakage rates per 10 000 picks :

1 unit	...	...	...	3·4,	2 units	...	...	...	2·6,

$$\text{Ingredient } A \begin{cases} \text{yarn } X & ... \quad 4·9, \\ \text{yarn } Y & ... \quad 2·5, \end{cases} \qquad \text{Ingredient } B \begin{cases} \text{yarn } X & ... \quad 2·5, \\ \text{yarn } Y & ... \quad 1·9. \end{cases}$$

For comparing the quantities, since there are 16 readings per mean, the standard error of the difference is $\pm \sqrt{(2 \times 0·712/16)} = \pm 0·30$, and the corresponding standard error of a difference between ingredients on one yarn is $\pm \sqrt{(2 \times 0·712/8)} = \pm 0·42$. The difference between ingredients on yarn Y is not significant.

Thus, the final conclusions from these experiments are that the use of two units of either ingredient instead of one reduces the warp breakage rate slightly on both yarns, that on yarn X ingredient B gives a considerably lower breakage rate than A and that on yarn Y there is little or no difference in response to the two ingredients. It is interesting to note that the breakage rate is higher on yarn X than Y, and although we have not tested to see whether this is due to the yarns or to loom and period variations, it may be that the higher breakage rate is necessary to give sensitivity to the form of ingredient.

An experiment of this kind in which the treatments form a pattern so that they can be subdivided into factors is called a *factorial experiment*. Factorial experiments find considerable application in some fields and lead to data in highly complex forms. The subject has been considerably elaborated, and readers who wish to follow it further should refer to Brownlee (1946), Fisher (1936a) and Yates (1937b).

7.43. The data of Table 7.43 are from a paper by Gould and Hampton (1936).* From a single " pot," about eighteen cylinders of spectacle glass are made on any one day or " journey." Two pots are heated together in the same furnace and glass may be made on several consecutive days from the same pair of pots, forming a " run." The quality measured, or variate, is the mean number of seed per unit area of glass, and this is given in Table 7.43 for three cylinders from each pot—the third, tenth and sixteenth in order of manufacture—and for the first five journeys in each of four runs. There is no significance in the numbering of the pots, and the runs are independent, being separated by several weeks and sometimes referring to different furnaces. The separate figures are given in the table, and various totals have also been computed.

Now each kind of manufacturing unit—cylinder, pot, journey or run—is a potential source of variation, since the causes that control quality may be consistently different for each unit. Further, since the journeys are consecutive days and the cylinders are in order of manufacture, there may be trends in quality. Clearly, the variations in density of seed shown in Table 7.43 are the result of the superimposition of variations from many possible sources. Precisely what are these sources ? Which have statistically significant effects ? What is their relative importance ? To answer these questions we shall analyse the variations in Table 7.43 completely.

First consider the fifteen readings in one pot-run, say the first pot and first run. This is of the two-factor basic form, the factors being between cylinders (two degrees of freedom) and between journeys (four degrees), the residual having eight degrees and the total sum of squares fourteen degrees. When the sums of squares and degrees of freedom are added for the eight pot-runs, the figures

---

* From Table IV of their paper. We give here only four of the five runs given there so as to make the analysis easier to follow. It might lead to some ambiguity in the argument if five runs and five journeys were retained.

given in rows (1) to (4) of Table 7.43a result. The sums of squares
are :

$$22\ 132\cdot53 = (248^2 + \ldots 294^2)/5 - (1\ 047^2 + \ldots 820^2)/15$$
$$37\ 916\cdot66 = (203^2 + \ldots 177^2)/3 - (1\ 047^2 + \ldots 820^2)/15$$
$$78\ 447\cdot33 = (\ 47^2 + \ldots\ 78^2)/1 - (1\ 047^2 + \ldots 820^2)/15.$$

TABLE 7.43

MEAN NUMBER OF SEED PER UNIT AREA

Run	Journey	Pot 1 Cylinder			Pot 2 Cylinder			Totals		
		3	10	16	3	10	16	Pot 1	Pot 2	Both Pots
1	1	47	56	100	52	61	88	203	201	404
	2	55	89	93	49	62	97	237	208	445
	3	35	57	56	34	60	72	148	166	314
	4	78	67	113	47	93	118	258	258	516
	5	33	40	128	16	29	130	201	175	376
	Totals	248	309	490	198	305	505	1 047	1 008	2 055
2	1	52	66	36	65	80	40	154	185	339
	2	21	61	49	122	97	79	131	298	429
	3	31	39	25	45	54	72	95	171	266
	4	43	72	52	109	120	80	167	309	476
	5	37	51	67	67	85	63	155	215	370
	Totals	184	289	229	408	436	334	702	1 178	1 880
3	1	50	61	60	75	139	130	171	344	515
	2	33	27	49	46	58	63	109	167	276
	3	24	39	24	15	33	39	87	87	174
	4	18	18	43	22	16	19	79	57	136
	5	28	42	28	27	19	22	98	68	166
	Totals	153	187	204	185	265	273	544	723	1 267
4	1	24	34	43	46	66	24	101	136	237
	2	24	49	42	40	117	105	115	262	377
	3	21	21	51	30	28	34	93	92	185
	4	21	69	48	36	64	53	138	153	291
	5	76	48	42	39	60	78	166	177	343
	Totals	166	221	226	191	335	294	613	820	1 433

Now, the eight pot totals may be arranged in a one-factor basic form, and be analysed to give the results in rows (5), (6) and (7) of Table 7.43a. The sums of squares are :

$$13\ 679{\cdot}90 = (2\ 055^2 + \ldots\ 1\ 433^2)/30 - 6\ 635^2/120$$
$$23\ 779{\cdot}47 = (1\ 047^2 + \ldots\ \ 820^2)/15 - 6\ 635^2/120.$$

TABLE 7.43a

ANALYSIS OF VARIANCE

Source of Variation	Sum of Squares	Degrees of Freedom	Variance
(a) *Within Pots*			
(1) Between cylinders ...	22 132·53	16	1 383·28**
(2) Between journeys ...	37 916·66	32	1 184·90**
(3) Residual within pots	18 398·14	64	287·47
(4) Total	78 447·33	112	—
(b) *Between Pots*			
(5) Between runs ...	13 679·90	3	4 559·96
(6) Residual between pots	10 099·57	4	2 524·89**
(7) Total	23 779·47	7	3 397·07**
(c) *Between Cylinders*			
(8) Common to all runs ...	9 132·88	2	4 566·44
(9) Common to both pots in run, less (8) ...	11 532·72	6	1 922·12
	20 665·60	8	2 583·20**
(10) Specific to pot ...	1 466·93	8	183·37
(11) Total	22 132·53	16	—
(d) *Between Journeys*			
(12) Common to all runs ...	9 684·00	4	2 421·00
(13) Common to both pots in run, less (12) ...	18 650·07	12	1 554·17
	28 334·07	16	1 770·88**
(14) Specific to pot ...	9 582·59	16	598·91*
(15) Total	37 916·66	32	—

The cylinder variations in row (1) of Table 7.43a may be analysed further. The cylinder totals for each run may be arranged in the two-factor basic form, those for run 1 being given in Table 7.43b ; the sources are between pots (one degree), between cylinders, the effect being common to both pots (two degrees) and

TABLE 7.43b

	Cylinder			Total
	3	10	16	
Pot 1	248	309	490	1 047
Pot 2	198	305	505	1 008
Total	446	614	995	2 055

a residual (two degrees) which is the cylinder-pot interaction or in other words an extra cylinder effect that is specific to each pot. The sums of squares and degrees of freedom, when added for the four runs, give rows (6), (8) and (9) combined, and (10), of Table 7.43a. Only one new sum of squares needs to be directly computed, it is :

$$20\ 665 \cdot 60 = (446^2 + \ldots 520^2)/10 - (2\ 055^2 + \ldots 1\ 433^2)/30.$$

We may sub-divide this sum of squares further by analysing the two-factor basic form of Table 7.43c, which is formed from the cylinder totals for the runs. The sources are the cylinder effect common to all runs (two degrees) of Table 7.43a, row (8), the between-run effect (three degrees, entered in row (5) of Table 7.43a), and a cylinder-run interaction (six degrees, entered in row (9) of Table 7.43a) which may be interpreted as a differential cylinder effect for each run but common for the two pots in a run. The only new sum of squares required is :

$$9\ 132 \cdot 88 = (1\ 733^2 + \ldots 2\ 555^2)/40 - 6\ 635^2/120.$$

The between-journey sum of squares in row (2) of Table 7.43a may be sub-divided in precisely the same way as the between-cylinder sum, to give the results in section (d) of Table 7.43a.

Before testing the variances in Table 7.43a for significance, it will be well to determine of what substantive variances they are estimates. Let the variances entered in the table be denoted by v

with a subscript corresponding to the row of the table, i.e. v_1, v_2, etc., and let the corresponding substantive variances be denoted by σ^2 with a corresponding subscript. Thus, σ_1^2 is the variance that would be found between the cylinder means within each pot if an infinite number of observations could be made on

TABLE 7.43c

	Cylinder			Total
	3	10	16	
Run 1	446	614	995	2 055
Run 2	592	725	563	1 880
Run 3	338	452	477	1 267
Run 4	357	556	520	1 433
Total	1 733	2 347	2 555	6 635

each cylinder and there were an infinite number of pots. Further, let the number of the original individuals contributing to the mean of each individual factor be n with an appropriate subscript. For example, n_1 is the number of readings per cylinder within each pot, $= 5$, n_9 is the number of readings per cylinder mean for each run, $= 10$, and so on. Then the values of the n's and the relations between the observed and substantive variances, expressed in the manner of equations $(7.1b)$, are as follows :

$$n_1 = 5 \qquad v_1 \rightarrow n_1\sigma_1^2 + \sigma_3^2$$
$$n_2 = 3 \qquad v_2 \rightarrow n_2\sigma_2^2 + \sigma_3^2$$
$$n_3 = 1 \qquad v_3 \rightarrow \sigma_3^2$$

$$n_5 = 30 \qquad v_5 \rightarrow n_5\sigma_5^2 + v_6$$
$$n_6 = 15 \qquad v_6 \rightarrow n_6\sigma_6^2 + \sigma_3^2$$

$$n_8 = 40 \qquad v_8 \rightarrow n_8\sigma_8^2 + v_9$$
$$n_9 = 10 \qquad v_9 \rightarrow n_9\sigma_9^2 + v_{10}$$
$$n_{10} = n_1 = 5 \qquad v_{10} \rightarrow n_{10}\sigma_{10}^2 + \sigma_3^2$$

$$n_{12} = 24 \qquad v_{12} \rightarrow n_{12}\sigma_{12}^2 + v_{13}$$
$$n_{13} = 6 \qquad v_{13} \rightarrow n_{13}\sigma_{13}^2 + v_{14}$$
$$n_{14} = n_2 = 3 \qquad v_{14} \rightarrow n_{14}\sigma_{14}^2 + \sigma_3^2$$

We shall now proceed to discuss the derivation of these expressions.

The relations between v_1, v_2 and v_3 are the same as those between the variances of Table 7.1b, except that we have combined the estimates of several tables. It will be noted that the cylinder and journey effects may vary from one pot or run to another and σ_1^2 and σ_2^2 may themselves be complex. The residual variance σ_3^2 is due partly to the fact that only a limited number of sections on each cylinder were examined for seed and partly to a real variation that could not be associated with any factor.

The relation between v_5 and v_6 follows from equation $(7.1b)$, and from the fact that the analysis of pot totals and division of the sums of squares by the number of readings per pot is equivalent to performing the analysis on the pot means and multiplying the sums of squares by the number of individuals per pot. Thus, when the analysis is performed on the pot means, the n_s of equation $(7.1b)$ is the number of pots per run $= 2$; but in effect we multiplied the sums of squares by the number of readings per pot, $= 15$, so in the above equation, σ_5^2 is multiplied by the product of these which is n_5. The residual variance measured between the pot means is the sum of two parts ; it is the corrected variance between pots, σ_6^2, plus the square of the standard error or variance due to the fact that the residual variations within a pot are only sampled by $n_6 = 15$ individuals ; this added variance is $\sigma_3^2/15$. The variance v_6 is n_6 times this measured variance between pot means. The cylinder and journey effects do not contribute to the error in a pot mean, since they are expressed as deviations from the pot mean.

The relations between v_8 and v_9, between v_9 and v_{10}, between v_{12} and v_{13}, and between v_{13} and v_{14}, may easily be deduced in a similar manner ; these variances have all been found from analyses like that in Table 7.1b. The apparent variance v_{10} is contributed to only by the part of the cylinder trend that is specific to the pot, σ_{10}^2, and by the first residual, σ_3^2, and the relation given above is easily deduced. Similar remarks apply to the journey effect.

We are now in a position to test the variances given in Table 7.43a for statistical significance, using the F test. If there is no cylinder effect, $\sigma_1^2 = 0$ and $v_1 = v_3$; the test for this effect consists in establishing the statistical significance of the difference between v_1 and v_3. Similarly, v_2 should be compared with v_3, v_5 with v_6, v_6 with v_3, v_8 with v_9, and so on. When these tests are carried out, the values of F corresponding to the variances marked with two asterisks are above the 1 per cent. point and that with one asterisk is between the 5 and 1 per cent. points ; we shall presume that these show the existence of significant effects ;* all the other values of F are below the 5 per cent. point.

The variances v_1 and v_2 are both significantly greater than v_3 ; if this had not been so, we should still have been justified in performing the further analyses of sections (c) and (d) of Table 7.43a.

The variance v_5 is not significantly greater than v_6, so it is reasonable to combine these to give an improved estimate of the residual variance (b) between pots, based on 7 degrees of freedom ; this is in row (7) of Table 7.43a. Similarly, v_8 is not significantly greater than v_9 and it is reasonable to work on the conclusion that the cylinder effect varies from run to run and is measured by the combined variance based on 8 degrees. This combined estimate of v_9 is significantly greater than v_{10}. We see, however, that v_{10} is not greater than v_3, and conclude that the cylinder effect does not vary from pot to pot within a run. Similar conclusions may be reached regarding the journey variances, except that v_{14} is greater than v_3. We are justified in combining rows (10) and (3) to obtain an improved estimate of v_3 based on 72 degrees of freedom ; it is 275·90.

The significant effects and their substantive variances estimated from the apparent variances of Table 7.43a may be summarised as follows :

Differences between pots,

$$\sigma_6^2 \rightarrow \frac{2\ 524 \cdot 89 - 275 \cdot 90}{15} = 149 \cdot 93$$

Cylinder effect varying from run to run,

$$\sigma_9^2 \rightarrow \frac{2\ 583 \cdot 20 - 275 \cdot 90}{10} = 230 \cdot 73$$

Journey effect, part due to variation from run to run,

$$\sigma_{13}^2 \rightarrow \frac{1\ 770 \cdot 88 - 598 \cdot 91}{6} = 195 \cdot 33$$

Journey trend, part due to variation from pot to pot within a run,

$$\sigma_{14}^2 \rightarrow \frac{598 \cdot 91 - 275 \cdot 90}{3} = 107 \cdot 67$$

Residual (unaccounted variation),

$$\sigma_3^2 \rightarrow \qquad\qquad 275 \cdot 90.$$

These estimates of substantive variance measure the relative

* The one variance with one asterisk has a value of F very little below the 1 per cent. point.

importance of the several factors in the way described in section 7.11. The estimates are valid, however, only in so far as the third, tenth and sixteenth cylinders are representative of the eighteen or so that may be made from a pot, and the first five journeys are representative of all the journeys possible in a run, in so far as there is any secular variation. For example, all the cylinders between the third and tenth could have fewer and those between the tenth and sixteenth could have more seed than the three measured, and this would be a source of variation entirely over-looked by our analysis, of which random errors take no account. We shall assume the representativeness of the cylinders and journeys.

All the above values of the substantive variances are estimates subject to random errors, since the cylinder and journey effects vary from run to run or from pot to pot, and the few that have provided the estimates are a random sample from an infinite population of trends obtained from an infinite population of runs. Had there been a significant cylinder effect common to all runs, it would not have been subject to random errors in quite the same way. However many runs there had been, there would have been but two degrees of freedom for v_8 ; the effect of a large number of pots is merely to increase n_8 in the equation

$$v_8 \rightarrow n_8\sigma_8^{\,2} + v_9$$

and reduce the error v_9, thus reducing the effect of random errors in v_9 in estimating $\sigma_8^{\,2}$. Similar remarks apply to the journey effect.

ORTHOGONALITY

7.5. In all the foregoing basic forms and in complex forms made up of basic forms, every representative or level of each factor is associated equally with every level of every other factor, so that provided the effects are additive, the means for the levels of any one factor estimate that factor effect free from the effects of the other factors. The sets of means for the factors are said to be mutually orthogonal and the form of the data has the property of *orthogonality*. Orthogonality has a mathematical definition, but its chief importance for statistics lies in its equivalence to the complete separability of factor effects.

The basic forms have the essential merit of orthogonality, but they are also very convenient because the separate effects can readily be estimated by computing simple means. In practice, particularly in experimental investigations, incomplete forms of data sometimes arise ; these will be dealt with in the next section.

Incomplete Forms

7.51. If an experiment is arranged in randomised blocks so that the data are in the two-factor basic form there must be as many values per block as there are experimental treatments. If the arrangement conforms to the Latin square, the total number of values equals the square of the number of treatments. These limitations are sometimes inconvenient when the number of treatments is large, but they may in some measure be evaded by using one of a number of standard incomplete forms that have been developed. Some of these forms are orthogonal, but their analysis is not as straightforward as for the basic forms. The whole subject and its application are dealt with by Brownlee (1946), Goulden (1939) and Yates (1936-40).

The treatments in factorial experiments are sometimes arranged in incomplete forms. Suppose that a factorial experiment is performed with s factors at n_1, n_2, ... n_s levels respectively. Then the complete orthogonal arrangement requires $n_1 n_2 \ldots n_s$ experimental treatments, and even with only 2 or 3 levels per factor the number of treatments often becomes much too large for any practicable experiment. Consequently the experimenter decides in advance that certain of the interactions need not be separated, and he adopts a design with fewer treatments than are required for the complete set. Some of the factors and interactions are then mutually orthogonal, but others are not ; the ones that cannot be separated are said to be *confounded*. Confounding is a regular part of factorial experimentation, and readers may learn more about it by referring to the books mentioned at the end of section 7.42.

Incomplete forms of data can arise where the original arrangement was in a basic form, but a few of the individual values are missing.

If one value is missing from data in a two-factor basic form with

p rows and q columns, the missing value x may be computed from the equation :

$$x = \frac{pP + qQ - T}{(p - 1)(q - 1)} \quad . \quad . \quad . \quad . \quad (7.51)$$

where P is the sum of the $q - 1$ values in the row from which the required value is missing,

Q is the sum of the $p - 1$ values in the column from which the required value is missing, and

T is the sum of the $pq - 1$ values.

The value of x estimated from equation (7.51) is put in place of the missing value and the analysis is conducted as for the complete form, except that the residual number of degrees of freedom is reduced by one.

For example, suppose the first value in Table 7.43 was missing (it is given as 47). Then for the first pot-run $p = 5$, $q = 3$, $P = 156$, $Q = 201$, $T = 1\,000$, and from equation (7.51)

$$x = \frac{780 + 603 - 1\,000}{4 \times 2} = 47 \cdot 9, \text{ or } 48 \text{ (say).}$$

Then the analysis is performed with 48 in the place of 47 in Table 7.43. The sums of squares will be very slightly different from those in Table 7.43a, but the only change in the degrees of freedom will be the reduction of that in row (3) to 63. If there is one missing value in any other pot-run, it is estimated in the same way and the degrees of freedom in row (3) are further reduced by one.

When the original form is a Latin square with p levels of each factor, the estimated missing value is

$$x = \frac{p(P + Q + R) - 2T}{(p - 1)(p - 2)} \quad . \quad . \quad . \quad (7.51a)$$

where P, Q and R are respectively the sums of the row, column and " treatment " (or level of the third factor) from which the value is missing, and T is the grand total.

If the first value in Table 7.2 (given as 1·4) happened to be missing, we would have for the first Latin square $p = 4$, $P = 15 \cdot 9$, $Q = 6 \cdot 7$, $R = 6 \cdot 4$, $T = 58 \cdot 0$ and (from equation (7.51a)) $x = 0 \cdot 0$. The residual degrees of freedom, given in Table 7.2a as 6, become 5.

If two values are missing in the same basic form, say x_1 and x_2, the procedure is to assume some value for x_1 (it does not matter much what value is assumed provided it is reasonable) and then to estimate x_2 by means of equation (7.51) or (7.51a); let it be x_2'. Then with x_2' and the known values, x_1 is estimated from equation (7.51) or (7.51a); let it be x_1'. Then x_1' is used and a new estimate of x_2 is made from equation (7.51) or (7.51a); let it be x_2''. This is then used to obtain another new estimate of x_1 and the whole procedure is continued until the last two estimates of x_1 agree sufficiently ; and similarly for x_2. The *iterative* procedure, as it is called, has not usually to be carried very far. This method can be extended to estimate several missing values. In the ultimate analysis of variance, the residual degrees of freedom are the number appropriate to the complete form, less the number of missing values estimated.

To adjust an analysis of data with estimates of missing values only by adjusting the residual degrees of freedom is to enhance the apparent significance very slightly, but not enough to matter in most practical situations. Readers should refer to Yates (1933) and to Yates and Hale (1939) for fuller details.

The Method of Least Squares

7.6. The analysis of the incomplete forms of data is based on a general procedure, of which that described for the basic forms is a special case. As this general procedure will have further application, it is described here.

The first step is to represent each value by an equation containing a number of constants plus a random term ; for the two-factor basic form the equation corresponding to equation (7.1) would be:

$$x = \bar{\xi} + \bar{\xi}_s' + \bar{\xi}_t' + x' \quad . \quad . \quad . \quad (7.6)$$

where x is the individual value in the sth row and tth column,

$\bar{\xi}$ is a constant which we may describe as the " true " grand mean from which all values are measured as deviations,

$\bar{\xi}_s'$ is another constant, which is the " true " mean for the sth row measured as a deviation from $\bar{\xi}$,

$\bar{\xi}_t'$ is a corresponding constant referring to the tth column, and

x' is a random deviation drawn from an infinite population distributed normally about a mean of zero.

Equation (7.6) is somewhat similar in form to equation (7.1), but there is a difference in the description of the terms. The

Greek symbol signifies a " true " value, and the prime signifies that it is a deviation. There is a value of $\bar{\xi}'_s$ for each row and one of $\bar{\xi}'_t$ for each column.

The *method of least squares* consists in choosing estimates of the constants so that the sum of squares of deviations from the estimated values is a minimum : i.e. if $\tilde{x}$, $\tilde{x}'_s$ and $\tilde{x}'_t$ are the estimates, the sum over all values of $(x - \tilde{x} - \tilde{x}'_s - \tilde{x}'_t)^2$ is a minimum. The deviations are the residual deviations. The process of estimation is described as *fitting* the equation to the data. For the complete basic form these estimates become $\tilde{x} = \bar{x}$, $\tilde{x}'_s = \bar{x}_s - \bar{x}$ and $\tilde{x}'_t = \bar{x}_t - \bar{x}$, the terms of equation (7.1). The general treatment of incomplete forms is based on the method of least squares, the estimates when one value is missing, for example, being those that would be obtained by estimating the missing value according to equation (7.51) and then calculating the means as though data were complete.

The usefulness of the method of least squares lies in the property, proved by Irwin (1931) that if for a set of say N independent values distributed normally u constants of a series of equations are independently estimated by the method, the sum of squares of the residual deviations divided by $(N - u)$ is an unbiased estimate of the population variance. For example, if we were to distribute the N observations at random among the p rows and q columns of the two-factor basic form ($pq = N$), there would be p values of $\tilde{x}'_s$ giving $p - 1$ independent constants for rows (since the sum of $\tilde{x}'_s$ is zero), $q - 1$ independent constants for columns, and one for $\tilde{x}$, giving $p + q - 1$ altogether ; and the sum of the squares of the residuals divided by $N - (p + q - 1)$ would be an unbiased estimate of the same variance as that estimated by $\mathrm{S}(x - \bar{x})^2$ divided by $N - 1$. A significant difference between the two estimates of variance is evidence of a significant row and column (combined) effect.

The two estimates are not, however, independent, since the $N - 1$ degrees of freedom contain the $N - u$ and the sums of squares are correspondingly related. By subtracting the smaller sum of squares from the larger and dividing by $(N - 1) - (N - u) = u - 1$ we have an estimate of variance that is independent of that based on the $N - u$ degrees, and the F test may be used to decide whether they are different. According to this, the sum of squares associated with any source is defined as a difference between the total sum of squares and that of the residuals—it happens to be the same as that computed directly for the basic forms.

The above procedure tests the significance of a set of constants as a whole : for example of the $\bar{\xi}$, $\bar{\xi}'_s$ and $\bar{\xi}'_t$ of equation (7.6) taken together. Let us suppose that some of the constants differ significantly from zero—say $\bar{\xi}$ and the values of $\bar{\xi}_s$ in equation (7.6), and that we wish to test the significance of the remaining constants—the values of $\bar{\xi}'_t$. We first determine $\tilde{x}$ and the p values of $\tilde{x}'_s$ by the method of least squares, and hence the sum of squares of the residuals which has associated with it $N - p$ degrees of freedom. Then we determine $\tilde{x}$, the p values of $\tilde{x}'_s$ and the q values of $\tilde{x}'_t$, and the sum of squares of the corresponding residuals, which are associated with $N - p - q + 1$ degrees. The second set of values of $\tilde{x}$ and $\tilde{x}'_s$ will not agree with the first unless the sets of constants are orthogonal. The difference between the two sums of squares divided by $(N - p) - (N - p - q + 1)$ $= q - 1$ degrees of freedom estimates independently the same population variance as the smaller sum of squares divided by $N - p - q + 1$, if the values of $\bar{\xi}'_t$ are zero ; and a significant difference between the two estimates indicates a real column effect. This result follows from an extension of the above-stated property of the method of least squares, and it applies irrespective of the significance of the first set of constants.

It can easily be seen how the procedure can be extended to any number of sub-sets of constants (e.g. those for a Latin square), fitting first one sub-set, then two, then three, and so on, and at each stage determining the difference in sums of squares of residuals and the associated degrees of freedom. When the sub-sets of constants are orthogonal, as they are when the data are in the complete basic forms, it does not matter in what order the sub-sets are fitted—whether the $\bar{\xi}'_s$ are estimated before or after the $\bar{\xi}'_t$; the results are the same, and in an absolute sense the various sums of squares can be associated with the corresponding sub-sets, and with the sources of variation that they describe. When the sub-sets are not orthogonal, the result depends on the order in which the sub-sets are estimated ; that is why the estimation of missing values by equations (7.51) and (7.51a) and the procedure described in the previous section does not give quite the correct results. In such circumstances, the appropriate order of fitting is often inherent in the practical problem. Thus, in equation (7.6) the values of $\bar{\xi}'_s$ may be a source of error and those of $\bar{\xi}'_t$ represent the effect of an experimental treatment, the significance of which it is desired to test. Then the order of fitting would be that given above.

We shall make considerable use of the results of this section in later sections of the book.

CHAPTER VIII

CORRELATION AND ASSOCIATION

CORRELATION TABLES AND SCATTER DIAGRAMS

8.1. When dividing the total variability of a quantity into parts, one of which is associated with arrays as in Table 6.2, it is by no means inevitable that the character which defines the arrays should be some qualitative description or serial number ; it also may be the groups of some quantitative variate. Tables 8.1 to 8.1*d* are examples in which the individuals are classified according to two quantitative variates ; these are called *correlation tables*. In the first of these the arrays are groups of eggs having a small sub-range of length ; each array is regrouped according to longitudinal girth. The association between the two quantities is well marked, and it is clear that there is also a tendency for the length to increase with the girth quite regularly. We have thus reached another stage in the treatment of variability ; for while the single distribution shows the extent and form of the variation and the table of arrays introduced in Chapter VI shows the association of parts of the variation with other factors now the correlation table discovers the nature of that association when the other factor is a quantitative variate. It will be noticed, however, that such a table may be approached in two ways ; either variate may be regarded as the one which is being analysed and both the columns and rows are arrays.

When arranging correlation tables it is convenient to choose the grouping so that there are from ten to twenty for each variate ; if any observation appears to fall exactly on the dividing line between two groups a half may be given to each, and similarly it may happen that a quarter of a unit may be assigned to each of four adjacent cells in the table. In specifying the characters either the sub-ranges of the groups may be given, as in Tables 8.1 and 8.1*c*, or the central values as in Table 8.1*d*. The actual process of making a correlation table may be carried out in two ways. The first is to mark the position of each observation in the table by means of a dot or a stroke and finally to count the marks. This, however, is only suitable for fairly small samples, for if one makes a mistake or loses the place there is nothing for it but to start

TABLE 8.1

Length and Longitudinal Girth of Eggs of the Common Tern

$$r = + 0.89$$

(Data from " A Co-operative Study," 1923)

Longitudinal Girth in cm.			Length in cm.										
		3·55-	3·60-	3·65-	3·70-	3·75-	3·80-	3·85-	3·90-	3·95-	4·00-	4·05-
		-11	-10	-9	-8	-7	-6	-5	-4	-3	-2	-1
9·80-	−14	1	—	—	—	—	—	—	—	—	—	—
9·90-	−13	—	—	—	—	—	—	—	—	—	—	—
10·00-	−12	—	—	—	—	—	—	—	—	—	—	—
10·10-	−11	—	—	—	—	—	—	—	—	—	—	—
10·20-	−10	—	—	—	—	—	—	—	—	—	—	—
10·30-	− 9	—	—	—	1	—	—	—	1	—	—	—
10·40-	− 8	—	—	—	—	1	—	1	—	—	—	—
10·50-	− 7	—	—	—	—	2	2	1	1	—	—	1
10·60-	− 6	—	—	—	—	1	6	2	4	2	—	—
10·70-	− 5	—	—	—	—	—	2	4	—	3	1	—
10·80-	− 4	—	—	—	—	1	3	3	8	9	8	2
10·90-	− 3	—	—	—	—	1	1	1	11	7	11	5
11·00-	− 2	—	—	—	1	—	—	1	2	20	20	23
11·10-	− 1	—	—	—	—	—	—	1	3	6	20	20
11·20-	0	—	—	—	—	—	—	1	1	7	6	21
11·30-	1	—	—	—	—	—	—	—	—	—	—	7
11·40-	2	—	—	—	—	—	—	—	—	—	2	3
11·50-	3	—	—	—	—	—	—	—	—	—	—	1
11·60-	4	—	—	—	—	—	—	—	—	1	—	—
11·70-	5	—	—	—	—	—	—	—	—	—	—	2
11·80-	6	—	—	—	—	—	—	1	—	—	—	—
11·90-	7	—	—	—	—	—	—	—	—	—	1	—
12·00-	8	—	—	—	—	—	—	—	—	—	—	—
12·10-	9	—	—	—	—	—	—	—	—	—	—	—
12·20-	10	—	—	—	—	—	—	—	—	—	—	—
12·30-	11	—	—	—	—	—	—	—	—	—	—	—
Totals ...	...	1	—	—	2	6	14	16	30	55	69	85

TABLE 8.1 (*continued*)

LENGTH AND LONGITUDINAL GIRTH OF EGGS OF THE COMMON TERN

$r = + 0.89$

(*Data from " A Co-operative Study," 1923*)

				Length in cm.								Totals
4·10-	4·15-	4·20-	4·25-	4·30-	4·35-	4·40-	4·45-	4·50-	4·55-	4·60-	4·65-	
0	1	2	3	4	5	6	7	8	9	10	11	
—	—	—	—	—	—	—	—	—	—	—	—	1
—	—	—	—	—	—	—	—	—	—	—	—	—
—	—	—	—	—	—	—	—	—	—	—	—	—
—	—	—	—	—	—	—	—	—	—	—	—	—
—	—	—	—	—	—	—	—	—	—	—	—	2
—	—	—	—	—	—	—	—	—	—	—	—	2
—	—	—	—	—	—	—	—	—	—	—	—	6
—	—	—	—	—	—	—	—	—	—	—	—	15
—	—	—	—	—	—	—	—	—	—	—	—	10
1	—	—	—	—	—	—	—	—	—	—	—	35
1	—	—	—	—	—	—	—	—	—	—	—	38
10	1	1	—	—	—	—	—	—	—	—	—	79
25	8	3	1	2	1	—	—	—	—	—	—	90
37	29	11	5	—	—	1	—	—	—	—	—	119
38	25	23	13	5	1	1	1	—	—	—	—	114
10	25	29	21	9	2	—	—	—	—	—	—	101
5	11	20	27	22	9	1	2	—	—	—	—	98
1	2	8	15	30	12	5	1	1	—	—	—	76
—	—	2	9	25	16	10	2	—	—	—	—	66
—	—	—	—	9	10	15	11	1	1	—	—	48
—	—	1	—	4	2	5	4	6	6	—	—	29
—	—	—	—	—	1	2	4	5	3	1	—	16
—	—	—	—	—	—	—	—	1	1	1	3	6
—	—	—	—	—	—	—	—	1	1	—	1	3
—	—	—	—	—	—	—	—	—	—	—	1	1
128	101	98	91	106	54	40	25	15	12	2	5	955

again ; further, the only means of checking the accuracy of the table is to repeat it. The second method is to write the values of the characters of each individual on a separate card and to sort the cards ; the first sorting is into groups according to one character and then each group is re-sorted according to the second character. It is then an easy matter to look through each pile of

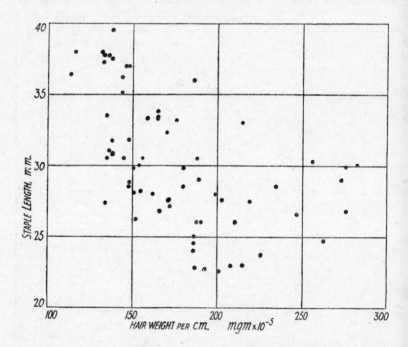

FIG. 8.i. Scatter diagram showing the relation between hair weight per cm. and staple length of different growths of cotton. The data are from Morton (1926).

cards to see that none is out of place and finally to count the cards and enter the numbers in a table. The writing of the cards takes some time but it is a saving in the long run, particularly if there are more than two characters ; it is often possible to collect the data on cards and so avoid copying.

If the observations are few, a correlation table is not suitable, and its place may be taken by a *scatter diagram*. This is just an ordinary graph in which x and y are the two variates, and points on this represent observations ; Fig. 8.1 is an example, and shows the relation between length and fineness of the hairs of a number of varieties of cotton. If the relationship between the two variates is exact the points in the scatter diagram lie on a smooth curve, while as the relationship weakens the diagram more and more resembles the result that would be obtained by sprinkling

TABLE 8.1a

NUMBERS OF PISTILS AND STAMENS IN *Ranunculus Ficaria Late Flowers.*

$r = +0.75$

(Data by Weldon, 1901)

		8	9	10	11	12	13	14	15	16	17	18	19	20	21	22	23	24	25	26	27	28	29	Totals
												Number of Stamens												
Number of Pistils	5	—	—	—	1	—	—	—	—	—	—	—	—	—	—	—	—	—	—	—	—	—	—	1
	6	—	—	1	1	—	1	—	3	—	—	—	—	—	—	—	—	—	—	—	—	—	—	6
	7	—	—	—	2	4	4	2	4	—	—	—	—	—	—	—	—	—	—	—	—	—	—	16
	8	—	—	1	—	—	3	10	14	2	1	3	1	—	—	—	—	—	—	—	—	—	—	35
	9	—	—	2	—	1	2	3	7	10	2	7	—	1	—	—	—	—	—	—	—	—	—	35
	10	—	—	—	—	—	—	1	3	4	6	5	13	4	1	—	—	—	1	—	—	—	—	38
	11	1	—	—	—	—	—	—	2	5	8	6	6	7	5	—	—	—	—	—	—	—	—	40
	12	—	—	—	1	—	—	—	2	4	4	3	5	7	6	3	—	—	—	—	—	—	—	35
	13	—	—	—	1	—	—	1	—	4	7	13	9	6	6	2	—	1	—	—	1	—	—	45
	14	—	—	—	—	—	—	—	1	—	2	8	7	12	4	2	—	—	—	—	—	—	—	36
	15	—	—	—	—	—	—	—	1	1	2	5	4	2	1	3	1	1	—	—	—	—	—	21
	16	—	—	—	—	—	—	—	—	2	3	—	5	3	5	1	1	2	1	—	—	—	—	23
	17	—	—	—	—	—	—	—	—	1	3	3	2	4	1	—	2	—	—	—	—	—	—	16
	18	—	—	—	—	—	—	—	—	—	—	1	2	2	2	—	—	—	—	3	—	—	1	11
	19	—	—	—	—	—	—	—	—	—	—	—	1	1	—	2	1	1	1	1	1	—	—	9
	20	—	—	—	—	—	—	—	—	—	—	—	—	1	—	—	—	—	—	1	—	—	—	2
	21	—	—	—	—	—	—	—	—	—	—	—	—	—	—	—	1	—	—	—	—	—	—	1
	22	—	—	—	—	—	—	—	—	—	—	—	—	—	—	1	—	—	—	—	—	—	—	1
	23	—	—	—	—	—	—	—	—	—	—	—	—	—	—	—	—	—	—	1	—	—	—	1
	24	—	—	—	—	—	—	—	—	—	—	—	—	—	—	—	—	—	1	—	—	—	—	1
Totals		1	—	4	6	5	11	23	43	35	31	66	43	42	19	17	7	4	6	6	2	1	1	373

the points evenly with a pepper-pot ; the former type of diagram is usually the experience of the physicist. The scatter diagram and correlation table are equivalent, except that in the latter the area is divided into a number of rectangles and the number of points in each one counted and substituted by the numerals. It is well to choose the scales of a diagram so that the range of variation is about the same in both directions and the diagram is nearly square.

TABLE 8.1b—NUMBERS OF PISTILS AND STAMENS IN *Ranunculus Ficaria* Early Flowers. $r = +0.51$

Number of Pistils (rows) × Number of Stamens (columns)

Pistils \ Stamens	18	19	20	21	22	23	24	25	26	27	28	29	30	31	32	33	34	35	36	37	38	Totals
2	—	—	—	—	—	—	—	—	—	—	—	—	—	—	—	—	—	—	—	1	—	1
3	—	—	—	—	—	—	—	—	—	—	—	—	—	—	—	—	—	—	—	—	—	—
4	—	—	—	—	—	—	—	—	—	—	—	—	—	—	—	—	—	—	—	—	—	—
5	—	—	—	—	—	—	—	—	—	—	—	—	—	—	—	—	—	—	—	—	—	—
6	—	—	—	—	—	—	—	—	—	—	—	—	—	—	—	—	—	—	—	—	—	—
7	—	—	—	—	—	—	—	—	—	—	—	1	—	—	—	—	—	—	—	—	—	1
8	—	—	—	—	—	—	—	—	—	—	—	—	—	—	—	—	—	—	—	—	—	—
9	—	—	—	—	—	—	—	—	—	—	—	1	—	—	—	—	—	—	—	—	—	1
10	—	1	—	—	—	—	—	1	—	—	—	—	—	—	—	—	—	—	—	—	—	2
11	—	—	—	2	—	—	—	1	—	—	—	—	—	—	—	—	—	—	—	—	—	3
12	—	—	3	1	2	1	1	3	1	1	—	—	—	—	—	—	—	—	—	—	—	13
13	—	1	1	1	4	1	1	1	—	—	1	1	—	—	—	—	—	—	—	—	—	12
14	—	4	3	—	1	2	4	1	2	3	1	1	—	—	—	—	—	—	—	—	—	22
15	—	—	1	—	2	4	3	7	4	4	5	2	1	—	1	1	—	—	—	—	—	35
16	1	—	—	2	—	—	1	5	3	5	4	5	3	2	—	—	—	—	—	—	—	31
17	—	—	—	—	2	2	1	4	2	3	1	2	5	2	1	—	—	—	—	—	—	25
18	—	—	—	1	—	2	4	3	1	7	1	3	2	1	—	2	—	—	—	—	—	27
19	—	—	—	—	—	1	2	—	5	4	1	4	1	1	1	1	—	—	—	—	—	21
20	—	—	—	—	2	—	—	1	1	2	2	1	3	4	2	1	—	—	—	—	—	19
21	—	—	—	—	1	—	—	—	2	2	—	2	4	1	1	—	—	—	—	—	—	13
22	—	—	—	—	—	—	1	—	2	3	—	1	2	3	1	2	—	—	—	—	—	15
23	—	—	—	—	—	—	—	—	1	1	—	2	1	1	2	—	—	2	—	—	—	10
24	—	—	—	—	—	—	—	—	1	1	—	2	—	—	—	—	—	—	—	—	—	4
25	—	—	—	—	—	—	—	—	—	—	—	—	1	—	2	—	—	—	—	1	—	4
26	—	—	—	—	—	—	—	—	—	—	—	1	—	—	2	—	—	—	—	—	—	3
27	—	—	—	—	—	—	1	—	1	—	—	—	—	—	—	—	2	—	—	—	—	4
28	—	—	—	—	—	—	—	—	—	—	—	—	—	—	—	—	1	—	—	—	—	1
29	—	—	—	—	—	—	—	—	—	—	—	—	—	—	—	—	—	—	—	—	—	—
30	—	—	—	—	—	—	—	—	—	—	—	—	—	—	—	—	—	—	—	—	—	—
31	—	—	—	—	—	—	—	—	—	—	—	1	—	—	—	—	—	—	—	—	—	1
Totals	1	6	8	9	16	12	22	26	26	38	14	23	20	20	13	7	1	4	—	1	1	268

TABLE 8.1c

DAILY MAXIMUM AND MINIMUM TEMPERATURES AT ROTHAMSTED FOR AUGUST 1878-1926 (Data by Fisher and Hoblyn, 1928.)* $r = +0.30$

Maximum Temperature ° F. (rows) × Minimum Temperature ° F. (columns)

Max \ Min	36–	38–	40–	42–	44–	46–	48–	50–	52–	54–	56–	58–	60–	62–	Totals
50–	—	—	—	—	1	—	—	—	—	—	—	—	—	—	1
52–	—	—	—	—	—	1	3	2	—	—	—	—	—	—	6
54–	—	—	1	—	4	2	4	3	3	1	—	—	—	—	21
56–	1	1	—	3	7	10	11	11	4	2	1	—	—	—	51
58–	—	1	4	2	11	13	24	22	13	8	4	—	—	—	102
60–	—	2	3	10	9	24	29	37	35	16	8	3	—	—	176
62–	—	2	3	6	16	25	43	39	54	28	12	3	—	—	231
64–	—	1	3	10	9	16	28	38	40	37	18	7	2	—	209
66–	2	—	2	9	16	19	20	33	35	35	33	12	2	—	218
68–	1	2	1	6	9	9	10	15	14	32	20	13	4	1	137
70–	—	—	1	3	6	10	9	14	19	19	25	14	5	—	125
72–	—	—	3	3	4	7	12	6	13	8	7	10	3	2	81
74–	—	—	—	—	5	3	8	4	7	8	8	7	3	1	54
76–	—	—	—	2	2	3	5	7	9	9	3	2	3	1	46
78–	—	—	—	1	2	—	3	5	8	3	5	1	—	—	28
80–	—	—	—	—	—	2	1	4	1	3	2	—	—	—	13
82–	—	—	—	1	—	1	—	—	1	—	2	2	1	—	8
84–	—	—	—	—	—	—	—	—	1	2	1	—	1	—	5
86–	—	—	—	—	—	—	1	—	—	1	1	—	—	—	3
88–	—	—	—	—	—	—	—	—	—	1	—	1	—	—	2
90–	—	—	—	—	—	—	—	—	1	—	—	—	—	—	1
92–	—	—	—	—	—	—	—	—	—	—	—	—	—	—	—
Totals	4	9	21	58	100	145	208	236	257	217	151	81	26	5	1 518

* This table is condensed from that of the original paper by doubling the sub-ranges of the arrays.

empirical *frequency surface*, and it must be noted that frequencies are measured by volumes.

Such a surface, of course, is made up of step-like figures (rather reminiscent of the basaltic columns of the Giant's Causeway in Northern Ireland) and shows irregularities ; but as the size of the sample is increased the irregularities disappear, and as the number of groups is increased the steps become smaller, until in the limit a smooth surface (analogous to the frequency curve for a single variate) results. The progress in devising systems of mathematical formulæ to describe such surfaces is less than has been made for the single variate distributions, and methods based on the *normal surface* are applied to most distributions. The equation to the normal surface is

$$df = \frac{N}{2\pi \, s_x \, s_y \sqrt{(1 - r^2)}} \, \mathrm{Exp} \left\{ - \frac{x^2/s_x{}^2 + y^2/s_y{}^2 - 2r \, xy/s_x s_y}{2(1 - r^2)} \right\} dx \, dy,$$

where x and y are the two variates measured as deviations from their means, s_x and s_y are constants equal to the standard deviations of the two variates, r is a constant equal to the correlation coefficient, N is the total number in the sample, and df is the element of frequency in the range $dxdy$ with its centre at (x, y). If we cut this surface by any vertical plane parallel to either the x- or y-axis, the section is a normal frequency curve of standard deviation $s_x\sqrt{(1 - r^2)}$ or $s_y\sqrt{(1 - r^2)}$. Fig. 8.21 shows the contours of surfaces in which correlation coefficients are 0, 0·3, 0·6 and 0·9, and the standard deviations of x and y are both equal to unity ; it will be seen that the surfaces all rise to a hump at the centre, but that they tend also to form a diagonal ridge which becomes narrower and sharper as r increases, as would be expected from the fact that the standard deviation of a sectional curve becomes smaller as r approaches unity. The correlation coefficient can never be greater than unity, and as it approaches that value, the ridge tends to become a thin outline in the form of a normal curve running diagonally ; when $r = 0$, vertical planes through the centre parallel to the x- and y-axes divide the surface into four equal quadrants. The correlation coefficient can be negative, but the only difference that makes is to cause the major axes of the ellipses to follow the other diagonal.

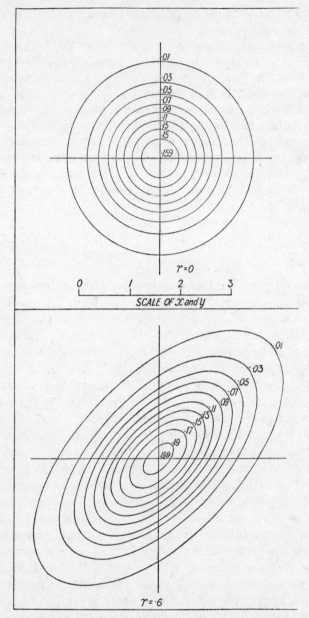

FIG. 8.21. Normal frequency surfaces for various values of the correlation coefficient represented by contour lines.

226

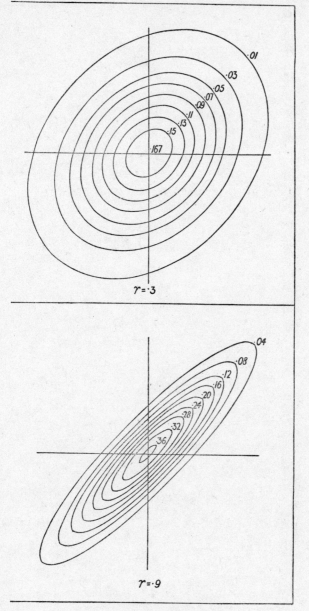

FIG. 8.21. (continued)

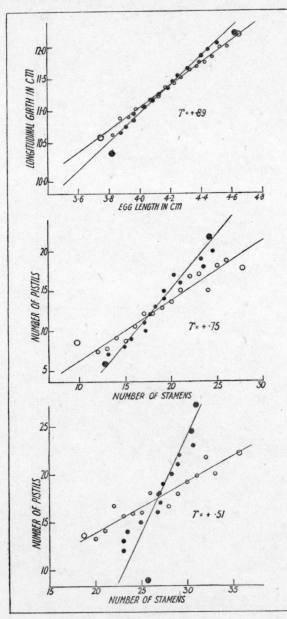

FIG. 8.22. Regression diagrams for the data of Tables 8.1, 8.1*a* and 8.1*b*.

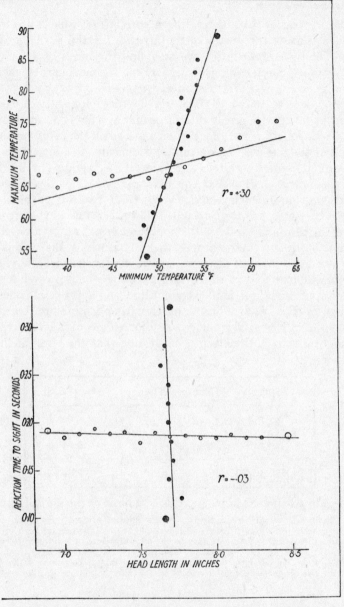

Fig. 8.22 (*continued*). Regression diagrams for the data of Tables 8.1*c* and
8.1*d*.

229

Regression Lines

8.22. An easier way of treating a correlation table is to draw a curve relating the means of the arrays of x and y. This can be done in two ways ; either we may find the mean of y for every array of x (i.e. referring to Table 8.1, find the mean girths when the lengths of the eggs are successively 3·55-3·60, 3·70-3·75, 3·75-3·80, etc., cm.) or we may find the mean of x for every array of y (mean lengths when the girths are successively 9·80-9·90, 10·30-10·40, 10·40-10·50, etc., cm.). In Fig. 8.22 are given the array means for each of the five correlation tables, the means of y for arrays of x being represented by circles and those of x for arrays of y by dots ; in the former x is called the *independent* and y the *dependent* variable, and in the latter vice versa.* The two sets of means are rather irregular but it is presumed that this is due to the errors of random sampling and that smooth curves drawn through the points represent more nearly the relationships that would be obtained if the size of the sample were increased indefinitely. The simplest curve that can be drawn, and one which is often a sufficient approximation, is the straight line, and appropriate ones are drawn on Fig. 8.22. For the maximum and minimum temperatures the circles giving the mean y for values of x lie above the straight line at both extremes suggesting that the straight line is

TABLE 8.22

Length	Number in Group	Mean Girth
3·575	I	9·85
3·725	2	10·70
3·775	6	10·67
Means 3·742	—	10·59

not quite adequate ; however, this is typical of the sort of data to

---

* The means of the extreme groups are naturally very inaccurate, being based on very few observations, and it is usual to combine several such groups. For example, in Table 8.1, if we assume the central values of lengths to be 3·575, 3·625, etc., cm., and those of girths to be 9·85, 9·95, etc., cm., we have the means in Table 8.22, with length as the independent variable. To combine the three readings, we find the weighted means of the length and girth. That of the length is

$$\frac{3·575 + 2 \times 3·725 + 6 \times 3·775}{9} = 3·742,$$

and similarly that of the girth is 10·59. Points obtained in this way are shown by larger circles and dots in Fig. 8.22.

which this method of correlation is often applied as an approximation, and we will use the straight lines. The two sets of means give two straight lines which become more divergent as the association decreases ; indeed, the diagram corresponding to Table 8.1d shows the two lines to be practically perpendicular. The line which is least inclined to the x-axis has x as the independent variable, and similarly the other, being more nearly parallel to the y-axis, has y as the independent variable.

The general equation of a straight line with x as the independent variable is

$$Y = ax + b \qquad \ldots \ldots \ldots \quad (8.22)$$

where a and b are constants and the capital letter Y denotes the value of the dependent variable given by the line, as distinguished from the actual value of an individual, denoted by y. The problem of estimating the most appropriate values of a and b to fit a line to any given data is analogous to that of determining estimates of parameters for fitting frequency distributions, and is the same as that mentioned in section 7.6 of determining the constants for an analysis of variance. The method of least squares provides a good solution, since the general properties of such a solution will be used in testing significances. Here the method involves choosing a and b to minimise the sum over all individuals of $(y - Y)^2$ (or for an infinite population, the mean value of this square). In a diagram the deviations $y - Y$ are represented by the distances of the individual points from the straight line, measured in a direction parallel to the y-axis ; they are not the perpendicular distances from the line. Further, there must be a separate deviation for each individual. A similar line may be obtained giving X in terms of y. The equations to the two lines are deduced in section 8.31 and may be written :

$$(Y - \bar{y}) = r \frac{s_y}{s_x} (x - \bar{x}) \qquad \ldots \ldots \quad (8.22a)$$

$$(X - \bar{x}) = r \frac{s_x}{s_y} (y - \bar{y}) \qquad \ldots \ldots \quad (8.22b)$$

where $\bar{x}$ and $\bar{y}$ are the two grand means, s_x and s_y are the two standard deviations and r is the correlation coefficient. The value of Y given by equation (8.22a) is the mean value for an array corresponding to the small sub-range about the given value of x, and that of X given by equation (8.22b) is similarly the mean corresponding to a given value of y. Equation (8.22a) represents the line more nearly parallel to the x-axis ; both lines pass through the point $(\bar{x},\ \bar{y})$. These are called *regression lines* and the coefficients

$$r \frac{s_y}{s_x} \quad \text{and} \quad r \frac{s_x}{s_y}$$

are called *regression coefficients*. The coefficients are the tangents of the angles the two lines make with the x- and y-axes respectively.

If $r = 0$, equation (8.22a) gives $(Y - \bar{y}) = 0$, an equation which is satisfied by a line parallel to the x-axis, and going through the mean, $\bar{y}$; similarly equation (8.22b) gives $(X - \bar{x}) = 0$, and this is satisfied by a line through the mean, $\bar{x}$, and parallel to the y-axis ; the two lines are perpendicular. The meaning of these two lines is that the mean value of y is the same for all values of x, and that the mean of x does not change with y ; or in other words, that there is no association between x and y ; and thus we see that r is zero for zero association or independence. If $r = 1$, one regression coefficient is equal to the inverse of the other, and the two lines coincide. This is the condition for perfect association, i.e. when x is uniquely determined by y (and vice versa) and is the state of affairs at which the physicist aims when he controls his experiment so that only the two factors vary and there are no extraneous disturbing influences. The biologist usually has to deal with materials subject to variations over which his control is limited, and consequently he obtains the kind of result illustrated in Tables 8.1 to 8.1d, where varying strengths of relationship are shown. If these tables are studied with Fig. 8.22, it will be noticed that the stronger the relationship, the greater is r and the closer together are the two regression lines. If $s_x = s_y$, or if the diagrams are plotted on such a scale that units of

$$\frac{x - \bar{x}}{s_x} \quad \text{and} \quad \frac{y - \bar{y}}{s_y}$$

are equal, the tangent of the angle between each regression line and the axis of the corresponding independent variable becomes equal to r. If r is positive, the slopes of the lines are in the direction indicating that x increases with y, while if r is negative the slopes are in the opposite direction showing that x increases as y decreases.

Analysis of Variance

8.23. The preceding section, dealing with regression, pays attention to the relationship between x and y, regarding the deviations rather as errors due to uncontrollable factors ; we will now consider the correlation table from the point of view of the variability. Adopting the method of Chapter VI, we can analyse the variance of say egg girth (Table 8.1) into two portions, one associated with differences between the array means for the various groups of length, and the other with residual deviations within the arrays. This can be done by finding the individual array means, as was done in Chapter VI, and calculating their variance and the variance of the residual deviations from them. For Table 8.1 we should combine the first five and the last two, giving 18 arrays, or 17 degrees of freedom on which to estimate the variance between arrays, and 937 on which to estimate the residual. If, however, we are satisfied that a straight regression line like equation (8.22a) sufficiently represents the trend, the value Y of the girth given by this line for various central values of the length (x) may be used instead of the array means $\bar{y}_s$. For Table 8.1 the line of regression of y on x (as computed in section 8.4) is

$$(Y - 11 \cdot 378) = 1 \cdot 756 \, (x - 4 \cdot 190) \; ;$$

when $x = 3 \cdot 575$, $Y - 11 \cdot 378 = -1 \cdot 080$ and $Y = 10 \cdot 298$,

when $x = 3 \cdot 725$, $Y - 11 \cdot 378 = -0 \cdot 817$ and $Y = 10 \cdot 561$,

and so on. For the sum of squares of the deviations of the array means from the grand mean ($11 \cdot 378$) we take $1 \times (-1 \cdot 080)^2 + 2 \times (-0 \cdot 817)^2$, etc., adding these quantities for all arrays ; for the squares of the residual deviations from the array means we take $(9 \cdot 85 - 10 \cdot 298)^2 + (10 \cdot 35 - 10 \cdot 561)^2 + (11 \cdot 05 - 10 \cdot 561)^2$, etc., adding these quantities for all cells in the table ; while for the total sum of squares we use the marginal totals as usual. These three sums may be found and entered in a table of analysis of variance in just the same way as if we had used the actual array means. This process can be carried out explicitly as indicated, and the reader is recommended to do it as an exercise ; alternatively, all the various sums of squares may be found from some of the constants of the table as shown below. We will set out the process algebraically.

Repeating equation (6.4), except that the variable is changed to y, we have for the first method of analysis,

$$S_s S'(y - \bar{y})^2 = S_s S'(y - \bar{y}_s)^2 + S_s n_s (\bar{y}_s - \bar{y})^2, \quad . \quad (8.23)$$

and for the second method, using the Y given by equation (8.22a) instead of $\bar{y}_s$, we have

$$S(y - \bar{y})^2 = S(y - Y)^2 + S(Y - \bar{y})^2, \quad . \quad (8.23a)$$

where $S = S_s S'$ is the summation over all individuals. This may be expressed in words—the sum of squares of deviations from the grand mean equals the sum of squares of deviations from the regression line plus the sum (over all observations) of squares of deviations of the regression values from the grand mean. The terms of equation (8.23a) are entered in Table 8.23, and it is shown in section 8.32 that the sums of squares are severally equal to those terms in the table which involve r^2. The constant r is again the

TABLE 8.23

ANALYSIS OF VARIANCE OF y (EGG GIRTH)

Source of Variation	Sum of Squares	Degrees of Freedom	Variance
Straight regression line	$S(Y - \bar{y})^2$ $= r^2 S(y - \bar{y})^2$	1	yv_s
Residual	$S(y - Y)^2$ $= (1 - r^2) S(y - \bar{y})^2$	$N - 2$	yv_r
Total	$S(y - \bar{y})^2$	$N - 1$	yv_T

correlation coefficient. If the reader has found the sums of squares directly as suggested in the last paragraph, he will also be able to check these relations. Similarly, by using the regression line of equation (8.22b) we may analyse the variance of x and arrive at the sums of squares in Table 8.23a.

In order to arrive at the degrees of freedom, let us consider the special case in which x and y are independent so that the regression of y on x in the infinite population is a line through the mean $\bar{y}$, parallel to the x-axis. Then $(y - Y) = (y - \bar{y})$ and the residual and total sums of squares are equal. But owing to sampling errors the regression line for a finite number of observations will be inclined slightly to the x-axis, and the residual sum of squares will be less than the total, since the method of least squares reduces the residual sum of squares to a minimum. The regression line of y on x involves two constants, a and b of equation (8.22), so that according to the result stated in section 7.6, the residual sum of squares divided by $N - 2$ is an unbiased estimate of the population variance. Accordingly $N - 2$ is entered as the number of degrees of freedom for the residual in Table 8.23, and when the association in the population is zero the three variances are estimates of the same population variance.

Table 8.23 is thus analogous to Table 6.2b for two arrays, or one degree of freedom between arrays. If there is no association $_yv_s$ and $_yv_r$ are independent estimates of the same variance ; if $_yv_s$ is the greater (significantly), there is evidence of association. The

TABLE 8.23a

ANALYSIS OF VARIANCE OF x (EGG LENGTH)

Source of Variation	Sum of Squares	Degrees of Freedom	Variance
Straight regression line	$S(X-\bar{x})^2$ $=r^2S(x-\bar{x})^2$	I	$_xv_s$
Residual	$S(x-X)^2$ $=(1-r^2)S(x-\bar{x})^2$	$N-2$	$_xv_r$
Total	$S(x-\bar{x})^2$	$N-1$	$_xv_T$

value $_yv_r$ is an estimate of the true variance within arrays, and hence of the variance of the distribution represented by a cross-section of the frequency surface in a vertical plane parallel to the y-axis. Corresponding arguments for x apply to the analysis in Table 8.23a.

It is thus seen that the two straight lines found by least squares are those which make the residual variances a minimum (or make the variance associated with themselves a maximum), and r is a measure of the amount of the total variation in each quantity associated with the appropriate line. If $r = 1$, the residual variance is zero and all the variation in one quantity is explained by variation in the other, while if $r = 0$, the residual variance is as great as the total, and there is no association between x and y. This point of view (since in fact it uses r^2) takes no account of the sign of r, but is merely concerned with measuring the strength of association without troubling whether y increases with x or whether it increases as x decreases.

ESTIMATION OF COEFFICIENTS

8.3. In the foregoing discussions we have been concerned merely to explain the meaning of the correlation and regression coefficients for an aggregate of individuals but, as for all statistical measures, the problem of estimation of population values from finite samples arises.

Considered as a constant of the normal frequency surface the correlation coefficient may be estimated by the method of maximum likelihood (section 3.7). For s_x and s_y it gives the estimates already deduced for single distributions ; for r it gives

$$r = \frac{S(x - \bar{x})\,(y - \bar{y})}{\sqrt{\{S(x - \bar{x})^2\, S(y - \bar{y})^2\}}} \quad \cdots \quad .(8.3)$$

where S is the summation over all individuals.

If N is the size of the sample, the quantity

$$p = \frac{S(x - \bar{x})\,(y - \bar{y})}{N}$$

is termed the *first product moment*, so that as an alternative to equation (8.3) we have

$$r = \frac{N}{(N - 1)} \quad \frac{p}{s_x s_y} \quad \cdots \quad (8.3a)$$

where s_x and s_y are estimated correctly on $N - 1$ degrees of freedom. If N is large, $N/(N - 1)$ may be taken as nearly equal to unity.

8.31. In order to deduce estimates of a and b in the regression equation (8.22) by using the method of least squares, we minimise $S(y - Y)^2$. We have for a sample

$$S(y - Y)^2 = S(y - ax - b)^2$$

and on differentiating this with respect to a and b in turn, and equating to zero (the usual method of evaluating parameters to make a function of them a maximum or a minimum), we have

$$- 2Sx(y - ax - b) = 0 \text{ and}$$
$$- 2S(y - ax - b) = 0 \, ;$$

and the expansion of these term by term, with a cancellation of the multiplier -2 which is common to both equations, leads to the simultaneous equations

$$\left. \begin{array}{l} Sxy = aSx^2 + bSx \\ Sy = aSx \; + bS_1 \end{array} \right\} \quad \cdots \cdots \quad (8.31)$$

where $Sx = N\bar{x}$, $Sy = N\bar{y}$ and $S_1 = N$. Thus,

$$\left. \begin{array}{l} a = \dfrac{Sxy - N\bar{x}\bar{y}}{Sx^2 - N\bar{x}^2} \\[3mm] b = \bar{y} - a\bar{x} \end{array} \right\} \quad \cdots \cdots \quad (8.31a)$$

Now we already know that $Sx^2 - N\bar{x}^2 = S(x - \bar{x})^2$, and by an extension of the argument of section 1.311 it can be shown that

$$S(x - \bar{x})(y - \bar{y}) = Sxy - N\bar{x}\bar{y} = Sxy - (SxSy)/N \quad . \quad (8.31b)$$

The substitution of these results in equations (8.31a) and of the resulting estimates of a and b in equation (8.22) leads to the regression equation :

$$Y - \bar{y} = \frac{S(x - \bar{x})(y - \bar{y})}{S(x - \bar{x})^2} \quad . \quad (x - \bar{x}) \quad . \quad . \quad (8.31c)$$

which reduces to equation (8.22a) when r, s_x and s_y are used in place of the sums of products and squares, suitably modified. If x and y are interchanged and the whole process is repeated, the regression of x on y is obtained.

For estimating the regression coefficients the most useful formulæ are

Regression of y on $x = \dfrac{S(x - \bar{x})(y - \bar{y})}{S(x - \bar{x})^2}$ $\cdots \cdots$ (8.31d)

and

Regression of x on $y = \dfrac{S(x - \bar{x})(y - \bar{y})}{S(y - \bar{y})^2}$ $\cdots \cdots$ (8.31e)

8.32. The sums of squares in Table 8.23 may be deduced by rewriting equation (8.23a), and substituting by equation (8.31c) for $(Y - \bar{y})$. Then the first term on the right-hand side of equation (8.23a) becomes

$$S(y - Y)^2 = S\{(y - \bar{y}) - (Y - \bar{y})\}^2$$

$$= S(y - \bar{y})^2 - 2S(Y - \bar{y})(y - \bar{y}) + S(Y - \bar{y})^2$$

$$= S(y - \bar{y})^2 - 2\frac{S(x - \bar{x})(y - \bar{y})}{S(x - \bar{x})^2} S(x - \bar{x})(y - \bar{y}) +$$

$$\frac{\{S(x - \bar{x})(y - \bar{y})\}^2}{S(x - \bar{x})^2}$$

$$= S(y - \bar{y})^2 - \frac{\{S(x - \bar{x})(y - \bar{y})\}^2}{S(x - \bar{x})^2} \quad \cdots \quad (8.32)$$

On multiplying the numerator and denominator of the last term of (8.32) by $S(y - \bar{y})^2$ and substituting r, the appropriate sum of squares in Table 8.23 is obtained. $S(Y - \bar{y})^2$ may then be obtained easily.

Computation of Coefficients

8.4. The standard deviations and sums of squares in the above equations may be computed by the methods of sections 1.31 and 6.3, and it is necessary to deal only with the product terms. To correspond with equations 1.31a we have

$$p = Sxy/N - \bar{x}\bar{y} \quad \cdots \quad (8.4)$$

and corresponding to equation (6.3)

$$S(x - \bar{x})(y - \bar{y}) = Sxy - N\bar{x}\bar{y} = Sxy - T_x T_y/N \quad (8.4a)$$

where x and y are measured from any convenient origin, $T_x = Sx$ and $T_y = Sy$. The correction term in the above equations may be positive or negative, and it is zero if either $\bar{x}$ or $\bar{y}$ is zero. It is sometimes convenient to divide all the values of x and y by some constant factor : then the regression coefficient must be corrected to the natural units after computation. The correlation coefficient, being a dimensionless number, requires no such correction.

When the number of observations is not large, say not greater than about 100, it is convenient to compute the sums of products from the individual observations. Then it usually saves confusion, especially when using a computing machine, to choose the origin so that all values of x and y, and hence all their products, are positive. Otherwise it is convenient to group the data and then an extension of the methods of section 1.31 may be used. All observations in any given group may be assumed to be at its centre and it is convenient to measure the deviations from a group near the middle of each distribution in terms of the sub-range h_x or h_y. Then if p' is the product moment in such units,

$$p = h_x h_y p' \qquad \qquad (8.4b)$$

Sheppard's corrections may be applied in calculating the denominators of equations (8.3) and (8.31d) from grouped data ; there is no corresponding correction for the numerator.

We shall compute the constants for Table 8.1 as an example, where the transformed values x' and y' are given in the column or row adjacent to that containing the true values of the variate. The computations are all contained in Table 8.4, where columns (1), (2), (3), (4), (7), (8), (9) and (10) contain all the data for obtaining the means and the second moments, and below the table all the calculations have been carried out as in the first chapter. Sheppard's corrections have been applied, and as the sample is a large one, the second moment has been obtained by dividing the sums of squares by the number of observations (995) instead of by the degrees of freedom.

To find the product moment, we must first find $Sx'y'$. This could be done directly by writing in the corner of each cell in Table 8.1 its $x'y'$ (the one in the top left-hand corner would be $-14 \times -11 = +154$, the next in the top row would be $-14 \times -10 = +140$, and so on), and then multiplying each $x'y'$ by the number in the cell and adding ; in this table, all the squares in the two quadrants containing most observations would have positive products, and those in the other two would have negative ones. A better method, however, is to do the summation in two parts, keeping y' constant first, summing all the x''s in each array of y' separately, and then adding the arrays. If we consider any array of y' with n_y observations :

$$Sx'y' = S_s y' S' x_y' = S_s y' n_y \bar{x}_y', \qquad (8.4c)$$

where S, S_s and S' are the summations used previously, and $\bar{x}_y'$ is the mean x' of all the observations in the sth array of y'.

The process is carried out in columns (5) and (6) of Table 8.4. In the array $y' = -14$, $\bar{x}_y'$ is $-11/1$, so $n_y\bar{x}' = -11$; $y' = -9$, $\bar{x}_y' = -12/2$, so $n_y\bar{x}_y' = -12$, and so on for the other quantities in column (5) ; the sum of this column is the sum of all the deviations

TABLE 8.4

(1) y'	(2) n_y	(3) n_yy'	(4) $n_yy'^2$	(5) $n_y\bar{x}'_y$	(6) $n_y\bar{x}'_yy'$
-14	1	-14	196	-11	154
-13	—	—	—	—	—
-12	—	—	—	—	—
-11	—	—	—	—	—
-10	—	—	—	—	—
-9	2	-18	162	-12	108
-8	2	-16	128	-12	96
-7	6	-42	294	-32	224
-6	15	-90	540	-75	450
-5	10	-50	250	-43	215
-4	35	-140	560	-117	468
-3	38	-114	342	-110	330
-2	79	-158	316	-141	282
-1	90	-90	90	-65	65
0	119	—	—	$+9$	—
1	114	$+114$	114	141	141
2	101	202	404	185	370
3	98	294	882	284	852
4	76	304	1 216	285	1 140
5	66	330	1 650	283	1 415
6	48	288	1 728	265	1 590
7	29	203	1 421	186	1 302
8	16	128	1 024	122	976
9	6	54	486	60	540
10	3	30	300	28	280
11	1	11	121	11	121
Totals ...	955	$+1\ 226$	12 224	$+1\ 241$	$+11\ 119$

$$yv'_1 = \bar{y}' = \frac{+1\ 226}{955} = +1.283\ 77. \quad h_y = 0.1 \text{ cm.}$$

$$\text{mean girth} = 11.25 + 0.128 = 11.378 \text{ cm.}$$

$$yv'_2 = \frac{12\ 224}{955} = \qquad 12.800\ 0$$

$$-yv'^2_1 = \quad -\ 1.648\ 1$$

$$yv_2 = \quad \overline{11.151\ 9}$$

$$\qquad -\ 0.083\ 3$$

$$y\mu_2 = \quad \overline{11.068\ 6}$$

$$s_y^2 = h_y^2 \times 11.068\ 6 = 0.110\ 69 \text{ cm.}^2$$

$$s_y = 0.332\ 70 \text{ cm.}$$

$$p' = \frac{+11\ 119}{955} = 11.642\ 9$$

$$-xv'_1yv'_1 = -\ 1.668\ 2$$

$$= +9.974\ 7$$

$$p = h_xh_y \times 9.974\ 7 \text{ cm.}^2 = +0.049\ 874 \text{ cm.}^2$$

$$r = +\frac{0.049\ 874}{0.332\ 70 \times 0.168\ 54} = +0.889$$

TABLE 8.4 (*continued*)

(7) x'	(8) n_x	(9) $n_x x'$	(10) $n_x x'^2$	(11) $n_x \bar{y}_x$	(12) $n_x \bar{y}_x x'$
-11	1	-11	121	-14	154
-10	—	—	—	—	—
-9	—	—	—	—	—
-8	2	-16	128	-11	88
-7	6	-42	294	-35	245
-6	14	-84	504	-75	450
-5	16	-80	400	-59	295
-4	30	-120	480	-105	420
-3	55	-165	495	-126	378
-2	69	-138	276	-119	238
-1	85	-85	85	-70	70
0	128	—	—	$+25$	—
1	101	$+101$	101	106	106
2	98	196	392	185	370
3	91	273	819	240	720
4	106	424	1 696	414	1 656
5	54	270	1 350	241	1 205
6	40	240	1 440	215	1 290
7	25	175	1 225	147	1 029
8	15	120	960	111	888
9	12	108	972	91	819
10	2	20	200	17	170
11	5	55	605	48	528
Totals ...	955	$+1\,241$	12 543	$+1\,226$	$+11\,119$

$$_x v_1' = \bar{x}' = \frac{+1\,241}{955} = +1{\cdot}299\,48, \quad h_x = 0{\cdot}05 \text{ cm.}$$

mean length $= 4{\cdot}125 + 0{\cdot}065 = 4{\cdot}190$ cm.

$$_x v_2' = \frac{12\,543}{955} = 13{\cdot}134\,0$$

$$- {}_x v_1'^2 = -1{\cdot}688\,6$$

$$_x v_2 = \overline{11{\cdot}445\,4}$$

$$-0{\cdot}083\,3$$

$$_x \mu_2 = \overline{11{\cdot}362\,1}$$

$$s_x^2 = h_x^2 \times 11{\cdot}362\,1 = 0{\cdot}028\,405 \text{ cm.}^2$$

$$s_x = 0{\cdot}168\,54 \text{ cm.}$$

Regressions—

$$y \text{ on } x = +\frac{0{\cdot}049\,874}{0{\cdot}028\,405} = +1{\cdot}756 \text{ cm./cm.}$$

$$x \text{ on } y = +\frac{0{\cdot}049\,874}{0{\cdot}110\,69} = +0{\cdot}450\,6 \text{ cm./cm.}$$

of x' from the arbitrary origin, and so should equal the sum of column (9). The terms of column (6) are the products of those in columns (1) and (5), and their sum is the required $Sx'y'$. As a check on the arithmetic this may be done the other way, summing first for each separate array of x' and adding the sums. This is done in columns (11) and (12), and if the arithmetic is correct the totals of columns (11) and (3) and those of columns (6) and (12) should be equal. There is no independent check of columns (4) and (10), and so they should be repeated carefully.

The product moment is calculated below Table 8.4 by applying equation (8.4) to the arbitrary values and then correcting by equation (8.4b). In finding r and the regressions, we have used p, s_x and s_y in the natural units of centimetres, but it would be just as easy to maintain arbitrary units throughout and then to correct the regressions by multiplying by h_y/h_x and h_x/h_y. The correlation coefficient, being a pure number, needs no such correction.

ASSUMPTIONS AND INTERPRETATIONS

8.5. The interpretation of the correlation coefficient as a parameter of the equation describing a normal frequency surface is of little other than theoretical value, but it serves to remind us that fundamentally it is like any other statistical measure : merely descriptive of a population of individuals. For instance, Weldon found that the correlation between number of pistils and stamens of late flowers of Table 8.1a was 0·75, while for the early ones, Table 8.1b, it was 0·51 ; this change in the strength of relationship is as much a characteristic of the flowers as a change (say) in mean height of the plants. Fisher and Hoblyn (1928) give tables to show that the correlation between maximum and minimum temperature is about 0·71 in January and 0·30 in August ; this change is gradual from month to month and is a quality of the climate.

For practical purposes, however, we choose to make other interpretations associated with the regression lines and the analysis of variance. Let us imagine that we have two urns, the first containing tickets with values of x and the second with an infinite population of tickets with random deviations of y distributed normally. Then each observation can be imagined as resulting from a draw of a ticket from the first urn and a random draw from the second, the first giving the value of x and hence by equation (8.22) of Y (a and b being also given constants of the universe), and the random deviation added to Y giving y. The residual variance of Table 8.23 is the variance of the deviations of y. If the values of x are distributed normally, this model gives rise to the normal frequency surface. As a model of the way in which regression lines and the components of variance arise, no assumptions need be made about the number or distribution of x tickets in the first urn, nor about the method of making the draw. It is necessary to assume only a constant linear relation between x and Y for all draws, and the normality and homogeneity of the deviations of y in the second urn.

The value of Y is sometimes used as a prediction of what y is likely to be for a given value of x, and the precision of such a prediction is measured by the standard deviation of the residual deviations. If x is not known, the standard error with which any one value of y can be predicted is s_y ; if x is known and the regression formula is used, the standard error is reduced to $s_y\sqrt{(1 - r^2)}$. The correlation coefficient is thus a complicated measure of the extent to which the use of a linear regression formula improves a prediction. This interpretation is legitimate provided the circumstances in which the prediction is used are the same as those in which the coefficients are estimated—provided the same urns are in use. This proviso is obvious but is apt to be overlooked in practical work when prediction is made from one set of experiences to another.

Sometimes the variations represented by the tickets in the first urn are thought of as causes of variations in y, operating through the relationship expressed by $Y = ax + b$. Then, if by control x can be kept constant, the variance of y is reduced from s_y^2 to $(1 - r^2)s_y^2$ and the standard deviations from s_y to $s_y\sqrt{(1 - r^2)}$. On this view, an increase in x is regarded as *causing*, on the average, an increase or decrease in y, according as the correlation coefficient is positive or negative ; and the coefficient is then used as evidence of a causal relationship.

Such inferences are sometimes erroneous when experimental control is so good that there are no random deviations and the correlation coefficient is unity, but they are particularly unsafe when there are uncontrolled variations and the relationship is not exact. Often two quantities are both affected in the same way by a third so that they appear to be related, when actually neither if altered independently would have any effect on the other. For instance, Yule refers to the fact that the proportion of marriages contracted outside the Church of England has for many years been increasing while the average age at death has also been increasing, and there is a positive correlation ; but no one supposes that there is a causal relationship and that a law prohibiting the solemnisation of marriage in churches would have the effect of improving the longevity of the nation. When investigating causation, it is usually well to decide first on other grounds that a causal relationship between two factors is likely, and then to conduct a close analysis of other possible factors before using the correlation coefficient as evidence. Care, common sense, imagination, and a technical knowledge of the subject to which it is applied, are particularly necessary in this use of correlation. We shall in Chapter X discuss methods of analysing data for other factors and of eliminating their effects.

When considered as an expression of the relationship between two quantities, the correlation coefficient measures the importance *relative to all other variations* of the variations in one quantity associated with variations in the other operating through that relationship. The appropriate regression coefficient measures more absolutely the technical importance of the associated variations, stating by how many units y changes, on the average, per unit change in x. It will be seen from equations $(8.22a)$ and $(8.22b)$ that according to the relative values of s_x and s_y, a high regression coefficient may occur with a low or a high correlation coefficient.

Some experience is necessary for arriving at an appreciation of the scale of values of r as a measure of the strength of association. In this connection, only the magnitude of r matters ; the sign does not. The ratios of the residual to the total variance, and of the corresponding standard deviations, are given in Table 8.5 for a few values of r. The scale is very uneven, since a correlation coefficient of 0·6 only reduces the residual standard deviation to 0·8 of the total, while even if the coefficient is as high as 0·9, the residual deviations have a standard deviation of 0·436 of the total. This unevenness of scale is shown by Tables 8.1 to 8.1d ; a far greater change in association is noticeable between Tables 8.1 and 8.1b for a smaller change in correlation coefficient than between Tables 8.1b and 8.1d ; i.e. a coefficient of 1·0 is much more than twice as good as one of 0·5.

The following typical cases may assist the reader. Yule (1927) gives the correlation coefficient between the ages of husbands and wives in England and Wales as 0·91, and that between the age and the standard of elementary school boys is about the same (Jones, 1910). The likeness between parents and children is expressed by a coefficient of about 0·47 as far as height and several other physical characters are concerned (Snow, 1911), and that between cousins or uncles and nephews, which is so small as scarcely to be noticeable to the " man in the street," has a correlation coefficient of about 0·26. Similarly, taking periods of six days as units, the correlation between the rainfall and hours of bright sunshine in Hertfordshire is negative (i.e. increased rainfall is associated with decreased sunshine) and about 0·2.

TABLE 8.5*

Correlation Coefficient r	Ratio of Variances Residual/Total	Ratio of Standard Deviations Residual/Total	z'
zero	1·00	1·000	zero
0·2	0·96	0·980	0·20
0·4	0·84	0·917	0·42
0·6	0·64	0·800	0·69
0·7	0·51	0·714	0·87
0·8	0·36	0·600	1·10
0·9	0·19	0·436	1·47
1·0	zero	zero	infinity

To sum up : there are three important constants that express the properties of a correlation table :

(1) The correlation coefficient that measures the importance of the variation in y associated with x relative to the total variation,

(2) The regression coefficient that measures the average amount of increase or decrease in y per unit increase in x, and

(3) The residual variance that measures the scatter of values of y about the regression line.

* The column under z' will be referred to in the next chapter.

245

For different populations, these constants are independent in that a high value of one constant does not necessarily mean a high or low value of either of the others.

Effects of Experimental Errors

8.51. In the experimental model of the urns introduced in the previous section we envisaged x and Y as being uniquely and exactly determined for each individual, and the random variations as affecting only y. Now let us consider the case in which two quantities u and v, measured from corresponding population means, are statistically correlated, and to each is added an independent random deviation, x' and y' respectively, so that the measured quantities are

$$\left. \begin{array}{l} (x - \bar{x}) = u + x' \\ (y - \bar{y}) = v + y' \end{array} \right\} \quad \cdots \cdots \quad (8.51)$$

In practice u and v could be true values of some quantities and x' and y' could be the experimental errors with which they are determined. For any individual, x' is independent of the value of u, v and y', and y' is independent of the value of u, v and x', so that

$$\text{S}x'u = \text{S}x'v = \text{S}x'y' = \text{S}y'u = \text{S}y'v = \text{o},$$

where S is the summation over all individuals.

Under these conditions, it is easy to show that

$$\left. \begin{array}{ll} \text{S}(x - \bar{x})\,(y - \bar{y}) = \text{S}uv \\ \text{S}(x - \bar{x})^2 \qquad\quad = \text{S}u^2 + \text{S}x'^2 \\ \text{S}(y - \bar{y})^2 \qquad\quad = \text{S}v^2 + \text{S}y'^2 \end{array} \right\} \quad \cdots \quad (8.51a)$$

and when divided by N or $N - 1$, these equations lead to corresponding relations between the product moments and variances. Equations (8.51a) enable estimates of the correlation and regression coefficients between u and v to be made from the observed data x and y, provided the error variances are known. It is unnecessary to develop the equations in detail but we shall work out an example.

In the evaluation of certain different growths of cotton two types of test were once used, the large-scale test yielding values of y and the small-scale test yielding values of x. Each test is, however, subject to errors, so that duplicate tests made on the same cotton give slightly different results. It is required to estimate the correlation coefficient between u and v, the true results freed from error, and (so that future true large-scale results may be predicted from experimental small-scale results) the regression coefficient of v on x.

There were 243 cottons, and the sums of products and squares of the deviations of the experimental values from their means, divided by 242, are in the second column of Table 8.51. The mean squares are of course estimates of the variances $s_x{}^2$ and $s_y{}^2$. The units of measurement are the technical units used in the spinning test. Each experimental value of x was the mean of two duplicate results. The variance within pairs estimated on 243 degrees of freedom according to section 5.1 is 4 611·3, so the $s_{x'}{}^2$ for the mean of two results is 2 306 ; this is entered in Table 8.51 as a correction. Only one large-scale test was made for each cotton, but from a separate set of replicate experiments made on somewhat similar cottons it is estimated on 72 degrees of freedom that $s_{y'}{}^2$ is 1 432,

TABLE 8.51

CORRELATION RESULTS, LARGE- AND SMALL-SCALE TESTS ON COTTON*

	Experimental Result	Correction	Corrected Result
Mean product ...	42 326	—	42 326
Mean square, x ...	45 482	2 306	43 176
Mean square, y ...	48 886	1 432	47 454

* Unpublished data by C. Underwood

as entered in Table 8.51. From the appropriate mean products and squares of Table 8.51 we compute :

Correlation coefficient between u and v,

$$r_{uv} = 42\ 326 / \sqrt{(43\ 176 \times 47\ 454)} = 0\text{·}935$$

and regression coefficient of v on x,

$$A_{vx} = 42\ 326 / 45\ 482 = 0\text{·}93 \text{ units.}$$

The interest in r_{uv} lies in knowing whether it is substantially equal to unity, that is to say whether discrepancies between the results of the two tests may be attributed to experimental errors. Unfortunately, the sampling errors of such estimates as r_{uv} have not been investigated. It may be noted that A_{vx} is unaffected by the experimental errors.

An interesting special case of equations (8.51) and (8.51*a*) occurs when u and v are exactly and linearly related such that

$$\left. \begin{array}{c} v = Au \\ \text{and} \\ r_{uv} = 1 \end{array} \right\} \quad \ldots \ldots \quad (8.51b)$$

Then it is easy to deduce from equations (8.51*a*) and (8.51*b*) that

$$A = a(1 + s_{x'}{}^2/s_u{}^2) = as_x{}^2/(s_x{}^2 - s_{x'}{}^2) \quad . \quad . \quad (8.51c)$$

where a is the regression coefficient of y on x, computed from the experimental results. The true regression A can thus be estimated only if the error variance, $s_{x'}{}^2$ is known. The effect of experimental errors is to reduce the apparent regression coefficient below the true value, the reduction being greater as the error variance becomes more important relative to the variance of the true values of u. For a given A and error variance, the apparent regression coefficient increases as $s_u{}^2$ increases. Readers who are interested to consider these relations further should refer to Eisenhart (1939).

CHAPTER IX

SAMPLING ERRORS IN SIMPLE CORRELATION ANALYSIS

In this chapter we shall consider the errors of sample estimates of the correlation and regression coefficients introduced in the last chapter, and how to take account of these errors when making inferences in a number of common situations.

It will be necessary to distinguish between sample estimates and population values for various quantities, and this we shall do by using Latin letters for sample estimates and equivalent Greek letters for the population values. It is only necessary to state particularly that η and H will be used as equivalents to y and Y.

When considering the variations in samples from a population of individuals on which two variates are measured, there are two main possibilities. The first is that x and y may both vary randomly from sample to sample, and the second is that only the residual deviations in the dependent variate may vary, the values of the independent variate being the same for each sample. When the samples are regarded as taken from a population expressible as a normal frequency surface as in section 8.21, only the first can be entertained as a possibility ; but both can be entertained in the interpretations involving regression lines and the analysis of variance, and may be described in terms of the model of the urns mentioned in section 8.5. According to the first possibility, values of x in the first urn form an infinite normal population as do those of the deviations of y in the second ; for each sample there is an independent and random draw of N tickets from each urn, the only thing that is constant being the α and β of the relationship between x and H (we are now thinking of the population value of equation (8.22)). According to the second possibility the same draw of N tickets from the first urn is used for all samples, sample variations arising entirely from the variations in the N residual deviations of y. This is the situation which arises in most experiments and in many studies of existing variability, where the values of the independent variable are more or less arbitrarily chosen or where their variation has no significance for the subject under investigation.

Correlation Coefficient when Association in Population is Zero

9.1. In order to test whether an observed correlation coefficient is significantly greater than zero we need to know the sampling distribution of r for $\rho = 0$ (ρ being the population value of the correlation coefficient). This is the same whether both or only one variable is subject to sampling variations.

For samples from such a population, the standard error of the distribution of r is $\pm 1/\sqrt{(N-1)}$ (or for large numbers, $\pm 1/\sqrt{N}$ is an adequate approximation) where N is the number of individuals, i.e. the number of pairs of readings of x and y. Unless the sample is very small, the distribution is near enough to normality to justify the use of the criterion that a value of r more than twice the standard error for zero association is above the 0·05 level of significance. For the data of Table 8.1d there are 4 690 observations, and the correlation between reaction time to sight and head length is $-0·034$, with a standard error of $\pm 0·015$. The value is a little more than twice its standard error, and so is suggestive of a real, although exceedingly weak, association. It would not be safe, however, to deduce very much from such a result ; indeed, a correlation of that sort might conceivably arise if there were a small personal error in measurement such that the observer who overestimated the head length tended slightly to underestimate the reaction time, and if several observers took the measurements, the same one always measuring both characters on the same individual. For the maximum and minimum temperatures of Table 8.1c, $N = 1\,518$, $r = +0·30$, and being more than ten times its standard error ($\pm 1/\sqrt{1\,518} = \pm 0·026$) is undoubtedly real. Hence, sufficient observations can establish the reality of an exceedingly weak association, and the probability of its significance is no guide to the closeness of the relationship.

We have seen, however, from Tables 8.23 and 8.23a that correlation may be expressed as an analysis of variance, where one degree of freedom is taken by the regression line and $(N-2)$ are taken by the residuals. For a sample from a population with zero correlation the two variances $_yv_s$ and $_yv_r$ are independent estimates of the same variance, and we may test for the significance of their difference by finding $F = r^2 (N-2)/(1-r^2)$ and testing with $\nu_1 = 1$ and $\nu_2 = N-2$, or $t = \sqrt{\{r^2(N-2)/(1-r^2)\}}$ and testing with $\nu = N-2$.

Fisher (1925c) has prepared tables giving values of the correlation coefficient on different levels of significance for samples of various sizes. When there are 12 degrees of freedom ($N = 14$), $r = 0.532\ 4$ lies on the 0.05 level, and making the above transformation, we find that $F = 4.747$ and $t = 2.179$. Both of these lie on the 5 per cent. level of their respective contributions. We can now check the assumption of the normal distribution of r for moderately large samples ; when $N = 20$ (say), $1/\sqrt{(N-1)} = 0.229$, and a correlation coefficient of 0.46 lies on the 0.05 level, while Fisher's tables give the exact value for $18 (= N - 2)$ degrees of freedom as 0.444 ; when $N = 10$ the corresponding values are $2 \times 0.333 = 0.67$ for the normal distribution and 0.632 for the true distribution, and at $N = 5$ they are $2 \times 0.500 = 1.0$ and 0.878. As far as the 0.05 level of significance goes, the assumption of normality is not likely to lead to serious error even for samples as small as 10, but below that it makes the test unnecessarily stringent ; the true test based on F or t, however, is correct for samples of all sizes.

Contrary to an opinion often expressed, an association measured by the correlation coefficient may be significant in a very small sample if it is strong enough ; and this is in accordance with common experience. A physicist, for instance, if he obtains on a graph half a dozen points which lie anywhere near a straight line does not say that there is no relationship but assumes one and draws his line. This is the more extreme case in which the association is high, and the correlation coefficient is a device for measuring and testing the association more objectively and exactly, and is particularly useful in border-line cases.

We shall take as example some data by Winter (1929), for which corn was grown for twenty-nine years in two series of plots ; in the first the seed for one year was from ears of corn in the previous year's crop in that series, selected because it had high protein content, and in the second the seed for one year was selected from the previous year's crop because of low protein content. The data given in Table 9.1 are the mean percentages of protein for each year, and the coefficients of variation per cent. from ear to ear, and we will call them y_1, y_2, v_1 and v_2. The mean protein percentages of the first series (y_1) seem to have increased progressively, and those of the second series (y_2) appear to have decreased, while it is difficult to see what tendency the variabilities show ; we shall

251

investigate these trends by means of the correlation coefficients, thus assuming them to be sufficiently well expressed by a linear

TABLE 9.1

PERCENTAGE PROTEIN CONTENT

Year t	Corn Selected for			
	High Protein Content		Low Protein Content	
	y_1 Mean	v_1 Variability	y_2 Mean	v_2 Variability
1896	10·93	9·50	10·93	9·50
1897	10·99	10·90	10·63	8·47
1898	10·98	11·15	10·49	12·61
1899	11·62	11·00	9·59	10·50
1900	12·62	8·09	9·13	11·34
1901	13·78	8·48	9·63	11·47
1902	12·90	8·50	7·86	9·60
1903	13·51	10·04	8·00	10·41
1904	15·03	9·05	8·17	9·91
1905	14·73	8·55	8·58	9·91
1906	14·26	9·19	8·65	10·64
1907	13·90	10·72	7·32	12·57
1908	13·94	11·91	8·96	14·06
1909	13·29	10·76	7·48	12·57
1910	14·87	9·68	8·26	10·41
1911	13·79	12·98	7·90	14·81
1912	14·49	7·80	8·23	9·96
1913	14·83	8·23	7·71	12·32
1914	15·04	9·44	7·67	12·39
1915	14·54	10·19	7·27	11·69
1916	15·66	8·56	8·68	11·86
1917	14·45	12·80	7·09	10·01
1918	15·49	8·78	7·13	10·52
1919	14·70	10·54	6·46	8·05
1920	14·01	12·78	7·54	11·80
1921	16·66	11·04	9·14	14·77
1922	17·34	7·15	7·42	9·43
1923	16·53	8·50	6·48	11·27
1924	16·60	7·17	8·38	13·96

relationship with time. The correlation coefficients between time and y_1, v_1, y_2 and v_2 are $+ 0.862$, $- 0.081$, $- 0.708$ and $+ 0.256$

respectively.* For 27 degrees of freedom, $r = 0.367$ lies on the 0.05 level of significance, so that on the average the mean percentages of protein have increased significantly in the first series and decreased in the second with time, but the continued selection has had no measurable effect on the variability.

CORRELATION COEFFICIENT WHEN ASSOCIATION IN POPULATION IS NOT ZERO

9.2. When ρ, the population value of the correlation coefficient, is not zero the sampling distribution of r differs according as both or only one variable is subject to sampling variations, but only the former case has been treated fully and is the basis of this and the next three sections.

The standard error of r is

$$\frac{1 - \rho^2}{\sqrt{(N - 1)}}$$

but this result is of little value, especially when ρ is high, because the sampling distribution of r is far from normal, and moreover considerable error may result from substituting the sample value r for ρ in the above expression when ρ is not known. However, the exact distribution has been deduced by Fisher (1915) and tables of ordinates and probabilities have been computed by David (1938). The use of these tables is fully described in the introduction to them.

It is more convenient, however, to use the following methods based on a transformation suggested by Fisher (1921). This consists in writing

$$z' = \tanh^{-1} r = \tfrac{1}{2} \log_e \frac{1 + r}{1 - r} \quad \cdots \quad (9.2)$$

This is not quite the same as the $z = \tfrac{1}{2} \log_e F$, so the prime has been added to make a distinction. The sampling distribution of z' is nearly normal, with a mean that is nearly but not quite equal to ζ' (i.e. z' estimates the population value ζ' with a small bias), and a standard error approximately equal to $1/\sqrt{(N - 3)}$ (i.e. independent of ζ'). As an approximation, therefore, the ordinary large sample theory outlined in Chapter III may be applied to z'. For example, when $N = 12$, the standard error of z' is $1/3$ and the

---

* The computation is much simplified if the year 1910 is chosen as zero time, and the others are labelled $-1, -2, \ldots, +1, +2, \ldots$; then $\bar{t} = 0$.

two values cutting off tails of 0·05 (the 0·05 and 0·95 levels) are 1·645/3 = 0·548 above and below the population value ζ'. For $\rho = 0·8$, $\zeta' = 1·099$, and the 0·05 and 0·95 levels of z are 1·099 $\pm$ 0·548 = 0·551 and 1·647, corresponding to values of r of 0·501 and 0·928. The correct values of r on these levels, obtained from David's tables, are 0·54 and 0·935. For $N = 20$ and $\rho = 0·8$, the 0·05 and 0·95 levels of r are : 0·624 and 0·899 obtained by the approximation and 0·62 and 0·91 obtained from David's tables. The z' approximation is good enough for most practical purposes. Clearly it can be used for, among other things, determining confidence limits.*

Fisher (1925c) gives a good table relating z' to r, and some of the values are entered in Table 8.5. When $r = 1·0$, $z' = \infty$, and the whole effect of the transformation is to give a more open scale for z' when the association is high when, as we saw in the last chapter, small changes in r correspond to important changes in the variance absorbed by the regression line.

Significance of Differences between Correlations

9.21. Because its distribution is more nearly normal, Fisher recommends the z' transformation when testing the significance of the deviation of an observed correlation from zero ; but the effect of the transformation is small for small values of r, and this step is not important. Differences of observed correlations from some assumed population value, or between pairs of observed correlations, may be tested by using z' and its standard error just as we did the mean and its standard error in large samples.

For example, Snow (1911) gives the correlation coefficient between brothers and sisters, measured for a variety of characters, as 0·521, while Fisher (1928a) found from 34 pairs of unlike sex from triplet births the correlation coefficient for cubit to be 0·645 ; can this difference be attributed to random errors ? The values of z' are 0·578 and 0·767, and the standard error of the second is $\pm 1/\sqrt{31} = \pm 0·180$ (we assume the first determination to be the exact population value, since it is based on many more

* It may be well to mention here a fairly common fallacy in the use of the standard error for testing the significance of an observed coefficient, r. As an approximation, $(1 - r^2)/\sqrt{(N - 1)}$ is often written for the unknown $(1 - \rho^2)/\sqrt{(N - 1)}$ and if any observed correlation is greater than twice the former standard error it is judged to be significant ; but if the hypothesis being tested is that $\rho = 0$, the true standard error of r is $1/\sqrt{(N - 1)}$ as shown in the previous section.

observations) ; the difference is less than twice the standard error
and is insignificant.

In this example, deviations of z' of $\pm$ 0·360 from the population
value (0·578) lie on the 0·05 level of significance, giving values of
z' on this level of 0·218 and 0·938 ; the corresponding values of r
are 0·214 and 0·734. Thus the chances are about 20 : 1 against a
random sample of 34 pairs giving values of r outside these limits,
but we regard values anywhere between them as common experience ; the deviations of the limits of r from 0·521 are $-$ 0·307
and $+$ 0·213, and their inequality shows the skewness of the
distribution of r.

The following is an example of the use of z' to test the significance of the difference between two observed correlations. Table
8.1a shows the correlation between number of stamens and pistils
measured on 373 flowers collected late in the season to be 0·745,
while a sample of 268 flowers collected earlier gave a correlation
coefficient of 0·506 ; making the transformation, we find $z' =$
0·962 and 0·557, and the difference, being 0·405 with a standard
error of $\sqrt{(1/370 + 1/265)} = $ 0·080, is quite significant.

Combination of Estimates of a Correlation

9.22. It sometimes happens that we have a number of correlation
coefficients estimated from several small samples from populations
having the same coefficient, and that we wish to combine them to
obtain a mean. This is best done by making the transformation,
finding the mean z', and then re-transforming back to r. If the
samples are not of equal size, we naturally give the larger ones
more weight than the smaller ones ; but the weights should be
proportional, not to N, the size of the sample, but to $(N - 3)$.
Thus if $z'_1, z'_2 \ldots$ are the individual estimates based on samples
of $N_1, N_2 \ldots$ pairs of observations, the weighted mean is

$$\bar{z}' = \frac{(N_1 - 3)z'_1 + (N_2 - 3)z'_2 + \ldots}{(N_1 - 3) + (N_2 - 3) + \ldots}$$

and the standard error of z' is

$$\frac{1}{\sqrt{(N_1 - 3 + N_2 - 3 + \ldots)}}.$$

In the language of section 3.62, $N_1 - 3$, $N_2 - 3$, etc., are the
quantities of information given by the samples. In finding the

mean of z' these quantities are the weights, and since the quantities are additive the variance of the mean z' is the inverse of the total quantity of information.

Table 9.22 contains the correlation coefficients between cephalic index and upper face form for samples of skulls belonging to thirteen races (Tschepourkowsky, 1905). The values of z' are in the fourth column and their mean, when weighted with $(N - 3)$, and standard error are

$$- 42\cdot408/696 = - 0\cdot060\ 9, \text{ and } \pm - 1/\sqrt{696} = \pm\ 0\cdot037\ 9.$$

The mean z' is not significant.

If an improved estimate of the correlation is obtained by combining a large number of very small samples in this way, there is a

TABLE 9.22

CORRELATION COEFFICIENTS BETWEEN CEPHALIC INDEX AND
UPPER FACE INDEX

Race	Number of Cases N	Correlation Coefficient	z'	$z'^2(N - 3)$
Australians ...	66	+ 0·089	+ 0·089	0·50
Negroes	77	+ 0·182	+ 0·184	2·51
Duke of York Islanders ...	53	− 0·093	− 0·093	0·43
Malays	60	− 0·185	− 0·187	1·99
Fijians	32	+ 0·217	+ 0·221	1·42
Papuans	39	− 0·255	− 0·261	2·45
Polynesians ...	44	+ 0·002	+ 0·002	0·00
Alfourous	19	− 0·302	− 0·312	1·56
Micronesians ...	32	− 0·251	− 0·257	1·92
Copts	34	− 0·147	− 0·148	0·68
Etruscans	47	− 0·021	− 0·021	0·02
Europeans ...	80	− 0·198	− 0·201	3·11
Ancient Thebans ...	152	− 0·067	− 0·067	0·67
				$\chi^2 = 17\cdot26$ $g = 13$

possibility of serious error in $\bar{z}'$ due to the fact that its distribution is not quite normal and there is a slight bias. For this reason, the number of coefficients combined should be small compared with the average size of sample.

Significance of Groups of Correlation Coefficients

9.23. If we have a group of correlation coefficients and wish to test whether as a whole they show association, we may find the separate significance probabilities, using perhaps the t test, and combine these by the method of section 5.62. Alternatively, and probably more efficiently, we may use a test involving z' and χ^2. Since the standard error of z' is $1/\sqrt{(N-3)}$, the quantity $z'\sqrt{(N-3)}$ is distributed approximately normally about a mean of zero and with unit standard deviation in samples from a population with zero association, and we may calculate

$$\chi^2 = S\{z'^2(N-3)\},$$

where S is the summation over the number of samples available. As we have indicated in section 2.73, this should be distributed as the χ^2 for g degrees of freedom if there are g samples, and we may find P, the probability that random samples from the hypothetical population would give χ^2 as great or greater than that observed.

When testing the correlations of Table 9.22 by finding the mean z', we implicitly assumed them to be samples from the same population and regarded the variations in r as due to random errors. It may be, however, that the variations are real racial differences, and that in general there is a correlation between cephalic index and face form, which is sometimes positive and sometimes negative, so that the mean is nearly zero ; we can now test this, using z' and χ^2. The values of $z'^2(N-3)$ are given in the fifth column of the table, and their sum gives a χ^2 of 17·26, which for 13 degrees of freedom lies between the 0·1 and 0·2 levels of significance. Thus the combined experience of Table 9.22 lends no support to the view that the two characters are associated, even after making allowance for the possibility of racial differences.

Having found a mean z' from a number of samples by the method of section 9.22, and found it to be significant, we may wish to test if the individual values as a whole differ significantly among themselves, and the χ^2 distribution may be used for this. If z' is an individual transformed correlation, $\bar{z}'$ the mean, and N the size of the individual sample,

$$\chi^2 = S\{(z' - \bar{z}')^2(N-3)\},$$

and the number of degrees of freedom (g) is one less than the number of samples (if the mean has been found from them). As

R   257

an example, we shall consider Table 9.23, which contains correlations between head length and breadth for Egyptians native to six districts ; the data have been taken from a paper by Orensteen (1920). The weighted mean z' is $+ 0.266\ 8$ (giving $r = + 0.260$), and the sum of the last column is $\chi^2 = 7.28$; for 5 degrees of freedom this lies almost exactly on the $P = 0.2$ level and we must conclude that there is no evidence of any difference in correlation among the six districts chosen. Comparing the Beheira

TABLE 9.23

CORRELATIONS BETWEEN HEAD LENGTH AND BREADTH

District	Number of Cases N	Correlation Coefficient	z'	$z' - \bar{z}'$	$(z' - \bar{z}')^2 (N-3)$
Alexandria	643	+0.244	+0.249	−0.017 8	0.20
Cairo ...	802	+0.244	+0.249	−0.017 8	0.25
Canal ...	127	+0.330	+0.343	+0.076 2	0.72
Beheira ...	526	+0.213	+0.216	−0.050 8	1.35
Gharbiya	1 104	+0.316	+0.327	+0.060 2	3.99
Minufiya	717	+0.230	+0.234	−0.032 8	0.77

and Gharbiya districts, we find the difference in z' is 0.111 with a standard error of $\pm \sqrt{(1/523 + 1/1\ 101)} = \pm 0.053$; this difference is about twice the standard error, and if the two samples came alone it might be regarded as significant ; but we must remember that it is just about the most significant one that could be taken from the six values, and bearing in mind the remarks in section 3.22 regarding significances of differences within groups of samples, we should compare the ratio 0.111/0.053, not with 2.0, the 0.05 level for a random pair, but with 2.9, the 0.05 level of the range for six samples (Table 3.22a).

REGRESSION COEFFICIENT WHEN ASSOCIATION IN POPULATION IS ZERO

9.3. All the following tests of the regression coefficient are based on the assumption that the values of x do not vary from sample to sample. When the population association is zero, the population value of the regression coefficient α in equation (8.22) is zero, and we may derive from Table 8.23, with suitable modification of symbols, a t test for significance based on $N - 2$ degrees of freedom. If a is a sample regression coefficient and $s'^2 = {}_y v_r$ is the estimated variance of the residual deviations from the fitted line, we see from Table 8.23 that

$$t = \frac{a}{s'/\sqrt{\{S(x - \bar{x})^2\}}} \quad \cdots \quad \cdots \quad (9.3)$$

The standard deviation s' may be estimated from equation (8.32).

It is easy to show that for constant values of x from sample to sample the above values of t in repeated samples from a population for which $\alpha = 0$ are distributed as the t of section 5.2 for $N - 2$ degrees of freedom. Mathematically this follows because, for values of x that do not vary from sample to sample, a is a linear function of normally and randomly distributed variables y with constant coefficients, which is itself normally distributed, and $s'/\sqrt{\{S(x - \bar{x})^2\}}$ is an estimate of its standard error based on $N - 2$ degrees of freedom.

REGRESSION COEFFICIENT WHEN ASSOCIATION IN POPULATION IS NOT ZERO

9.4. It is not difficult to show that when the regression coefficient is α, the quantity

$$t = \frac{a - \alpha}{s'/\sqrt{\{S(x - \bar{x})^2\}}} \quad \cdots \quad \cdots \quad (9.4)$$

is distributed as the t equation (9.3) for $N - 2$ degrees of freedom, where s' is the standard deviation of the residual deviations from the fitted regression line, and the denominator estimates the standard error of α. Hence can be calculated any required confidence or fiducial limits for an observed value of a. If N is large, a is normally distributed about a mean of α with a standard error of

$$\frac{\sigma'}{\sqrt{\{S(x - \bar{x})^2\}}} = \frac{\alpha}{\rho} \sqrt{\left(\frac{1 - \rho^2}{N} \right)} \quad \cdots \quad \cdots \quad (9.4a)$$

where ρ is population value of the correlation coefficient and σ' that of the standard deviation of the residual deviations of y from the regression line.

SIGNIFICANCE OF GROUPS OF REGRESSIONS

9.5. The methods of analysis of variance as applied in section 7.6 can be readily extended to testing the significance of differences between groups of straight regression lines, and this will be illustrated in the next three sections. Each section will test one hypothesis and the tests follow the same general principle, which will emerge as the examples are studied.

Throughout these tests, it is assumed that the residual variance of y is the same for all series of data and values of x, and that the values of x are not subject to sampling errors.

9.51. *Hypothesis : That a number of samples are from populations having the same regression coefficient.*

Consider the data of Table 9.51, taken from a paper by Glanville and Reid (1934). They are the crushing strengths of specimens of mortar and concrete made from seven different cements ; specimens were broken at three different ages. These data form part of the result of an investigation into the use of tests on mortar as a guide to the behaviour of the cement in concrete. If the corresponding strengths of mortar and cement are plotted a marked

TABLE 9.51

CRUSHING STRENGTH OF MORTAR AND CONCRETE, LB. PER SQ. IN. ÷ 10

Cement	One Day		Seven Days		Twenty-eight Days	
	Mortar x	Concrete y	Mortar x	Concrete y	Mortar x	Concrete y
A	263	138	750	507	895	679
B	493	278	936	653	1 066	818
C	137	49	453	425	632	651
D	477	293	893	662	1 100	842
E	233	104	545	437	716	603
F	568	350	797	735	897	832
G	230	141	631	439	846	724
$S_s(x-\bar{x}_s)^2$ ...	164 786		193 074		173 057	
$S_s(y-\bar{y}_s)^2$ ...	76 259		99 933		55 482	
$S_s(x-_s)(y-\bar{y}_s)$	111 205		117 648		82 646	

correlation will be apparent, and we may ask if the slopes of the regression lines of concrete strength on mortar strength for the three ages are significantly different. Whether or not the means for the three ages are different does not here concern us, nor the possibility of any variations in the variance of mortar strength from one age to another.

We may eliminate the mean strengths for the three ages by measuring the individual strengths as deviations from those means. Then we may either (1) fit one regression line to all the deviations, which is equivalent to fitting a series of parallel lines going through the means for the various ages, or (2) fit separate regression lines for the ages. The data are plotted in Fig. 9.51, where the parallel lines of system (1) are full lines and the separate ones of system (2) are dotted. The dotted lines fit the data more closely than the full ones in the sense that the sum of squares of deviations of concrete strength is less from the dotted lines. The separate regressions are only significantly different, however, if this difference in sums of squares is real after allowing for degrees of freedom absorbed in fitting and for random errors. This is tested by calculating residual variances. If the hypothesis is correct, the lines with separate slopes will give the same residual variance as those with the common slope, within the limits of sampling errors; if the second residual variance is significantly less than the first, the hypothesis is rejected and it is inferred that the separate lines give a closer representation of the data than the common line and are significantly different in slope. We shall set out the process algebraically.

If there are u samples of $N_1 N_2 \ldots$ individuals and we fit a separate regression line to each, viz. :

$$(Y - y_1) = a_1(x - \bar{x}_1),$$
$$(Y - y_2) = a_2(x - \bar{x}_2),$$
$$\cdot \quad \cdot \quad \cdot \quad \cdot \quad \cdot \quad \cdot \quad \cdot$$

the residual sums of squares and corresponding degrees of freedom after fitting the lines are given by equation (8.32) as :

$$\left. \begin{array}{l} \textit{Sums of squares :} \ S'(y - \bar{y}_1)^2 - \dfrac{\{S'(x - \bar{x}_1)\,(y - \bar{y}_1)\}^2}{S'(x - \bar{x}_1)^2}, \\[2ex] \qquad\qquad S''(y - \bar{y}_2)^2 - \dfrac{\{S''(x - \bar{x}_2)\,(y - \bar{y}_2)\}^2}{S''(x - \bar{x}_2)^2} \\[2ex] \qquad\qquad\qquad\qquad \text{etc., etc.,} \end{array} \right\} \cdot \quad 9.51$$

Degrees of freedom : $N_1 - 2$, $N_2 - 2$. etc.,

where $S'\, S'' \ldots$ are summations over all individuals in the respective samples. The sum of these sums of squares divided by

$(N_1 + N_2 + \ldots - 2u)$, the sum of the degrees of freedom, provides an estimate of the residual variance of y in the population, which is assumed to be the same for all samples.

Now, assuming the samples to have one regression coefficient but different means of y for a given value of x, the residual sum of

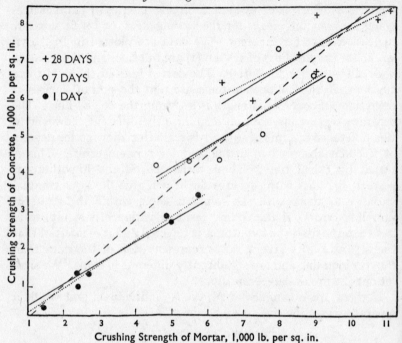

FIG. 9.51. Scatter diagram relating the crushing strength of mortar and concrete test-specimens of various ages, made from different cements [see Table 9.51]. The various regression lines are subjected to tests of significance in the text.

squares from the regression lines with common slope, and the degrees of freedom are :

Sum of squares :

$$\left. \begin{array}{l} S'(y - \bar{y}_1)^2 + S''(y - \bar{y}_2)^2 + \ldots \\[4pt] \quad - \dfrac{\{S''(x - \bar{x}_1)(y - \bar{y}_1) + S''(x - \bar{x}_2)(y - \bar{y}_2) + \ldots\}^2}{S''(x - \bar{x}_1)^2 + S''(x - \bar{x}_2)^2 + \ldots} \end{array} \right\} \quad 9.51a$$

Degrees of freedom : $N_1 + N_2 + \ldots - u - 1.$

The degrees of freedom are made up of the $N - 1$ contributed by each sample minus the one absorbed in fitting the common regression. The sum of squares divided by the degrees provides another estimate of the residual variance of y.

We cannot test the difference between the two variances obtained from (9.51) and (9.51a) for significance by the F test, because the variances are not independent. However, if we subtract the sum of squares of (9.51) from that of (9.51a) and divide by the corresponding difference in degrees, we have an estimate of the variance that is independent of the estimate of (9.51), and may be compared with it. The differences in sum of squares and degrees of freedom are:

Sum of squares :

$$\frac{\{S'(x-\bar{x}_1)(y-\bar{y}_1)\}^2}{S'(x-\bar{x}_1)^2}+\frac{S''\{(x-\bar{x}_2)(y-\bar{y}_2)\}^2}{S''(x-\bar{x}_2)^2}$$
$$+\ldots$$
$$-\frac{\{S'(x-\bar{x}_1)(y-\bar{y}_1)+S''(x-\bar{x}_2)(y-\bar{y}_2)+\ldots\}^2}{S'(x-\bar{x}_1)^2+S''(x-\bar{x}_2)^2+\ldots},$$

$$(9.51b)$$

Degrees of freedom : $u-1$.

Then F may be calculated from the ratio of the variances estimated from (9.51b) and (9.51) and tested for significance for degrees of freedom, $v_1 = u-1$, $v_2 = N_1 + N_2 + \ldots - 2u$.

For the data of Table 9.51, the total sum of squares of concrete strengths from equation (9.51) is*

$$76\ 259 - \frac{(111\ 205)^2}{164\ 786} + \ldots = 45\ 471,$$

and there are 15 degrees of freedom, giving a variance of 3 031. The sum of squares in equation (9.51b) is

$$\frac{(111\ 205)^2}{164\ 786} + \ldots - \frac{(311\ 499)^2}{530\ 917} = 3\ 441,$$

and for two degrees of freedom this gives as an estimate of variance the value 1 720. This is not greater than the variance from (9.51), and the slopes of the lines are not significantly different.

9.52. *Two samples are from populations having the same regression coefficient.*

The above test may be reduced to the t test when there are only

* All results for this example are in units of 10 lb. per sq. in.

two samples. The variance from (9.51*b*) is, in this instance, based on one degree of freedom, the square root of its ratio to the variance from (9.51) is *t*.

If the residual variance estimated from (9.51) is written s'^2 and the regression coefficients of the two samples are a_1 and a_2, it is easy to show from equations (8.31*d*), (9.51) and (9.51*b*) that

$$t = \frac{a_1 - a_2}{s'\sqrt{\{1/S'(x - \bar{x}_1)^2 + 1/S''(x - \bar{x}_2)^2\}}},$$

where s' is estimated from $N_1 + N_2 - 4$ degrees of freedom.

This test is parallel to that given in section 5.3 for the difference between two means. It follows from this that the standard error of the difference between the two regression coefficients may be derived from those of the separate coefficients by the standard method, using equation (3.21).

As an example we may consider the seven and twenty-eight day results of Table 9.51. The residual variance s'^2 is obtained from equation (9.51) applied to the last two ages, and is 4 426 based on 10 degrees of freedom. The standard error of the difference between the two regression coefficients is

$$\frac{\sqrt{4\,426}}{\sqrt{(1/193\,074 + 1/173\,057)}} = 0.220.$$

The regression coefficients are 117 648/193 074 = 0·609 3 and 82 646/173 057 = 0·477 6. Hence $t = 0.6$, and for 10 degrees of freedom this is near the 0·6 level; the difference in regression coefficients is not significant.

9.53. *Hypothesis : That a number of samples are from populations having the same regression line.*

We are postulating here, not only that the true regression lines for the separate samples are parallel, but that they *coincide*. The true means and variances of the independent variable *x* need not be equal for the populations, so those of *y* are not necessarily equal, but if our hypothesis is true, the true mean value of *y* and the variance for any given value of *x* must be the same for all samples. This hypothesis is not quite the same as postulating that the samples come from the same population. Again, we are not considering the possibility of the residual variance of *y* changing from sample to sample, and so are not testing it.

The general procedure is the same as that used in section 7.6. We fit the separate lines shown dotted in Fig. 9.51 and estimate a residual sum of squares and variance from equation (9.51). The common line is shown in Fig. 9.51 by a broken line ; it is fitted to the deviations of the values from the grand means for all samples. If $\bar{x}$ and $\bar{y}$ are the grand means and S is the summation over all individuals, we have for the residuals from this line :

$$\left.\begin{array}{l} \textit{Sum of squares} : \text{S}(y - \bar{y})^2 - \dfrac{\{\text{S}(x - \bar{x})\,(y - \bar{y})\}^2}{\text{S}(x - \bar{x})^2}, \\[2mm] \textit{Degrees of freedom} : N_1 + N_2 + \ldots - 2. \end{array}\right\} \quad (9.53)$$

The difference between the sums of squares in (9.53) and (9.51) divided by the difference in degrees of freedom, $2u - 2$, is the independent estimate of variance that may be compared with the residual variance from (9.51). There is no further algebraic reduction of the expressions.

We shall test the hypothesis on the data of Table 9.51 analysing the variance of the concrete strengths. The sum of squares of deviations from the common line is 111 792, the sum of squares of deviations from the separate lines is 45 471 and the difference is 66 321 for $19 - 15 = 4$ degrees, giving as an estimate of variance the value 16 580. The residual variance based on 15 degrees is 3 031, and since this is significantly less than the estimate based on four degrees ($F = 5.5$ lies just beyond the 0·01 point), we conclude that the regression lines differ. In this instance, since we have shown in section 9.51 that the lines do not differ significantly in slope, we may say that they differ only in level.

To test for a difference in level, assuming the slope to be constant, it would be legitimate to compare the residual after fitting a number of lines having different means but the same slope, with the residual after fitting a common line. Such a test is used in section 10.41.

SAMPLING ERRORS OF PREDICTED VALUES

9.6. A regression value, Y, calculated from the equation

$$Y = \bar{y} + a(x - \bar{x}) \quad . \quad . \quad . \quad . \quad . \quad (9.6)$$

where $\bar{y}$ and a are estimated from a sample according to section 8.31 is subject to sampling errors on account of the errors in $\bar{y}$ and a. These two constants are statistically independent, so that if

V_Y, $V_{\bar{y}}$ and V_a are respectively the sampling variances or the squares of the standard errors of Y, $\bar{y}$ and a,

$$V_Y = V_{\bar{y}} + (x - \bar{x})^2 V_a.$$

If we assume that the values of x are not subject to sampling errors, sampling variations in $\bar{y}$ arise only because of the residual variations from the regression line, and $V_y = \sigma'^2/N$ where σ'^2 is the true residual variance of y. From this and the result of equation (9.4a) we see that

$$V_Y = \sigma'^2 \left(\frac{1}{N} + \frac{(x - \bar{x})^2}{S(x - \bar{x})^2} \right) \quad \cdots \cdots \quad (9.6a)$$

and the standard error can be obtained by extracting the square root.

If σ' the population value is known, Y is distributed normally, since it is a linear function of independent quantities that are themselves distributed normally. If, as usually happens, the sample value s' is substituted for σ', $Y/\sqrt{V_Y}$ is distributed as t for $(N - 2)$ degrees of freedom. Thus, confidence limits for different values of Y can be determined. According to our assumptions $S(x - \bar{x})^2$ is a constant. The standard error of Y and hence the width of any given confidence band increases as the value of x for which the prediction is being made deviates more from $\bar{x}$.

It was stated in section 8.5 that when H deduced from the population values of the regression constants is used to predict what an individual value of y is likely to be, the standard error of the prediction is the residual standard deviation σ' (we are using symbols appropriate to population values). When a sample estimate Y is used, the sampling error variance is increased because of the sampling error of Y, and since Y and the deviations of y are independent,

$$V_y \text{ (y predicted from regression line)} = V_Y + \sigma'^2$$

$$= \sigma'^2 \left(\frac{N + 1}{N} + \frac{(x - \bar{x})^2}{S(x - \bar{x})^2} \right) \quad \cdots \cdots \quad (9.6b)$$

Biological Assay

9.61. Another situation arises typically in biological assay, where it may be required to determine the potency of a particular preparation of a certain drug by measuring its biological effect, either absolutely or in comparison with that of a standard preparation. Several measured doses of the drug are given to groups of, say animals, and some measure of the effect of each dose on the animals, the " response," is obtained—the response may be the average result of some chemical test on the animals in each group, or the proportion of animals that survive the treatment. Whatever the measure of dose and response, some mathematical transformation is usually found (e.g. by taking logarithms) such that the transformed response is linearly correlated with the transformed dose ; these transformed variables are respectively y and x. Now x is an independent variable in a physical as well as a mathematical sense and is determined with relatively high precision, whereas y shows the usual biological variation, so that the form of equation (9.6) is suitable for expressing the relationship between x and y. In practice, however, it is required to find the value of x, which we may specify as X, corresponding to a given standard response Y, for it is that value which specifies the relative potency of the preparation of drug. For this situation, therefore, we rearrange equation (9.6) and find that

$$X = \frac{(Y - \bar{y})}{a} + \bar{x} \quad \cdots \quad (9.61)$$

What is the sampling error variance of X ?

If we apply the method of section 4.15, remembering that Y is given, that $\bar{x}$ is not subject to sampling errors, and that the sampling variations of a and $\bar{y}$ are independent, we find :

V_X (X predicted from equation 9.61)

$$= \frac{1}{\alpha^2} \left\{ V_{\bar{y}} + \left(\frac{Y - \bar{\eta}}{\alpha} \right)^2 V(a) \right\}$$

$$= \frac{\sigma'^2}{\alpha^2} \left\{ \frac{1}{N} + \left(\frac{Y - \bar{\eta}}{\alpha} \right)^2 \frac{1}{S(x - \bar{x})^2} \right\} \quad \cdots \quad (9.61a)$$

If Y itself is not given with absolute precision, but has a sampling error, being perhaps the experimentally determined response to a standard dose of a standard preparation of the drug, equation (9.61a) must be modified accordingly.

The sampling variation of X determined in this way is different, of course, from that of X determined from a form of equation (8.22b) with Y as the independent variable. Moreover, X determined from equation (9.61) is not a linear function of a and so is not distributed normally. Consequently equation (9.61a) may be interpreted in the usual way only as a large-sample approximation. Confidence limits for X may be determined precisely by working backwards from those of Y determined by equation (9.6a).

This section merely gives the beginnings of the regression analysis underlying biological assay. Readers who wish to follow the subject further will find a good survey with references to the literature in Finney (1947a and b). The statistical methods can, of course, have other applications but these have so far been only occasional.

REGRESSION COMBINED WITH OTHER COMPONENTS OF VARIANCE

9.7. Regression analysis may sometimes be a part of the analysis of variance of data in more complex forms than the simple form so far dealt with in this chapter. The varieties of form that can arise are very many, but here an attempt will be made only to illustrate the general principle by way of an example.

An experiment was made in a weaving factory to investigate the effect of loom speed on loom output. A Latin square arrangement was adopted, and this, together with the results, is in Table 9.7. There are five weaving periods each of about one week, and five weavers each of whom attended to eight looms. For

TABLE 9.7

LOOM OUTPUT (AVERAGE EFFECTIVE PICKS PER LOOM PER MINUTE) AND IN BRACKETS, LOOM SPEED (PICKS PER MINUTE) FOR WEAVERS A TO E

Period	Weaver					Totals*
	A	B	C	D	E	
I	154·7 (174)	168·9 (185)	137·2 (169)	167·5 (191)	163·4 (177)	91·7
II	156·5 (185)	149·7 (169)	143·4 (191)	151·0 (177)	156·1 (174)	56·7
III	150·6 (169)	151·2 (174)	145·1 (177)	157·2 (185)	154·5 (191)	58·6
IV	157·0 (177)	167·1 (191)	141·1 (174)	142·0 (169)	152·4 (185)	59·6
V	159·3 (191)	160·9 (177)	144·3 (185)	150·5 (174)	147·5 (169)	62·5
Totals*	78·1	97·8	11·1	68·2	73·9	329·1
Speed† Totals*	0 27·0	5 53·6	8 77·4	16 79·3	22 91·8	51 329·1

one period all the looms of one weaver were run at the same speed, and the average rate of output was measured as the total output in " picks," divided by the working length of the period in minutes and the looms per weaver. The average effective picks per loom per minute is less than the speed because the loom stops at intervals for routine causes.

* These are of outputs measured from 140·0 as an arbitrary origin.
† The speed is measured from 169 as an arbitrary origin.

The results of the standard analysis of variance for the three-factor basic form are in the left-hand parts of the columns of the top section of Table 9.7a. The values of F for periods, weavers and speeds are respectively 2·7, 13·6 and 9·5, and the probability levels are (from Chart E1) approximately 0·08 for the first and less than 0·005 for the other two. The weaver effect is significant and was well worth eliminating from the experimental error ; the speed effect is also probably real.

TABLE 9.7a

ANALYSIS OF VARIANCE OF LOOM OUTPUT

Source of Variation	Sum of Squares		Degrees of Freedom		Variance	
Periods	170·96		4		42·7	
Weavers	847·75		4		211·9	
Speeds { Regression	529·42 {	434·20	4 {	1	132·4 {	434·2
{ Deviations		95·22		3		31·7
Residual	187·23		12		15·60	
Total	1 735·36		24		—	
Analysis of Deviations from *Output* ∝ *Speed* Law						
Speeds { Regression	257·7 {	162·5	4 {	1	64·4 {	162·5
{ Deviations		95·2		3		31·7

When we inspect the totals for the speeds in Table 9.7, however, we see that they increase progressively with speed, and common sense tells us that such a result is more significant than similar variations not following a regular pattern would be. The variance of 132·4 in Table 9.7a takes no account of the pattern, but we may do so by expressing the relationship between output and speed as a linear regression and analysing the variance accordingly.

If we represent output (measured from 140·0) as y and speed (measured from 169) as x, the sum of squares associated with the regression line calculated from the 25 values is, from section 8.31,

$$\{S(x - \bar{x}) (y - \bar{y})\}^2 / S(x - \bar{x})^2,$$

where S is the summation over the 25 values. The computation may be simplified by remembering that there are only five speeds, x_1 to x_5. Then if $\bar{y}_1$ to $\bar{y}_5$ are the corresponding mean outputs (x_s and $\bar{y}_s$ will be the values for the sth speed), the above expression equals

$$\{5S_s(x_s - \bar{x})\ (\bar{y}_s - \bar{y})\}^2/5S_s(x_s - \bar{x})^2$$

where S_s is the summation over the five speeds. On our applying equations (8.31b) and (6.3) this expression becomes

$$\{5S_s x_s \bar{y}_s - 25\overline{xy}\}^2/5\{S_s x_s{}^2 - 5\overline{x^2}\}.$$

For Table 9.7 the numerator of this expression is

$$\{0 \times 27{\cdot}0 + 5 \times 53{\cdot}6 + \ldots - 10{\cdot}2 \times 329{\cdot}1\}^2 = 818{\cdot}78^2,$$

and the denominator is

$$5\{0^2 + 5^2 + \ldots - 10{\cdot}2 \times 51\} = 1\ 544,$$

and the required sum of squares is $818{\cdot}78^2/1\ 544 = 434{\cdot}20$, as entered in Table 9.7a. The sum of squares for the deviations is obtained by difference. These are obtained entirely from the five speed means, and the factor of 5 in the above expressions is merely to give the sums of squares suitable weights for inclusion in Table 9.7a.

If we use the same residual as before to express the error with which the speed effect is determined, $F = 27{\cdot}8$ and is still well beyond the 0·005 level of significance. The advantage of using the regression in this way appears only when the effect is less highly significant. For the deviations from the regression $F = 2{\cdot}03$ and is far from being statistically significant ($P = 0{\cdot}16$ approximately). Had it been significant, the inference would have been that the speed effect was not entirely described by the straight regression line—it could have been curvo-linear (e.g. quadratic), or the output at the different speeds could have been affected by some irregular factor not influencing the residual. We might imagine, for example, that some particular speeds set up vibrations in the machinery that distress all the operatives enough to cause a drop in output ; such an effect is very unlikely at the speeds in question, but the suggestion may help readers to appreciate the statistical point.

The regression coefficient is $+\ 818{\cdot}78/1\ 544 = 0{\cdot}530$, and its standard error is, by equation (9.4a) (estimating s' from the residual variance in Table 9.7a), $\sqrt{(15{\cdot}60/1\ 544)} = 0{\cdot}100\ 5$. Had output been proportional to speed, the regression coefficient would have been the mean output divided by the mean speed, viz. 153·164/179·2 = 0·857. The estimated value differs from this by the ratio 0·327/0·100 5 = 3·25, and we test the significance of this by entering the tables or chart of t for 12 degrees of freedom. From Chart C we see that $P = 0·006$ (approximately) ; but a significant value in excess of 0·857 is technically inconceivable, so we must use the " single tail " test and take $P = 0·003$ as a measure of the significance.

Thus we infer that output increases with speed, but less than in proportion, and (taking 0·95 confidence limits) that the increase is probably between 0·530 ± 2·18 × 0·100 5 = 0·31 and 0·75 effective picks per minute per unit increase in speed.

It is a good statistical exercise to test more directly the hypothesis that the increase in output is proportional to the increase in speed. Instead of performing the analysis of variance on deviations from the grand mean output, we measure each deviation from the value of output that would result if it were proportional to speed. This output is the speed multiplied by 153·164/179·2. The only quantity in this expression subject to random errors is the mean output, 153·164 ; and in so measuring the deviations only one degree of freedom is absorbed, as when measuring them from the mean output. It is not necessary to find the 25 deviations, for the only rows in Table 9.7a that are affected are those for speeds and the total ; and the sums of squares for speeds can be calculated from the speed means. If we represent by $[y_s]$ the mean output for the sth speed calculated according to the postulated law of proportionality, measured as a deviation from the arbitrary origin of 140·0, the five values of $[y_s]$ are (to three decimal places) :

$$4·446 \quad 8·720 \quad 11·284 \quad 18·121 \quad 23·250.$$

The sum of squares due to speeds may be computed directly as $5S_s(\bar{y}_s - [y_s])^2 = 257·7$. That due to the linear regression on speeds is :

$$\{5S_s x_s(\bar{y}_s - [y_s])\}^2/5S_s(x_s - \bar{x})^2 = \{-500·940\}^2/154\ 4 = 162·5$$

(x_s is used instead of $x_s - x$ because the mean value of $\bar{y}_s - [y_s]$ is zero). These sums of squares together with that for the deviations from the regression obtained by difference are entered in the bottom section of Table 9.7a. The regression line expresses the same relationship of speed with output as before, but measured from a different base, and the sum of squares of the deviations is as before. The variance for the departure of the regression from the postulate of proportionality gives a value of $F = 162\cdot5/15\cdot60 = 10\cdot42$, which for 1 and 12 degrees of freedom is statistically significant ($t = \sqrt{F} = 3\cdot23$ is the same as deduced above, when allowance is made for approximations due to using few decimal places in the computations).

ASSUMPTIONS

9.8. Readers are reminded of the assumptions underlying the tests of significance of this chapter. The assumption that x is a random variate is made only for some of the tests. For most, no assumption is made about the distribution of x or y, but it is assumed that the residual deviations of y from the regression line are distributed normally; this is probably not a very important assumption since quite marked departures from normality are unlikely to have much effect on the tests.

The second assumption applying to all tests is that a straight regression line adequately represents the relationship between x and y so that the residual deviations of y from that line are in every sense of the word random. Non-linear regression will be dealt with in the next chapter.

The other important assumption is that the variability of the residual deviations of y is homogeneous. In simple correlation this involves the variability being the same about all parts of the line—about the ends as about the middle, and about one end as about the other. In more complex instances the assumption may be that the residual variance is the same for various groups of data. For example, the separate residual variances for concrete of the three ages in Table 9.51 are 243, 5 649 and 3 203, each being based on 5 degrees, and the first is significantly less than the other two. In consequence, some little doubt may be thrown on the inferences of sections 9.51 and 9.53. We do not propose attempting to extend the statistical analysis to deal with such instances, and if the matter is of importance suggest either that more data should be procured or that here the hypotheses could be tested on the 7- and 28-day values only.

In calculating correlation coefficients from samples of grouped data, Sheppard's corrections are often used in determining the standard deviations of x and y, and the corrections tend to increase the value of r. For this reason it is safer to ignore them in making tests of significance, particularly when the grouping is broad, although their use probably leads to an estimate of r which is nearer the population value.

TESTS FOR ASSOCIATION IN RANKED DATA

9.9. Sometimes it is impossible to measure some characteristic, but the individuals can be ranked in order with respect to two or more characteristics. For example, Table 9.9 (data from Binns, 1934) shows the order in which ten worsted fabrics were ranked by 50 skilled assessors on three bases. The bases of assessment are : *sight*, the best cloth being that judged to have the smartest and most acceptable appearance ; *touch*, the best cloth felt softest ; and *full*, the best being that which the assessors would choose, all things considered, if the cloths were all offered at the same price. Cloth J_1 was the best for sight and cloth Q the worst ; cloths G_2 and H_2 were bracketed third and fourth for touch ; and the ten cloths are given in order of preference on the full assessment.

TABLE 9.9

RANKINGS OF CLOTHS ASSESSED ON THE BASIS OF SIGHT, TOUCH, AND FULL QUALITIES

Fabric	F	G_1	H_1	J_1	L_1	G_2	M_1	H_2	P	Q
Basis					*Ranking*					
Sight ...	4	3	6	1	2	5	8	7	9	10
Touch ...	2	7	1	6	5	3·5	9	3·5	10	8
Full ...	1	2	3	4	5	6	7	8	9	10

Had the three bases of assessment yielded measurements, we might have calculated correlation coefficients, and tested them for significance in order to decide how far sight and touch affect the full assessment, and which of the two is more important. In this section we shall deal with this sort of problem for ranked data.

Measures of association have been proposed to deal with this type of situation and have been developed to cover the analogies of partial and multiple correlation when there are several sets of ranks. Tests of significance have also been developed. I have no practical experience of the application of these methods, and indeed am sceptical of their usefulness in any but the simplest situations, largely on the ground that it is usually impracticable to rank more than 20 or so individuals by qualitative assessment, and in such small samples any measure of association is subject to very large sampling errors. Accordingly, only one simple method of rank correlation is here introduced, and is dealt with superficially, purely for the sake of illustration. Readers who wish to follow the subject further should refer to the very comprehensive account in Kendall's (1948) book.

9.91. The most obvious measure of association, and the first to be used, is the correlation coefficient between the rank numbers, known as Spearman's coefficient and designated by the symbol ρ.* If for each individual we take the difference between the two rank numbers, d, ρ may be conveniently calculated from the equation

$$\rho = 1 - \frac{6S(d^2)}{N^3 - N} \quad \cdots \quad (9.91)$$

where S is the summation over the N individuals. We may approximately test the significance of ρ by calculating

$$t = \rho \sqrt{\left(\frac{N-2}{1-\rho^2}\right)} \quad \cdots \quad (9.91a)$$

and applying the ordinary t test for $N-2$ degrees of freedom, the value of ρ in (9.91a) being that found from the sample. In order to arrive at a rough idea of the strength of association signified by a given value of ρ we may imagine the two qualities in respect of which the individuals are ranked to be measurable by quantities that in the population are normally distributed and correlated with a coefficient of r. Then r is roughly estimated from the equation

$$r = 2 \sin \frac{\pi\rho}{6} \quad \cdots \quad (9.91b)$$

For the sight and full rankings in Table 9.9, the values of d are 3, 1, 3, −3, etc., and $\rho = 0.76$. By equation (9.91a) $t = 3.3$, and on 8 degrees of freedom this is significant on the $P = 0.011$ level of significance. The two bases of assessment are related. The estimated value of r, according to (9.91b), is 0.80, but this is only a very crude estimate of the population value of the correlation

---

* ρ here has a meaning that is new for this chapter and is confined to this section. It is not the population value corresponding to r.

coefficient of the assumed underlying normal measures of cloth quality.

When in the ranking order two or more individuals are placed together as equal or indistinguishable, they are said to be " tied." The presence of " ties " complicates the analysis, but at the superficial level at which we are treating the whole subject it is sufficient, unless there are many ties, to give the individuals the average of the numbers of the places they occupy, and to apply equations (9.91) and (9.91b). Unfortunately the test of significance of ρ is doubtful when there are ties. For the assessment of the fabrics of Table 9.9 for touch, fabrics G_2 and H_2 together occupy the third and fourth places, and are numbered 3·5. The value of ρ for association between the full and touch assessment is 0·58 and t, according to equation (9.91a), is 2·0 ; r, from equation (9.91b), is 0·59. The association is not statistically significant (particularly having regard to the effect of the ties), but of course that is not to say that there is no association. Sight seems to have had more weight than touch in arriving at the full assessment, but whether this can be inferred as a generalisation depends on the result of a test of the significance of the difference between the two values of ρ, or on further experience.

CHAPTER X

MULTIPLE AND PARTIAL REGRESSION AND CORRELATION

MULTIPLE REGRESSION AND CORRELATION

10.1. The methods of correlation analysis can be readily extended to the case where there are several measurements made on the same individuals, and the relationships can be expressed as a system of straight lines, with random deviations superimposed.

There is a multi-variate correlation surface in hyperspace, corresponding to the surface described in section 8.21. It is difficult to visualise and, having virtually no practical application, it will not be referred to further.

A linear regression equation may be formed relating one variate, the dependent, to the others, the independent variates. The choice of the dependent variate is determined by the technicalities of the problem.

We shall represent the dependent variate by y, the value given by the regression equation by Y, and the values of the independent variates by x_a, x_b, ... x_k, each subscript referring to a different variate.* It will be convenient to measure these quantities from their corresponding means and to represent the deviations by Y', x'_a, x'_b, ... x'_k. The population value H' is measured from the population mean, $\bar{\eta}$, and Y' estimated from a sample from the sample mean, $\bar{y}$; and individual values y' for a sample are also measured from the sample mean. The regression equation is

$$H' = \alpha x'_a + \beta x'_b + \dots \kappa x'_k \quad \dots \quad (10.1)$$

where $\alpha, \beta, \dots \kappa$ are constants which may be positive or negative. By extending the proofs of section 8.31 it is easily shown that the least squares estimates of these constants are obtained by solving equations (10.1a) :

$$\left. \begin{aligned}
Syx'_a &= a\,Sx'^2_a + b\,Sx'_ax'_b + \dots k\,Sx'_ax'_k \\
Syx'_b &= a\,Sx'_ax'_b + b\,Sx'^2_b + \dots k\,Sx'_bx'_k \\
&\quad \dots \quad \dots \quad \dots \quad \quad \dots \quad \dots \\
Syx'_k &= a\,Sx'_ax'_k + b\,Sx'_bx'_k + \dots k Sx'^2_k
\end{aligned} \right\} \quad . \quad (10.1a)$$

* A letter in the subscript specifies an independent variate ; a number in a subscript a particular group of individuals.

where S represents the summation over all individuals in the sample, and $a, b, \ldots k$ are the estimates of $\alpha, \beta \ldots \kappa$ respectively.

We shall, as an illustration, deal with the data of Table 10.1 referring to fifty different cottons. The highest standard yarn count is a measure of the quality of yarn spun from the cotton, the standard fibre weight is a measure of the average coarseness of the fibres, and the effective fibre length is a special average calculated from the frequency distribution of the lengths of the fibres. The figures in Table 10.1 are in convenient, arbitrarily chosen units, and we shall continue the discussion in terms of those units, and refer to the variates as y, x_a and x_b. A fuller analysis of

TABLE 10.1

HIGHEST STANDARD YARN COUNT (y), STANDARD COTTON FIBRE WEIGHT (x_a = mgm. per cm. — 150), AND EFFECTIVE FIBRE LENGTH (x_b = thirty-seconds of an inch — 30)

y	x_a	x_b	y	x_a	x_b
49	64	7	58	9	12
47	56	8	38	31	7
40	65	6	44	23	12
48	60	7	60	10	12
47	42	7	70	2	10
37	74	5	70	12	11
47	43	5	60	37	10
36	50	2	52	42	9
45	63	7	54	42	9
46	49	4	41	59	9
49	55	6	40	49	9
49	62	6	45	58	9
50	54	6	58	22	10
58	80	3	59	32	10
45	71	4	55	8	10
47	69	5	55	30	12
35	67	4	50	39	10
52	51	7	49	36	8
38	62	6	67	10	11
38	59	7	58	26	9
40	61	9	62	11	10
43	66	8	29	62	5
32	70	5	30	53	3
37	66	6	17	112	4
56	14	11	22	89	7

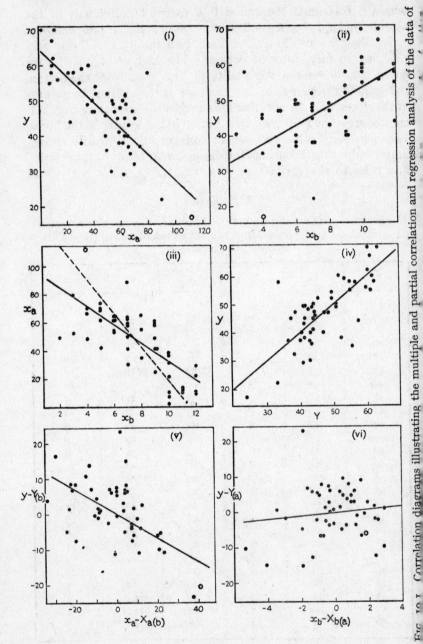

FIG. 10.1 Correlation diagrams illustrating the multiple and partial correlation and regression analysis of the data of

similar data, and a discussion of the technological implications is given by Underwood (1935). The data have their limitations, but we shall for the present ignore these and refer to them in section 10.5.

The variate y is measured by means of a somewhat laborious spinning test, whereas x_a and x_b are fibre characters that can be measured in the laboratory ; and it is of scientific as well as technical interest to express y in terms of x_a and x_b. Scatter diagrams are plotted in Fig. 10.1, sections (i), (ii) and (iii) ; these show a marked correlation which appears to be substantially linear, and a regression equation of the form of (10.1) is appropriate. The various sums of squares and products are :

$$Sy'^2 = 6\,283\cdot68 \qquad Sx_a'^2 = 27\,210\cdot42$$
$$Sx_b'^2 = 334\cdot18 \qquad Sy'x_a' = -10\,158\cdot16$$
$$Sy'x_b' = +924\cdot68 \qquad Sx_a'x_b' = -2\,268\cdot66$$

On entering these in equations (10.1a) and solving for a and b we find for the regression equation :

$$(Y - 47\cdot08) = -0\cdot331\,507\,(x_a - 47\cdot54) + 0\cdot501\,491\,(x_b - 7\cdot58).$$

The 50 values of Y have been calculated from this equation and y is plotted against them in Fig. 10.1 (iv).

Now we may perform an analysis of variance after the manner of section 8.23, dividing the sum of squares of y' into two parts, the first being $S(Y'^2)$ associated with the regression equation and

TABLE 10.1a

ANALYSIS OF VARIANCE

Source of Variation	Sum of Squares	Degrees of Freedom
Multiple Regression	$SY'^2 = R^2Sy'^2$	p
Residual	$S(y' - Y')^2 = (1 - R^2)Sy'^2$	$N - p - 1$
Total	Sy'^2	$N - 1$

the second being $S(y' - Y')^2$ associated with the residual deviations. The general analysis for the case in which there are N individuals and p independent variates is set out in Table 10.1a. There are $N - p - 1$ degrees of freedom for the residual because the regression equation contains $p + 1$ constants estimated from the data ($\bar{y}$ and the p constants $a, b, \ldots k$) ; by difference the degrees of freedom associated with the regression equation are p. If there is no relation between y and the x's in the population, and the a's differ from zero only because of random errors, the variances for Table 10.1a will be estimates of the same variance (this follows from section 7.6). Thus the F test may be used to test the significance of a multiple regression equation.

The symbol R entered in Table 10.1a is termed the *multiple correlation coefficient*. It is defined by analogy with the simple correlation coefficient, R^2 being the fraction of the total sum of squares associated with the multiple regression, and is used as a measure of the strength of the association of y with the x's. If the values of Y are computed from the regression equation and correlated with the values of y by the methods of Chapter VIII, the value of r so obtained will equal R. It is necessarily positive in sign.

Some care is necessary in the interpretation of the multiple correlation coefficient, except when p is negligibly small compared with N, for the value of R is enhanced by random errors. Thus, if

TABLE 10.1b

ANALYSIS OF VARIANCE OF HIGHEST STANDARD COTTON YARN COUNT

Source of Variation	Sum of Squares	Degrees of Freedom	Variance
Multiple Regression ...	3 831·22	2	1 916
Residual	2 452·46	47	52·1
Total	6 283·68	49	—

the variances of Table 10.1a are equated it will be seen that for zero association R^2 tends to equal $p/(N-1)$.

It is instructive as an exercise to compute the values of Y directly, and hence to obtain the various sums of squares, but for general use it is more convenient to use the following result, which may easily be proved by squaring the terms of equation (10.1) with sample values inserted, summing, and substituting the terms of equations (10.1a).

$$SY'^2 = aSy'x_a' + bSy'x_b' + \ldots kSy'x_k' \quad . \quad . \quad (10.1b).$$

For the cotton data of Table 10.1 we have $SY'^2 = 3\ 831·22$, and the analysis of variance is as shown in Table 10.1b. The multiple correlation coefficient is $\sqrt{(3\ 831\cdot22/6\ 283\cdot68)} = 0\cdot780\ 8$.

Fisher (1925c) has developed a computing scheme that has several conveniences. It consists in solving, instead of the one set of p equations (10.1a), the p sets represented by equations (10.1c).

$$
\left.
\begin{array}{cccc}
(1) & (2) & . & . & (p) \\
1 & 0 & . . & 0 = aSx_a'^2 + b\,Sx_a'x_b' + \ldots kSx_a'x_k' \\
0 & 1 & . . & 0 = aSx_a'x_b' + bSx_b'^2 + \ldots kSx_b'x_k' \\
. & . & . . & . \qquad\qquad . \qquad\qquad . \\
0 & 0 & . . & 1 = aSx_a'x_k' + bSx_b'x_k' + \ldots kSx_k'^2
\end{array}
\right\} \quad (10.1c)
$$

For the first set, the quantities to the left of the = sign are those in column (1), the other columns being ignored. For the second set, the quantities on the left of the = sign are those in column (2), the terms on the right being the same as before ; and so on. The solutions for the first set are written

$$a_1,\quad b_1, \ldots \ldots k_1.$$

The solutions for the second set are written

$$a_2,\quad b_2, \ldots \ldots k_2$$

and so on, the solutions for the last set being

$$a_p,\quad b_p, \ldots \ldots k_p.$$

It is a consequence of the symmetry of the equations that $a_2 = b_1$, $a_p = k_1$, $b_p = k_2$, and so on. It will be noted that these quantities involve only the x's.

The regression coefficients of equation (10.1a) may then be evaluated as :

$$
\left.
\begin{array}{l}
a = a_1Sy'x_a' + a_2Sy'x_b' + \ldots a_pSy'x_k' \\
b = b_1Sy'x_a' + b_2Sy'x_b' + \ldots b_pSy'x_k' \\
. \qquad\qquad . \qquad\qquad\qquad . \\
k = k'Sy'x_a' + k_2Sy'x_b' + \ldots k_pSy'x_k'
\end{array}
\right\} \quad . \quad (10.1d)
$$

For the data of Table 10.1 the first set of equations is :

$$1 = 27\ 210\cdot42a_1 - 2\ 268\cdot66b_1$$
$$0 = -2\ 268\cdot66a_1 + 334\cdot18b_1$$

whence $a_1 = 0\cdot000\ 081\ 59$ and $b_1 = 0\cdot000\ 537\ 79$. The second set is :

$$0 = 27\ 210\cdot42a_2 - 2\ 268\cdot66b_2$$
$$1 = -2\ 268\cdot66a_2 + 334\cdot18b_2$$

and $b_2 = 0\cdot006\ 450\ 31$; $a_2 = b_1$.

Then a is $-10\ 158\cdot16 \times 0\cdot000\ 081\ 59 + 924\cdot68 \times 0\cdot000\ 537\ 79 = -0\cdot331\ 5$ as before. This method of obtaining the regression coefficients is economical when, and only when, several regression equations are to be determined for several dependent variates, all associated with the same set of values of the independent variates. We might, for example, wish to correlate several yarn properties in turn with the fibre characteristics of the fifty cottons of Table 10.1.

The solutions of equations 10.1d are useful also for computing standard errors.

Sampling Errors

10.11. In order to test the statistical significance of a multiple regression we apply the F test to the variances of Table 10.1a, or if the association is expressed in terms of a multiple correlation coefficient, to

$$F = \frac{R^2(N - p - 1)}{(1 - R^2)} \quad . \quad . \quad . \quad . \quad (10.11)$$

For the cotton count variances of Table 10.1b, $F = 37$, and for 2 and 47 degrees of freedom is very highly significant. This test is based on the assumption that x_a and x_b are not subject to sampling errors, but for testing the hypothesis that there is no association the assumption is irrelevant.

The sampling distribution of the multiple correlation coefficient when the population value is not zero is fully discussed by Fisher (1928b). It is complicated and has been evaluated for only a few special cases.

If the multiple regression equation is known for the population, $H = H' + \bar{\eta}$ (equation 10.1) predicts an individual value of y with a standard error of σ', where σ'^2 is the population value corresponding to the residual variance of Table 10.1a. If the regression equation is determined from a sample the sampling variance of Y must be added to σ'^2 after the manner shown in section 9.6.

If we write V with a subscript for the sampling variance (the square of the standard error) of a quantity specified by the subscript,

$$V_Y = V_{\bar{y}} + V_{Y'},$$

and by applying the method of section 4.15 to equation (10.1) we have for Y' corresponding to a given value of $x'_a, x'_b, \ldots x'_k$

$$V_{Y'} = x'^2_a V_a + x'^2_b V_b + \ldots x'^2_k V_k$$
$$+ 2x'_a x'_b C_{ab} + \ldots 2x'_a x'_k C_{ak}$$
$$+ \ldots 2x'_j x'_k C_{jk}.$$

where C with a subscript is the mean product of sampling deviations of the quantities specified by the subscript and is termed the sampling *co-variance* of those quantities. Co-variance is a mean product in the same way as variance is a mean square. According to Fisher (1925c), the required variances and co-variances are

$$\left. \begin{array}{l} V_a = s'^2 a_1, \ V_b = s'^2 b_2, \ldots V_k = s'^2 k_p \\ C_{ab} = s'^2 a_2 = s'^2 b_1, \ldots C_{ak} = s'^2 a_p = s'^2 k_1 \end{array} \right\} \quad (10.11a)$$

PARTIAL REGRESSION AND CORRELATION

10.2. Sometimes it is desired to express, not the relationship between one variate and a group of others taken together, but between selected pairs of variates when others are kept constant. Thus, the first two sections of Fig. 10.1 show that y is related to both x_a and x_b, and the third section shows a relationship between x_a and x_b. The relationship between y and x_a shown in Fig. 10.1 (i) discloses partly the direct effect of x_a operating alone, and partly the effect of x_b operating through its effect on x_a We may ask, therefore : what is the relationship between y and x_a when x_b is kept constant ? The theory of partial correlation attempts to answer this question in the following manner.

First the simple regression of y on x_b is determined. The equation is

$$(Y_{(b)} - 47 \cdot 08) = + 2 \cdot 686 \, 62 (x_b - 7 \cdot 58),$$

the subscript (b) denoting that Y has been calculated from the regression on x_b. This line is drawn in Fig. 10.1 (ii). The deviations $(y - Y_{(b)})$ measured from this line represent the variations that would occur in y were x_b kept constant. One typical value is represented by a circle in Fig. 10.1 (ii) and its deviation is $17 - 37 \cdot 5 = -20 \cdot 5$. Next the regression of x_a on x_b is determined ; it is

$$(X_{a(b)} - 47 \cdot 54) = -6 \cdot 591 \, 49 (x_b - 7 \cdot 58)$$

and is the full line drawn in Fig. 10.1 (iii). The deviations $(x_a - X_{a(b)})$ from this line represent the variations that would occur in x_a were x_b kept constant. The circle in Fig. 10.1 (iii) marks values corresponding to those similarly marked in Fig. 10.1 (ii), and the deviation of x_a is $112 - 71 \cdot 1 = +40 \cdot 9$. The two sets of deviations $(y - Y_{(b)})$ and $(x_a - X_{a(b)})$, as plotted in Fig. 10.1 (v) [the value $(+40 \cdot 9 - 20 \cdot 5)$ is marked by a circle], provide the answer to our question. A regression equation and correlation coefficient can be computed and interpreted in the usual way. The quantities so derived are in the terminology qualified by the adjective *partial*.

The foregoing procedure is worth undertaking in full as an exercise, but it is convenient to note that the partial regression coefficient is the corresponding coefficient in the multiple regression equation. The partial correlation coefficient is represented by $r_{oa,b}$, the subscript o refers to the variate y and the subscripts a and b to x_a and x_b respectively, the placing of the dot signifying that the correlation is between y and x_a, x_b being kept constant ; and by following out the procedure of the previous paragraph algebraically it may be shown that

$$r_{oa,b} = \frac{r_{oa} - r_{ob} \, r_{ab}}{\sqrt{(1 - r_{ob}^2)} \, \sqrt{(1 - r_{ab}^2)}} \quad . \quad . \quad . \quad (10.2)$$

where r_{oa}, etc., are the simple or *total* correlation coefficients between the pairs of variates. In applying this equation, tables of $\sqrt{(1 - r^2)}$ for different values of r, given by Miner (1922), will be found very useful. A partial correlation coefficient may be positive or negative, and it may be different in sign from the corresponding total coefficient.

For the data of Table 10.1 the sums of squares and products lead to the following :

$$r_{oa} = -0 \cdot 776 \, 86 \quad r_{ob} = +0 \cdot 628 \, 77 \quad r_{ab} = -0 \cdot 741 \, 32,$$

and on applying equation (10.2) we have $r_{oa,b} = -0 \cdot 595 \, 4$. The elimination of the effect of x_b has slightly weakened the correlation between y and x_a, as can be seen by comparing Figs. 10.1 (i) and (v).

It is possible, and reasonable, to apply the same procedure in order to determine the partial correlation between y and x_b, x_a being kept constant. The regression of y on x_a is shown in Fig. 10.1 (i) ; the regression of x_b on x_a is shown by the dotted line in Fig. 10.1 (iii) ; and the deviations $(y - Y_{(a)})$ and $(x_b - X_{b(a)})$

are plotted in Fig. 10.1 (vi), the regression values being denoted by $Y_{(a)}$ and $X_{b(a)}$. The partial correlation coefficient is

$$r_{ob.a} = \frac{+ 0.628\ 77 - 0.776\ 86 \times 0.741\ 32}{\sqrt{(1 - 0.776\ 86^2)}\ \sqrt{(1 - 0.741\ 32^2)}} = + 0.125\ 1.$$

Most of the apparent relationship between y and x_b is due to the indirect effect of the relationship with x_a, and when this is eliminated the correlation is very low.

It would be possible also to determine the partial correlation and regression between x_a and x_b, y being kept constant—i.e. to compute $r_{ab.o}$; but the result would have no technical meaning. Here, y has been singled out for the dependent variate as being physically an effect as opposed to a cause ; sometimes all the variates have equal status from the point of singling out any one as dependent.

10.21. Partial correlation analysis can most easily be extended to the case of more than three variates by repeated application of the methods of the foregoing section. If, for example, the variates are y, x_a, x_b and x_c, simple regression equations of y, x_a and x_b respectively on x_c can be used to eliminate the effect of x_c and the deviations of y, x_a and x_b from their respective regressions, viz. $(y - Y_{(c)})$, $(x_a - X_{a(c)})$ and $(x_b - X_{b(c)})$ say, be correlated to give $r_{oa.c}$, $r_{ob.c}$ and $r_{ab.c}$. Further, these three sets of deviations can be treated as variates to eliminate the additional effect of $(x_b - X_{b(c)})$, leading to $r_{oa.bc}$, or to eliminate $(x_a - X_{a(b)})$ and give $r_{ob.ac}$. The other partial correlation coefficients can be obtained by treating the variates in other combinations.

It is more practicable, however, to determine the partial regression coefficients by fitting the multiple regression equation, and the partial correlation coefficients by repeatedly applying equation (10.2). For example,

$$r_{oa.bc} = \frac{r_{oa.b} - r_{oc.b}\ r_{ac.b}}{\sqrt{(1 - r_{oc.b}^2)}\ \sqrt{(1 - r_{ac.b}^2)}}$$

The stage-by-stage calculation and interpretation of partial correlation coefficients will be illustrated from some data given by Mumford and Young (1923). Table 10.21 gives some correlation coefficients determined from physical measurements made on 1 110 boys. It would appear at first sight that there is a strong tendency for tall boys to have a large vital capacity (the correlation coefficient is 0·835), but the older boys tend to be taller and (as might be expected) to have a larger vital capacity. It is reasonable, therefore, to suppose that a good deal of the apparent association between vital capacity and height may be due to the fact that the taller boys are also older, and before the true connection can be found, correction must be made for age. Similar

TABLE 10.21*

CORRELATION COEFFICIENTS

Vital capacity and height + 0·835	Vital capacity and weight + 0·851
Vital capacity and age ... + 0·662	Weight and age ... ... + 0·701
Height and age ... ... + 0·714	Height and weight ... + 0·897

* We include only a portion of the data in the paper.

arguments apply to the correlations between vital capacity and weight and between height and weight, and, using equation (10.2) to find the three partial correlations with age eliminated, we obtain the results in the upper part of Table 10.21a. The first three coefficients show that the relationships between vital capacity, height and weight continue to exist, even though the age is kept constant, although they are a little less strong. We

TABLE 10.21a

PARTIAL CORRELATION COEFFICIENTS

Vital capacity and height (age eliminated) ... ... + 0·690	
Vital capacity and weight (age eliminated) ... ... + 0·724	
Height and weight (age eliminated) ... ... + 0·794	
Vital capacity and height (weight and age eliminated) ... + 0·271	
Vital capacity and weight (height and age eliminated) ... + 0·399	

are still, however, far from a complete knowledge; part of the association between vital capacity and height may really be an indirect consequence of the fact that tall boys are also heavy, and weight may be the determining factor, or, conversely, height may have the direct and weight the indirect connection with vital capacity. Again we may use the formula of equation (10.2) to eliminate further, and in turn, weight and height, and the results are in the lower part of Table 10.21a. The correlations are now much reduced, but are still real, and it appears that the association of vital capacity with height is a little less important than that with weight. Mumford and Young in their paper consider other factors (stem length and chest girth), and the conclusions even of the second part of Table 10.21a cannot be regarded as final.

Sampling Errors

10.22. Fisher (1924b) has shown that the sampling distributions of the partial and total correlation coefficients are the same when the number of degrees of freedom for the residuals is the same. Thus all the tests of sections 9.1 and 9.2 may be applied provided N minus the number of variates eliminated is used instead of N.

For the data of Table 10.1 $N = 50$, so that the standard error of a partial correlation coefficient with one variate eliminated is $1/\sqrt{48} = 0.144$. The values of -0.595 and $+0.125$ in the previous section are respectively 4.1 and 0.87 times this; one is highly significant and the other is insignificant.

For the situation where the values of the independent variates are not subject to sampling variations, the standard error of the partial regression coefficients is the square root of the error variances given in equation (10.11a). The residual variance, s'^2 is usually estimated on $N - p - 1$ degrees of freedom, and the quantities $(a - \alpha)/s'\sqrt{a_1}$, $(b - \beta)/s'\sqrt{b_2}$, etc., are distributed as t with $N - p - 1$ degrees of freedom.

For the data of Table 10.1 we have calculated that $a = -0.332$, $s'^2 = 52.1$ measured on 47 degrees of freedom (Table 10.1b), $a_1 = 0.000\ 081\ 59$, and the standard error of a is $\sqrt{52.1} \times \sqrt{0.000\ 081\ 59} = 0.065\ 2$. For testing the hypothesis that $\alpha = 0$ we have $t = 0.332/0.065\ 2 = 5.1$, and as for $r_{oa.b} = -0.595$, this is highly significant. Had the exact sampling distribution for the correlation coefficient been used, the tests of both the correlation and regression coefficient would have given the same probability level. For testing $b = 0.501$, $t = 0.86$. This is very nearly the ratio obtained when testing the corresponding partial correlation coefficient—the effects of the approximation in the distribution of the correlation coefficient are not great for the smaller ratios.

It can happen that each partial regression and correlation

coefficient is statistically insignificant, whereas the multiple regression and correlation is significant. This is not paradoxical. It means only that owing to the interrelations between the x factors, the effect of each one of them separately can be adequately described by a regression equation containing all the others. For this reason, the tests developed in the next section are more useful.

10.23. Sometimes it is required to know whether a regression equation with a larger number of independent variates gives a significantly better description of the variations in y—a " closer fit "—than one with a smaller number : whether there is any advantage in including the extra variates in the equation. In connection with cotton yarn and fibre data of Table 10.1, for example, we may ask whether the regression equation containing x_b and x_a predicts y more closely than a simple equation containing either x_a or x_b alone.

This kind of question may be answered by applying the same

TABLE 10.23

ANALYSIS OF VARIANCE

Source of Variation		Sum of Squares		Degrees of Freedom	
Regression with q variates	Regression with p variates	$R_q^2 Sy'^2$	$R_p^2 Sy'^2$	q	p
	Difference between regressions		$(R_q^2 - R_p^2) Sy'^2$		$q - p$
Residual from regression with q variates		$(1 - R_q^2) Sy'^2$		$N - q - 1$	
Total		Sy'^2		$N - 1$	

kind of argument as was used in sections 9.5 to 9.53 for testing the significance of introducing additional regressions. The regression equation with the larger number, q, of variates, is determined and the variance analysed as shown in part of Table 10.23. Then the equation with the smaller number, p, is determined and the sum of squares associated with the difference in regressions determined by subtraction, as shown in Table 10.23. The significance of the additional terms in the second regression is that of the variance associated with the difference in regressions in Table 10.23. If R_p and R_q are respectively the multiple correlation coefficients for the regressions with the lesser and larger number of variates, the significance of the difference in regressions is that of

$$F = \frac{(R_q{}^2 - R_p{}^2)(N - q - 1)}{(1 - R_q{}^2)(q - p)} \qquad . \quad . \quad (10.23)$$

For Table 10.1 let us test the significance of the equation with two variates as compared with that involving x_a alone. Then $p = 2, q = 1, R_q{}^2 = 0.609\ 7, R_p{}^2 = r_{oa}{}^2 = 0.603\ 5, N - q - 1 = 47,\ q - p = 1$, and $F = 0.75$. The variance associated with the addition of the regression on x_b is less than the residual, and

TABLE 10.23*a*

ANALYSIS OF VARIANCE OF HIGHEST STANDARD COTTON YARN COUNT

Source of Variation	Sum of Squares	Degrees of Freedom	Variance
Regression on x_a	3 792·23	1	3 792
Difference due to addition of regression on x_b	38·99	1	39·0
Residual	2 452·46	47	52·2
Regression on x_b	2 484·26	1	2 484
Difference due to addition of regression on x_a	1 346·96	1	1 347
Residual	2 452·46	47	52·2
Total	6 283·68	49	—

we infer that an equation in terms of x_a alone predicts y as closely as one in terms of x_a and x_b. If we consider taking x_b alone, $R_p{}^2 = r_{ob}{}^2 = 0.395\ 4$ and $F = 25.9$, and on 1 and 47 degrees of freedom this is highly significant. An equation involving x_a and x_b is better than one involving x_b alone.

The analyses of variance for these regressions are set out in

Table 10.23a. The variance associated with the regression on x_a in the top section of the table is different from that associated with the regression on x_a after x_b has been taken into account in the lower section ; and similarly for x_b. The terms in the multiple regression equation are not orthogonal and no variance can be associated with each regression constant in any absolute or unique sense, as can be done when the analysis is of data in one of the basic forms. The variance attributable to each of the regressions depends on the order in which they are taken. If the order is defined by the technicalities of the situation, a useful and unique set of variances can be deduced. Otherwise, common sense suggests that the variates should be taken in the order of the strength of their correlation with y, although such a selection will unduly enhance the apparent statistical significance of the result. An example with three independent variates is worked out in my *Technological Applications of Statistics* (Chapter XII).

10.24. We shall illustrate further the application of these tests by an example which presents several special features ; the data are in Table 10.24. Fifty groups of varying numbers of cotton fibres were weighed and measured, and the weights of the groups were expressed as multiples of 10^{-8} grammes per centimetre. These were then swollen in caustic soda and placed in three classes, A, B and C, according to their appearance under the microscope. The problem is to determine if the three classes show real differences in average fibre-weight per centimetre. A regression formula of the form of equation (10.1) may be obtained to express the weight of a group of fibres in terms of the number in each of the three classes ; if we put y equal to the group weight, and x_a, x_b and x_c the numbers in the three classes, a, b and c are the corresponding mean fibre-weights per centimetre. Similarly a second regression may be obtained in which only the average fibre-weight for all classes and the total number of fibres in the group are used ; this is the ordinary case with one constant. Now the former regression, absorbing three degrees of freedom, will necessarily have associated with it a little more of the variance in weights of the groups than the second, but if the three groups really have different fibre-weights, the equation with three constants will fit the data very much better than that with only one, and the difference in the associated variances will be *significantly* greater than zero. We may therefore investigate the problem by finding the regressions and variances, and testing the significance of the difference in the latter.

TABLE 10.24*

NUMBERS OF COTTON FIBRES AND WEIGHTS (IN 10^{-8} GRAMMES)

Numbers of Fibres				Weight	Numbers of Fibres				Weight
A	B	C	Total		A	B	C	Total	
15·4	7·6	—	23	3 243	14·5	3·4	1·1	19	3 401
25·0	4·0	1·0	30	5 580	10·5	3·5	—	14	2 016
22·3	6·7	—	29	4 872	24·0	10·0	—	34	6 596
45·6	7·4	1·0	54	11 880	25·5	7·4	1·1	34	6 290
51·0	4·0	—	55	13 420	66·7	13·2	1·1	81	15 147
63·3	12·7	1·0	77	16 632	81·9	13·1	4·0	91	20 790
88·5	17·5	—	106	22 684	77·9	5·1	—	83	18 260
71·9	8·1	—	80	18 240	63·1	14·8	1·1	79	15 642
53·8	6·2	—	60	13 380	42·9	7·1	—	50	8 950
41·0	4·0	—	45	9 180	24·9	2·1	—	27	4 887
13·0	—	—	13	3 185	3·0	—	—	3	561
7·9	1·1	—	9	1 818	4·0	—	—	4	660
2·7	4·0	1·3	8	816	12·3	3·7	—	16	2 272
8·2	1·8	—	10	2 190	9·8	2·8	1·4	14	2 072
15·0	8·0	—	23	3 864	15·0	7·0	—	22	3 762
14·5	5·5	—	20	4 400	24·0	6·0	2·0	32	6 144
17·6	12·4	1·0	31	6 045	31·0	7·0	—	38	8 018
47·6	12·4	—	60	14 880	54·4	8·6	—	63	14 238
70·9	19·0	1·1	91	20 657	97·3	17·6	1·1	116	23 896
50·0	17·0	—	67	13 601	95·6	14·4	—	110	23 870
71·0	16·0	3·0	90	17 910	54·6	15·4	—	70	14 350
34·0	15·9	1·1	51	8 670	27·9	3·1	—	31	6 231
27·0	6·0	1·0	34	6 154	30·3	2·7	—	33	5 346
10·8	3·2	—	14	2 464	5·0	—	—	5	840
7·0	—	—	7	1 190	5·0	—	—	5	710

* Some of the groups have fractional numbers because one or two hairs were lost between weighing and classifying, and these were assumed to be distributed proportionately in all classes. The weights were supplied as mean weights per centimetre of hair to the nearest unit, and those in this table are the means multiplied by the number of hairs in the group. The effect of these approximations in the data is exceedingly small. The data were supplied by Mr. J. Gregory.

To find a, b and c we solve equations (10.1a), and for these we need to determine the sums of squares and products from the data. It is not fair, however, to give all groups, whether large or small, the same weight in finding these sums. If the number of fibres in a group is n, and the variability of weights of single fibres is approximately the same in all classes, with a standard deviation of σ, the standard error of the mean weight per fibre for the group is $\sigma/\sqrt{n}$, and that of the total weight is n times this, and so is proportional to $\sqrt{n}$; hence the variance of the total weight of a group due to variations between fibres within the same class is proportional to n, the number in the group. We may use the results of section 3.62 and regard $1/n$ as the quantity of information; then in making summations, each term may be weighted with this quantity, multiplying each product and square by $1/n$ before summing. For example, the weighted sum,

$$Syx_a = \left(\frac{3\ 243 \times 15\cdot4}{23} + \frac{5\ 580 \times 25\cdot0}{30} + \ldots\right).$$

A further modification is necessary; a group with no fibres naturally has zero weight, so we shall make our regression line pass through the origin and not through the mean, and shall measure all deviations from zero; that is, in equations (10.1) and (10.1a) we write x and y instead of x' and y'. It may assist some to think of the data of Table 10.24 as a half of the complete data, the other half having equal negative values, so that the mean is zero, and the sums of squares and products we obtain are half the total for the imaginary complete results.

The appropriate sums of squares and products are set out in equations below, and their solution yields the regression equation following them.

$$363\ 785\cdot7 = 1\ 468\cdot85a + 288\cdot83b + 18\cdot42c$$
$$73\ 472\cdot3 = 288\cdot83a + 74\cdot73b + 4\cdot94c$$
$$4\ 646\cdot0 = 18\cdot42a + 4\cdot94b + 1\cdot04c$$
$$Y = 226\cdot255\ 7x_a + 114\cdot127x_b - 82\cdot16x_c.$$

Although the data are to some extent approximate, the arithmetic must be performed with considerable precision if the final results are to have any accuracy at all. In finding $Sx_a y/n$ we calculated x_a/n to five decimal places, and then summed $y \times x_a/n$ on a machine; as a check, we then calculated y/n and summed $x_a \times y/n$. In performing the divisions for the solution of the simultaneous equations we had to work to nine or ten significant figures to obtain the accuracy of the constants shown in the regression. It is not claimed that the four decimal places for a have any physical meaning, but as a constant of the sample which will be used to find the sum of squares of group weights, that accuracy is necessary. Classes A and B have differing mean fibre-weights per centimetre, while the fibres of C appear to have a negative one; however, there were very few of class C, and this irrational result is due to sampling variations, and signifies nothing. To find the sum of squares associated with the regression we use equation (10.1b), and find

$$226\cdot255\ 7 \times 363\ 785\cdot7 + 114\cdot127 \times 73\ 472\cdot3 - 82\cdot16$$
$$\times 4\ 646\cdot0 = 90\ 312\ 000.$$

This could not have been given correct even to five figures if we had determined the regression coefficients correct only, say, to three. The weighted sum of squares of the fibre-weights is

$$\frac{3\,243^2}{23} + \frac{5\,580^2}{30} + \ldots = 91\,220\,148,$$

and we shall use this to five significant figures only.

We now have to find a regression equation using one constant, the mean fibre-weight per centimetre for all classes. Using only the first term and equation of (10.1a), and finding the weighted sums of products and squares, we have

$$S\left(\frac{yx}{n}\right) = a'S\left(\frac{x^2}{n}\right);$$

since there is only one class, $x = n$, and we obtain $Sy = a'Sn$, which is the straightforward relationship, *mean fibre-weight = total weight of all groups divided by the total number of fibres*. This gives $a' = 203\cdot736$, and the sum of squares of weights associated with it is $203\cdot736 \times 441\,904 = 90\,032\,000$ (correct to five significant figures).

The analysis of variance is in Table 10.24a, and in reckoning the degrees of freedom it must be remembered that deviations are not

TABLE 10.24a

ANALYSIS OF VARIANCE OF WEIGHTS OF GROUPS OF COTTON FIBRES

Source of Variation	Sums of Squares	Degrees of Freedom	Variance
Multiple regression—			
Simple regression ...	90 032 000 ⎫	1 ⎫	90 032 000
Difference in regres-	⎬ 90 312 000	⎬ 3	
sion	280 000 ⎭	2 ⎭	140 000
Residual	908 000	47	19 300
Total	91 220 000	50	—

measured from a mean determined from the data, but from the origin, so that the fifty groups contribute fifty degrees to the sum of squares. In order to test the significance of the difference in regressions, we find that $F = 7\cdot25$ and, from Chart E1, that P is less than 0·005. Thus we conclude that the two classes of fibres A and B, as determined by swelling in caustic soda, have significantly different mean fibre-weights per centimetre. This result could not have been obtained directly, because there were no means of weighing the fibres individually, and it was not practicable to obtain the individual classes for separate weighing.

DISCRIMINANT FUNCTIONS

10.3. Table 10.1 refers to three groups of cottons. The first 24 are Northern Nigerian growths, the next 22 are from Uganda, and the last four are from the Belgian Congo. For this section we shall confine attention to the first two sets, and deal with the problem of using the values of x_a and x_b to provide a means of discriminating between the sets, so that when given only the values of x_a and x_b for a further cotton belonging to one or other set, we can say with some degree of assurance to which it belongs. We shall make no use of the measured values of y in Table 10.1. This problem arises characteristically when a skull is found belonging to a known race but of unknown sex, and it is required to determine the sex.

The values of x_a and x_b for the two sets are plotted in the upper part of Fig. 10.3. For each character the two distributions are distinct, and an analysis of variance or t test would establish the significance of the difference between the means. But the two distributions for each character also overlap. A cotton with a value of x_a up to 35 or so almost certainly belongs to set 2, and one with x_a greater than about 60 to set 1; but it is doubtful to which set a cotton with a value of x_a between 40 and 60 belongs. For the purpose of identifying an individual cotton, x_a does not provide complete discrimination; and the same may be said of x_b.

If we were to use, say, x_a for purposes of discrimination and as an approximation were to assume the same within-set variance for each, we would reasonably allocate to set 1 all cottons with a value of x_a greater than $(\bar{x}_{a1} + \bar{x}_{a2})/2$, and to set 2 all others, where $\bar{x}_{a1}$ and $\bar{x}_{a2}$ are the estimated means for the two series. Moreover, it would be easy to estimate the probability of misclassification through a cotton actually belonging to set 1 having a value of x_a less than $(\bar{x}_{a1} + \bar{x}_{a2})/2$, and a cotton belonging to set 2 having a value of x_a greater than $(\bar{x}_{a1} + \bar{x}_{a2})/2$. Similar calculations can be performed for x_b.

If we had to choose between x_a and x_b for purposes of discrimination, we should prefer the variate with the greater value of t in the t test—i.e. with the greater ratio of difference between means to within-set sum of squares, for this would give the lower probability of misclassification. But we may hope to do better by using both x_a and x_b, combining them into a function known as a *discriminant* function. We shall develop this in a form allowing for p variates, denoting the pth by x_k.

The simplest form of discriminant function is the linear equation

$$Y = ax_a + bx_b + \ldots kx_k \quad \ldots \quad (10.3)$$

Let the mean values for the first set be

$$\overline{Y}_1 = a\overline{x}_{a1} + b\overline{x}_{b1} + \ldots k\overline{x}_{k1};$$

let those for the second set be

$$\overline{Y}_2 = a\overline{x}_{a2} + b\overline{x}_{b2} + \ldots k\overline{x}_{k2};$$

and let the differences between the means be

$$\overline{Y}_1 - \overline{Y}_2 = D; \quad \overline{x}_{a1} - \overline{x}_{a2} = d_a; \quad \ldots \overline{x}_{k1} - \overline{x}_{k2} = d_k$$

so that

$$D = ad_a + bd_b + \ldots kd_k.$$

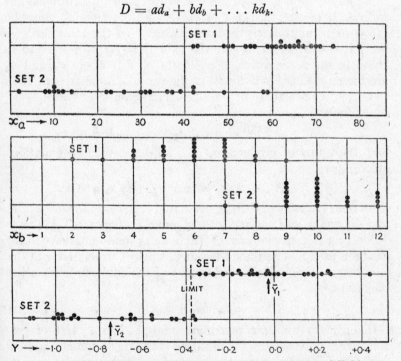

FIG. 10.3. Diagram showing how two sets of the cottons of Table 10.1 may be discriminated by fibre weight (x_a), fibre length (x_b), and a discriminant function of both quantities (Y).

The discriminant function is best when $a, b \ldots k$ are chosen so as to maximise the ratio

$$\frac{D^2}{S_1(Y_1 - \overline{Y}_1)^2 + S_2(Y_2 - \overline{Y}_2)^2}$$

where S_1 and S_2 are summations over set 1 and set 2 respectively. This criterion only defines the relative values of the constants a, b, etc., for if they are multiplied by one factor, the numerator and denominator of the above ratio are both multiplied by the square of that factor.

By differentiating the above ratio successively with respect to $a, b, \ldots k$ it is possible to arrive at a series of simultaneous linear equations which can be solved to give quantities proportional to the required constants. Fisher (1938 and 1940) has shown, however, that equivalent results are obtained by giving each individual a dummy variate y, which has one of two values according as the individual belongs to set 1 or set 2, and determining equation (10.3) as a multiple regression equation. To the individuals in set 1 it is convenient to give the value $y = n_2/(n_1 + n_2)$ and to those in set 2 the value $y = -n_1/(n_1 + n_2)$, where n_1 and n_2 are the numbers of individuals in the two sets respectively. Then it is easy to see that, if S is the summation over the $n_1 + n_2$ individuals,

$$\bar{y} = 0 \text{ and } Sy^2 = n_1 n_2/(n_1 + n_2) = \lambda^2 \text{ (say)},$$

and the sums of products on the left-hand side of equations (10.1a) are

$$Sy'x'_a = \lambda^2 d_a, \quad Sy'x'_b = \lambda^2 d_b, \ldots . Sy'x'_k = \lambda^2 d_k.$$

Equations (10.1a) can then be evaluated and solved for $a, b, \ldots k$, and the analysis of variance of y becomes as shown in Table 10.3. Table 10.3 is a special case of Table 10.1a, and equation (10.1b) has been used to determine the sum of squares associated with the regression. Algebraically the square of the multiple correlation coefficient is

$$R^2 = ad_a + bd_b + \ldots kd_k \quad . \quad . \quad . \quad . \quad (10.3a)$$

In ordinary multiple regression analysis, the F test of significance may be used on the resulting variances on the assumption that the x's are fixed and the residual y varies normally and at random. Here y is fixed and the x's vary, but it has been shown that the variances in Table 10.3 may nevertheless be tested in the same way as those in Table 10.1a. The usefulness of this lies in the application of an analysis similar to that in Table 10.23 to testing

TABLE 10.3

ANALYSIS OF VARIANCE OF $y = n_2/(n_1 + n_2)$ OR $-n_1/(n_1 + n_2)$

Source of Variation	Sum of Squares	Degrees of Freedom
Regression	$\lambda^2(ad_a + bd_b + \ldots kd_k) = \lambda^2 R^2$	p
Residual	$\lambda^2(1 - ad_a - bd_b - \ldots kd_k) = \lambda^2(1 - R^2)$	$n_1 + n_2 - p - 1$
Total	λ^2	$n_1 + n_2 - 1$

the improvement in discrimination achieved by using an increased number of variates.

We now need to analyse the variance of the values of Y into two parts : between and within sets. The total sum of squares is $\lambda^2 R^2$, as given in Table 10.3, and the sum of squares between sets is

$$n_1(\overline{Y}_1 - \overline{Y})^2 + n_2(\overline{Y}_2 - \overline{Y})^2 = \lambda^2 R^4,$$

where $\overline{Y}$ is the weighted mean of $\overline{Y}_1$ and $\overline{Y}_2$. The analysis of

TABLE 10.3a

ANALYSIS OF VARIANCE OF Y

Source of Variation	Sum of Squares	Degrees of Freedom
Between sets	$\lambda^2 R^4$	p
Within sets	$\lambda^2 R^2(1 - R^2)$	$n_1 + n_2 - p - 1$
Total ...	$\lambda^2 R^2$	$n_1 + n_2 - 1$

variance is in Table 10.3a. The degrees of freedom between sets are p rather than 1 on account of the p constants that have been determined from the data to minimise the within-set variance as compared with that between sets. The F for testing the significance of the difference between sets—i.e. for testing the significance

297

of the discriminant function—is the same as that derived from Table 10.3a.

It is useful to note that
$$Y_1 - \overline{Y}_2 = R^2,$$
and the standard deviation of Y within sets
$$= \sqrt{\{\lambda^2 R^2 (1 - R^2)/(n_1 + n_2 - p - 1)\}} \quad . \quad (10.3b)$$

Now let us apply these results to the data for the 46 cottons of Fig. 10.3. The following are the various calculated quantities :
$$d_a = 33{\cdot}428\ 031, \quad d_b = -4{\cdot}166\ 667, \quad \lambda^2 = 11{\cdot}478\ 261.$$
The linear equations are :
$$383{\cdot}695\ 7 = \quad 20\ 753{\cdot}24a - 1\ 920{\cdot}565b$$
$$-47{\cdot}826\ 09 = -1\ 920{\cdot}565a + 300{\cdot}608\ 7b$$
and their solution gives
$$a = 0{\cdot}009\ 211\ 3, \quad b = -0{\cdot}100\ 247.$$
On inserting the appropriate values in equation (10.3a), we find that
$$R^2 = 0{\cdot}725\ 61.$$

For testing the significance of the function we have
$$F = (n_1 + n_2 - p - 1)R^2/p(1 - R^2) = 56{\cdot}5$$
and on 2 and 43 degrees of freedom this is overwhelmingly significant. The standard deviation of Y within sets is, from equations (10.3b), $0{\cdot}231$, and the difference between means, $\overline{Y}_1 - \overline{Y}_2 = 0{\cdot}726$ is $3{\cdot}18$ times the within-set standard deviation. So far we have not evaluated Y. As we are concerned with differences, it does not matter from what origin we measure Y, so we may take as the discriminant function
$$Y = 0{\cdot}009\ 211\ x_a - 0{\cdot}100\ 25\ x_b,$$
measuring x_a and x_b as in Table 10.3. Then
$$\overline{Y}_1 = -0{\cdot}024\ 8, \quad \overline{Y}_2 = -0{\cdot}750\ 4.$$
If for any unknown cotton Y is less than $-0{\cdot}387\ 6$, it is attributed to series 2 ; if greater it is attributed to series 1. The limit differs from each mean by $1{\cdot}57$ times the within-set standard deviation. If Y is distributed normally, the probability of a cotton belonging to set 2 having a Y greater than the limit and so being wrongly classified as belonging to set 1 is (by Chart B) $0{\cdot}058$; the probability of a cotton belonging to set 1 being wrongly classified is similarly $0{\cdot}058$; this is the probability of misclassification.

The values of Y are plotted in the lowest part of Fig. 10.3, and to the eye it appears that Y gives greater discrimination than either x_a or x_b.

Discriminant analysis has been developed for more than two groups when an actual measure of y is available.

Classical papers on the subject of discriminant analysis are by Barnard (1935) and Fisher (1936). A good expository paper with a large bibliography is by Brown (1947).

THE ANALYSIS OF CO-VARIANCE

10.4. In Chapter VI the analysis of variance was developed by measuring deviations of individual values from discrete array or group means, and in Chapter VII deviations were measured from row, column and treatment means, and so on. In section 8.23 we applied the same ideas to regression analysis by measuring deviations of y from regression values, and in section 10.2 partial regression was developed by correlating deviations of y and x_a from regression lines on x_b. In this section we shall combine these procedures and deal with the partial correlation of deviations from discrete group means.

Table 10.4 shows the mean grain and straw yields for each of 64 plots (the units do not concern us here), there being eight different manurial treatments and eight replicates on each. The data are selected from a paper by Eden and Fisher (1927), and are merely used here for illustrative purposes ; readers who are interested in the agricultural aspect must consult the original paper. Further, we shall for the moment ignore the fact that the sample is small with comparatively large sampling errors, and shall treat the statistical constants as though they were almost exact. The treatments were distributed at random within blocks and we have in Table 10.4a analysed the variance of grain and straw yields into three parts ; the fifth, eighth and ninth columns should be ignored for the moment. The block variation is much greater than the residual for both grain and straw, and so is the treatment variation for straw, while the variance of grain yields is less for the treatments than for the residual (although not significantly so) ; thus the variations in the yields of Table 10.4 are heterogeneous. Now in order to find the relation between grain and straw yields, we may correlate the sixty-four pairs of readings, and the crude correlation of the actual readings gives a coefficient of $+0.524$, indicating a positive relationship. This, however, is not the whole story ; the variations are produced by three groups of causes, changes in soil fertility, changes in treatments, and that complex of unknown causes which we call random, and it is unlikely that the relationship between grain and straw yields is

TABLE 10.4

GRAIN AND STRAW YIELDS

Treatment	Block 1		Block 2		Block 3		Block 4	
	Grain	Straw	Grain	Straw	Grain	Straw	Grain	Straw
A	620	242	646	321	681	261	644	317
B	644	267	745	382	542	201	711	316
C	523	215	713	330	686	298	688	381
D	601	212	693	292	685	265	714	255
E	664	322	693	370	666	284	516	323
F	514	200	637	261	697	259	710	361
G	550	260	708	318	663	266	673	340
H	521	203	661	275	594	207	730	331
	Block 5		Block 6		Block 7		Block 8	
A	706	255	615	331	552	216	726	295
B	705	280	637	285	543	200	646	309
C	692	300	612	294	635	256	748	284
D	699	238	697	309	701	283	746	324
E	656	232	663	393	657	351	683	363
F	633	234	595	258	697	306	712	376
G	671	362	626	400	655	276	671	385
H	625	229	644	266	745	276	747	328

the same for the three types of variation. Indeed, in a general way, plots that produce most grain might be expected to produce most straw ; but the treatments which had an effect on the straw yield had none on the grain, and this relationship cannot hold for treatment variations. It is thus necessary to separate out the effects and to find several correlations, and this is done by a fairly straightforward extension of the analysis of variance

Let us suppose first that the block and residual variations are due to the same thing (soil variability), and that we wish to separate them from those due to manurial treatments, and to correlate them. This may be done quite straightforwardly by finding the 64 pairs of deviations from the treatment means and correlating them, by finding the sums of their products and squares. We may also correlate the eight pairs of treatment means (or totals). Using the same notation as before, but calling the

TABLE 10.4a—ANALYSIS OF VARIANCE AND CO-VARIANCE OF GRAIN AND STRAW YIELDS

Source of Variations	Degrees of Freedom	Sums of Squares		Sums of Products	Variances		Co-variance	Correlation Coefficient
		Grain	Straw		Grain	Straw		
Blocks ...	7	86 045·8	75 841·5	56 073·6	12 292·3	10 834·5	8 010·5	+0·694
Treatments	7	12 496·8	32 985·0	−6 786·6	1 785·3	4 712·1	−969·5	−0·334
Residual...	49	136 972·6	71 496·1	58 549·0	2 795·4	1 459·1	1 194·9	+0·592
Total ...	63	235 515·2	180 322·6	107 836·0	—	—	—	+0·524

grain yield y and the straw yield x, the values of an individual pair of readings in the sth treatment as deviations from the grand means are

and
$$\left. \begin{aligned} (x - \bar{x}) &= (x - \bar{x}_s) + (\bar{x}_s - \bar{x}) \\ (y - \bar{y}) &= (y - \bar{y}_s) + (\bar{y}_s - \bar{y}), \end{aligned} \right\} \quad . \quad . \quad (10.4)$$

and their product summed for the sth treatment is

$$S'(x - \bar{x})(y - \bar{y}) = S'(x - \bar{x}_s)(y - \bar{y}_s) + n_s(\bar{x}_s - \bar{x})(\bar{y}_s - \bar{y}) \\ + (\bar{y}_s - \bar{y})S'(x - \bar{x}_s) + (\bar{x}_s - \bar{x})S'(y - \bar{y}_s),$$

where n_s is the number of plots per treatment. The last two terms are zero, since $S'(x - \bar{x}_s)$ and $S'(y - \bar{y}_s)$ are the sums of deviations from the mean and are zero, so this equation, when summed further over all treatments, gives

$$S(x - \bar{x})(y - \bar{y}) = S_s S'(x - \bar{x}_s)(y - \bar{y}_s) \\ + S_s n_s(\bar{x}_s - \bar{x})(\bar{y}_s - \bar{y}). \quad . \quad (10.4a)$$

The term on the left-hand side is the sum of products used in correlating the crude deviations from the grand mean, the first term on the right-hand side is used in correlating the deviations from the treatment means and the second term in correlating the treatment means themselves. This equation is exactly parallel to equation (6.4) deduced for the analysis of variance, and may similarly be entered in a table of analysis of *co-variance*. The degrees of freedom are reckoned up in the same way, and the sum of products divided by the number of degrees of freedom gives the mean product or co-variance. The sums of squares and variances can be entered in the same table, and the co-variance of any cause of variation when divided by the square root of the product of the variances [equation (8.3)] gives the corresponding correlation coefficient.

We can deal with the co-variance in exactly the same way as the variance, using all the arguments and equations previously used, except that co-variance may sometimes be negative while variance must always be positive. We saw in the last chapter that variance may be analysed into more than two parts, and now will use the same methods to analyse the co-variance of the yields of Table 10.4 into three parts. For a single plot in the sth treatment and tth block,

$$(x - \bar{x}) = (\bar{x}_s - \bar{x}) + (\bar{x}_t - \bar{x}) + x',$$
$$(y - \bar{y}) = (\bar{y}_s - \bar{y}) + (\bar{y}_t - \bar{y}) + y',$$

where x' and y' are residual deviations ; and by a similar argument to that used above, summing over all treatments and blocks gives

$$S(x - \bar{x}) (y - \bar{y}) = S_s n_s(\bar{x}_s - \bar{x}) (\bar{y}_s - \bar{y})$$
$$+ S_t n_t(\bar{x}_t - \bar{x}) (\bar{y}_t - \bar{y}) + Sx'y', \quad . \quad (10.4b)$$

where n_s is the number of plots in a treatment and n_t the number in a block. This is exactly parallel to equation (7.1a),* and the terms have been entered in Table 10.4a under the *sums of products* column, and when divided by the degrees of freedom, as co-variances. For convenience of computing, equation (8.4a) may be applied to find the terms of the above ; i.e.

$$S(x - \bar{x}) (y - \bar{y}) = Sxy - N\bar{x}\bar{y},$$
$$S_s n_s(\bar{x}_s - \bar{x}) (\bar{y}_s - \bar{y}) = S_s n_s \bar{x}_s \bar{y}_s - N\bar{x}\bar{y},$$

and so on ; but particular care must be taken of signs, as co-variance may be negative. The correlation coefficients in Table 10.4a have been found from the sums of squares and products, and whereas the coefficient for block and residual variations is about $+ 0.6$, for the treatment variations it is $- 0.3$; the difference is

* If n_s and n_t are constant, they may be placed outside the summation sign.

important. The residual deviations are independent of block and treatment differences, and their correlation coefficient is a *partial* coefficient with both block and treatment factors eliminated. The eight treatment totals are independent of the blocks and the block totals are independent of the treatments, but both are to some extent affected by the residual deviations, and although their correlation coefficients are in some degree partial, only *one* factor has been eliminated. However, as there are several plots per block and treatment, the effects of these two factors predominate over the residual in the correlation coefficients.

The maximum and minimum temperatures given in Table 8.1c are daily readings taken in the month of August for 49 years, and we may now be led to inquire if the variations between and within years are of the same nature. Fisher and Hoblyn give the sums of squares and products, and we repeat them in Table 10.4b, together with the correlation coefficients.* The variances show that the between-year variations are real, and the correlation coefficients

TABLE 10.4b—ANALYSIS OF VARIANCE AND CO-VARIANCE
Maximum and Minimum Temperatures

Source of Variations	Degrees of Freedom	Sums of Squares		Sums of Products	Variances		Correlation Coefficient
		Maximum	Minimum		Maximum	Minimum	
Within years ...	1 469	38 360 589	28 565 319	8 483 383	26 113	19 445	+0·256
Between years ...	48	14 127 693	3 549 394	3 772 672	294 327	73 946	+0·533
Total ...	1 517	52 488 282	32 114 713	12 256 055	—	—	+0·298

show that the association between maximum and minimum temperatures is stronger for these variations than for those within the year ; that is to say, if we know the average maximum temperature for the month of August in any one year we can estimate the average minimum for that month with a little greater accuracy than we can the minimum for any one day, knowing the corresponding maximum. Other facts are also presented by Table 10.4b ; the maximum temperature is a little more variable from day to day during the month than the minimum (the variances are 26 113 and 19 445), while between the monthly means for different years, the maximum is very much more variable than the minimum temperature.

* The data of Table 10.4b have been calculated from Fisher and Hoblyn's full correlation table and not from the condensed Table 8.1c.

If these data for the 49 years were separated, and from the 49 correlation coefficients a mean were found, using Fisher's transformation as shown in section 9.2, it would be something like the value of 0·256 of Table 10.4b. When the full data are available, however, it is always better to add the 49 sums of products and squares separately, and to find the single correlation coefficient from them in the way we have just shown.

Correction of Treatment Effect on one Factor for Variations due to a Correlated Factor

10.41. In an experiment like that measuring grain and straw yields in the previous section, it is sometimes desirable to know the effect of the treatments on one factor when the other is kept constant. Thus, the apparent effect of the treatments on grain yield measured by the variances in Table 10.4a is due not only to any possible direct effect of the treatments but also to the indirect effect of variations in the yield of straw, since straw and grain yields are positively correlated. It may be asked, " What is the effect of the treatments on grain yield when plots having the same straw yield are compared ? " Such a question may be somewhat unreal in this instance, unless the straw yield may be taken as a measure of the relative fertility of the plots, but when the variable to be eliminated is the number of plants per plot, or the yield on the same plots resulting from a uniformity trial during a previous year, the practical relevance of such questions is more obvious. We shall show how the analysis of co-variance technique gives an answer to the question.

The method is similar to those used in sections 9.5 to 9.53 for testing various hypotheses regarding regression constants. First, a single regression line is fitted to the data and the sum of squares of the residual deviations of grain yield is found. Then separate regression lines are fitted, one for each treatment, and the sum of squares of the residual deviations of grain yield from these lines is found. The degrees of freedom associated with the two sums of squares are also noted. Then, if the variance estimated from the reduction in residual sum of squares due to fitting the separate lines is significantly greater than the final residual variance from the separate lines, the treatments have a significant effect on grain, when corrected for straw yield.

Since the block variations have been eliminated from the treatment comparisons, we are only concerned with the treatment and residual variations, and may add the corresponding degrees of freedom and sums of squares and products in Table 10.4a to give new totals, within blocks. Let y'' be the grain and x'' the straw yields measured as deviations from the block means, and let the above sums of squares and products be Sx''^2, Sy''^2 and $Sx''y''$. The sum of squares of deviations of y'' from the one line is, according to equation (8.32),

$$Sy''^2 - \frac{(Sx''y'')^2}{Sx''^2}.$$

This is entered in the first row of Table 10.41. Before fitting the regression line, there were 56 degrees of freedom for this total, and since the line absorbs one, 55 remain for the deviations.

In fitting the separate regression lines for the treatments, we may assume the correlation between variations within the treatments in grain and straw yields to be the same for all treatments, and the lines will have the same slope, but will lie at different levels of y.* Indeed, they will go through the separate treatment means, and the various sums of squares and products will be those given in the residual row of Table 10.4a. The sum of squares of deviations from these lines is

$$Sy'^2 - \frac{(Sx'y')^2}{Sx'^2}$$

and this is entered in the second row of Table 10.41. The degrees of freedom are one fewer than those for the residual in Table 10.4a, due to the correction for the common slope of the regression lines. The effect of allowing for the treatments is measured by subtracting the residual sum of squares and degrees of freedom in Table 10.41 from the " Total " and estimating the corresponding variance ; this is given in the last row of Table 10.41. The variance due to treatments is now significantly greater than the residual, so that after correction for the straw yield, the treatments have a significant effect on grain yield. This is partly because of the considerable reduction in the residual variance resulting from the

* This has been mentioned in section 9.53. If a common slope may not be assumed, the residuals from the following two systems of lines may be compared : (1) lines having different slopes but a common constant b [equation (8.22)] and (2) lines with separate slopes and constants b. The method of fitting the first system is not given.

important partial correlation between the two yields. We make no attempt to give a biological interpretation of this result.

If a is the regression of grain on straw yield for the residual

TABLE 10.41

ANALYSIS OF VARIANCE OF GRAIN YIELD AFTER CORRECTION FOR REGRESSION ON STRAW YIELD

Source of Variations	Sum of Squares	Degrees of Freedom	Variance
Total within blocks ...	123 825·1	55	2 251·4
Residual	89 026·1	48	1 854·7
Treatments (difference)	34 799·0	7	4 971·3

deviations as estimated from the third row of Table 10.4a, the treatment means corrected for variations in straw yield are

$$\bar{y}_s \text{ (corrected)} = \bar{y}_s - a(\bar{x}_s - \bar{x}).$$

Here,

$$a = \frac{Sx'y'}{Sx'^2} = 0.818\ 91.$$

If a were the true population value, the standard error of the difference between any two corrected means would be calculable from the corrected residual variance in Table 10.41. As it is, the error in a also contributes somewhat to the standard errors of the corrected treatment means. It is for this reason that the variance due to treatments in Table 10.41 cannot be obtained directly from the corrected means.

ASSUMPTIONS AND INTERPRETATIONS

10.5. The assumptions underlying the methods of this chapter are substantially those discussed in section 8.5 for simple correlation and regression analysis, extended as is appropriate for multivariate analysis ; but in the complications of the analysis they are apt to be overlooked, and it is well to consider them again.

First it is assumed that a straight line law adequately expresses the relationships between the variates, and further, that the relationship between any two variates is the same at all values of the other variates. For example, in the analysis of Table 10.1 it is assumed that the relationship between y and x_a is the same for cottons having low values of x_b as for those having high values.

If the analysis is in terms of correlation coefficients, the assumption is that all the variates are random. This is not justified for Table 10.1, since the cottons belong to three main groups, two of which are shown in Fig. 10.3 to differ markedly. The multiple correlation analysis would have meaning only if one could imagine a homogeneous population of cottons from which those measured were selected at random.

For regression analysis the independent variates need not be random, and the analysis of Table 10.1 would be valid as statistically describing the effects of the factors x_a and x_b on y for the fifty particular cottons, in so far as the error with which each value of x_a and x_b is determined can be neglected as compared with the variations between cottons.

The residual variance is assumed to be homogeneous—there is, for example, a suggestion in Fig. 10.3 that the variance of x_a is greater for set 2 than for set 1, and if this is so the tests of significance are in some degree invalidated, although probably not enough to affect the conclusions in this instance.

It is a good thing to plot the data for multi-variate analysis in order to see how far the assumptions are justified. If they are not, the methods of this chapter can often be used to provide an approximate solution to the problem ; otherwise, special methods beyond the scope of this book must be used. Readers may refer to *Methods of Correlation Analysis* by Ezekial (1930).

The regression coefficients do not estimate the physical connection between the variates, for the reasons developed in section 8.51, and as statistical measures they are valid, at the best, for application to other cottons selected from the same universe. They would not apply, for example, to American or Egyptian cottons.

When it was first introduced, it was apparently hoped that partial correlation analysis would help in tracing causal relationships in complex situations, but it is doubtful if that hope has been realised. The mathematical model embodied in the assumptions is very simple for application to the real world, and partial correlation coefficients can be taken as evidence (evidence, not proof !) of causal relationships only if all causal factors are included in the analysis. The *a priori* knowledge required to establish the validity of any partial correlation coefficients as evidence of causation has (in my experience) been so great that the coefficients themselves add little to knowledge. I suggest, for example, that the partial correlation coefficients between vital capacity, height, etc., in Table 10.21*a* illuminate the mind of the physiologist but little ; rather he needs *a priori* knowledge to explain the coefficients.

In some situations multiple and partial correlation and regression analysis are the only tools that can be used. But any consequent conclusions should be reached cautiously and accepted with reserve. Fruitful applications of the analysis of co-variance to experiments and of discriminant analysis seem to be much more numerous.

CHAPTER XI

NON-LINEAR REGRESSION

11.1. The methods of Chapters VIII, IX and X are all based on the assumption that the regressions are straight lines ; in this chapter we shall deal with adaptations of the methods to data that do not justify this assumption.

If the data are regarded from the point of view of a regression surface, as in section 8.21, and the assumption is not justified, little can be done ; the mathematical model is inapplicable and no other models of the same kind have so far been developed, at

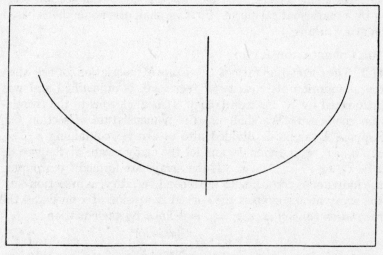

Fig. 11.1.   Curve representing an imaginary regression of y on x with the corresponding straight regression of x on y.

least to the extent of making them usable.   We shall regard the data as representable by a regression line, which may be curved, with random deviations in the dependent variate superimposed.

When the true regression line is curved and a straight regression line is fitted, the straight line may be regarded as an approximation to the curved one, which will be more or less adequate according as the effect of the curvature is small or large compared with the random deviations.   Then the correlation coefficient, which is a measure of the proportion of the total variance associated with the straight line, will underestimate the degree of association properly expressed by a measure of the proportion of the total variance associated with the curved line. We can imagine an extreme case as illustrated in Fig. 11.1, in which the curved line is the regression of y on x (i.e. x is the independent variate) and the straight line is the corresponding regression of x on y. The correlation coefficient would be nearly zero, for the best straight line that could be drawn to fit the curve would be one almost parallel to the x-axis ; but the points on the scatter diagram could nevertheless be closely clustered around the curve, indicating a high degree of association.

When the regression is not linear, it may be represented as a series of array means, such as those introduced in section 8.22, or by a mathematical curve. First we shall discuss methods based on array means.

The Correlation Ratio

11.2. The correlation ratio is a measure of association for use when the assumption of linearity of regression is unjustified and was introduced by K. Pearson (1905). It is analogous to the correlation coefficient. We shall use the nomenclature of section 6.2. Suppose a sample is divided into m arrays, containing n_1, n_2, ... n_s, ... n_m individuals, and let the array means of the variate x be $\bar{x}_1$, $\bar{x}_2$, ... $\bar{x}_s$, ... $\bar{x}_m$. If the arrays are formed by grouping the individuals according to the second variate y, as in section 8.22, the array means express the curved regression of x on y and the *correlation ratio of x on y*, $\eta_{x/y}$, is defined by the equation

$$1 - \eta_{x/y}{}^2 = \frac{S(x - \bar{x}_s)^2}{S(x - \bar{x})^2} \quad \cdots \quad (11.2)$$

where S is the summation over all individuals. If we refer to Table 6.2b we see that $1 - \eta_{x/y}{}^2$ is the ratio of the residual to the total sum of squares, just as for linear regression $1 - r^2$ is the corresponding ratio (see Table 8.23a). If s_x is the standard deviation of x and s'_x is that of the residual deviations from the regression line or series of array means, and if the number of arrays is small compared with the number of individuals in the sample we have :

for linear regression $s'_x{}^2 = (1 - r^2)s_x{}^2$,
for non-linear regression $s'_x{}^2 = (1 - \eta_{x/y}{}^2)s_x{}^2$.

In large samples, therefore, the correlation ratio may be

interpreted as a measure of association in the same way as the correlation coefficient.

With the two variates x and y, arrays of y may be formed by grouping according to sub-ranges of x, and the regression of y on x be expressed by array means. This leads to a correlation ratio of y on x, viz. $\eta_{y/x}$, which is usually different from that of x on y. The analysis with y as the independent variate is in general unconnected with that with x as the independent variate ; the two analyses have a connection only when the regression is linear.

The definition of the correlation ratio of x on y in equation (11.2) does not contain y, and a set of array means and correlation ratio can be determined when the variate describing the arrays is qualitative or discrete. Thus, for the ovules per ovary of Tables 6.2 and 6.2a we have :

$$1 - \eta^2 = \frac{3\ 026 \cdot 350}{5\ 379 \cdot 775}, \eta = 0 \cdot 66$$

and the strength of association comes somewhere between that of pistils and stamens of early and late flowers in Tables 8.1a and 8.1b. For the lengths of cuckoos' eggs of Tables 6.4 and 6.4a we have :

$$1 - \eta^2 = \frac{2\ 356 \cdot 21}{3\ 429 \cdot 70} \text{ and } \eta = 0 \cdot 56.$$

The strength of association is much the same as that shown in Table 8.1b.

It will be clear from Chapter VI that, other things being equal, the correlation ratio increases with the number of arrays, since the random errors of the array means contribute to the ratio. Indeed, even if there is no association and the variations between array means is random, the correlation ratio is necessarily positive and greater than zero. In this respect the correlation ratio is closely parallel to the multiple correlation coefficient and as a measure of association is misleading unless the number of arrays is negligibly small compared with the number of individuals in the sample—say less than one-twentieth.

TESTS FOR NON-LINEARITY OF REGRESSION

11.3. In order to test whether any given set of array means departs significantly from linearity it is only necessary to apply the general method of section 7.6. A straight regression line and a set of array means are fitted to the data, and an analysis of variance performed to ascertain whether the variance associated with the deviations from the linear regression is significantly greater than the final residual. Algebraically this is in effect a combination of Table 6.2*b* (generalised and written for the variate y) and

TABLE 11.3
ANALYSIS OF VARIANCE

Source of Variation	Sums of Squares	Degrees of Freedom
Linear regression ⎫ Between Deviations from ⎬ arrays linear regression ⎭ Residual within arrays	$r^2 S(y-\bar{y})^2$ ⎫ ⎬$S_s n_s(\bar{y}_s-\bar{y})^2$ difference ⎭ $S(y-\bar{y}_s)^2$	$\left.\begin{matrix}1\\ \\m-2\\N-m\end{matrix}\right\}m-1$
Total	$S(y-\bar{y})^2$	$N-1$

Table 8.23, and is set out in Table 11.3. S_s is the summation over the m arrays; the sums of squares can all be expressed in terms of S $(y-\bar{y})^2$, r, and η, if desired.

We shall apply the test to the data of Table 11.3*a* (Zinn, 1923) which gives the protein content of 100 commercial Ohio wheats and the loaf volume of standard loaves baked from them. The

TABLE 11.3a—PROTEIN CONTENT OF WHEAT AND LOAF VOLUME

		Protein Content, per cent.									Totals
		9·0	10·0	11·0	12·0	13·0	14·0	15·0	16·0	17·0	
Loaf Volume, c.c.	1 600–	2	—	1	—	1	—	—	—	—	4
	1 700–	—	2	1	—	2	—	—	—	—	5
	1 800–	6	5	5	2	1	—	—	—	—	19
	1 900–	5	4	6	7	—	—	—	—	—	22
	2 000–	2	3	9	10	2	1	—	—	—	27
	2 100–	1	—	3	3	5	2	1	—	—	15
	2 200–	—	—	1	2	—	2	1	—	—	6
	2 300–	—	—	—	—	—	—	—	1	1	2
Totals ...		16	14	26	24	11	5	2	1	1	100

correlation coefficient (without Sheppard's corrections) is + 0·529 78, and the analysis of variance is in Table 11.3*b*. The variance for the deviations from linear regression is not significantly greater than the residual.

It will be noticed that the distribution of protein content is

312

far from normal, but that does not invalidate the test, which assumes only that the distribution of loaf volume within arrays is normal. As far as can be judged from a sample of this size the assumption is justified.

The example of the analysis of loom speeds and outputs dealt with in section 9.7 is another one that tests the adequacy of a linear regression.

If deviations from the linear regression are significant, that

TABLE 11.3b

ANALYSIS OF VARIANCE OF LOAF VOLUMES
(Units, 10 000 c.c.²)

Source of Variation	Sums of Squares	Degrees of Freedom	Variance
Linear regression ... ⎫	64·66 ⎫	1 ⎫	64·66
Deviations from ⎬ Between	⎬ 78·21	⎬ 8	
linear regression ⎪ arrays			
sion ... ... ⎭	13·55 ⎭	7 ⎭	1·94
Residual within arrays ...	152·15	91	1·67
Total	230·36	99	—

merely shows that the straight regression line is not adequate; it does not show that a curved line would be. The array means could form a very irregular sequence.

POLYNOMIAL REGRESSION CURVES

11.4. A mathematically expressed regression curve, with constants determined from the data, is useful where the data are few or for any reason cannot be grouped into arrays. The form most developed for use in statistics is the polynomial

$$Y = a + bx + cx^2 + \ldots \qquad \ldots \quad (11.4)$$

and according to the method of least squares the constants a, b, c, etc., may be obtained by solving a series of linear equations

$$\left. \begin{aligned} Sy &= aS1 + bSx + cSx^2 + \ldots \\ Sxy &= aSx + bSx^2 + cSx^3 + \ldots \\ Sx^2y &= aSx^2 + bSx^3 + cSx^4 + \ldots \end{aligned} \right\} \quad . \quad . \quad (11.4a)$$

using as many equations as there are constants. The summations are taken over all individuals and may be determined by fairly straightforward extensions of the methods of sections 1.3 and 8.4. S1 is N, Sx and Sy are N times the respective means and the other sums are N times various moments and product moments measured about the origin. Any convenient arbitrary origin may be used in finding the summations provided the same origin is used in expressing the result in (11.4). If the data are grouped into arrays, the array means $\bar{y}_s$ may be used instead of the individual values, and the summations are then $S_s n_s \bar{y}_s$, $S_s n_s$, $S_s n_s x_s$, etc., using the same notation as before. A similar series of equations obtained by interchanging x and y in equations (11.4) and (11.4a) gives the regression of x on y.

Equations (11.4) and (11.4a) are very similar to equations (10.1) and (10.1a), and indeed the fitting of a polynomial may be treated exactly as the determination of a multiple regression equation of y on $x_b = x$, $x_c = x^2$, etc.

The polynomial equation is very adaptable, and according to the values of the constants a, b, c, etc., it may take a wide variety of forms with only a comparatively few constants. Indeed, for practical purposes it is a suitable way of expressing nearly all kinds of regression except those in which the curve of y undulates and has more than two or three maxima and minima.

In the analysis of variance given in section 11.3, a polynomial equation may be used instead of the array means, and it absorbs as many degrees of freedom as there are constants, the constant a accounting for the one degree previously attributed to the grand mean of y. Curves of the first, second, third and higher orders may be fitted successively if desired, and as more and more terms are used, the equation fits the observations more and more closely, until ultimately an equation with as many constants as there are observations does so perfectly. This progressive improvement in the closeness of fit may be seen by finding the deviations of the observed values from those given by the regression and squaring and adding them, i.e. by finding $S(y - Y)^2$. As more and more terms are used this sum of squares decreases until when the fit becomes perfect, it becomes zero. If the constants are determined by the method of least squares and the fluctuations in y are purely random, the reduction in sum of squares at each stage tends to be the same ; it is the variance associated with one degree of freedom, differing from the true variance only by the extent of the random errors. If the data show a comparatively simple form of variation predominating over the random fluctuations, the earlier terms of the equation, which express the simpler movements, reduce the sum of squares by an amount significantly greater than the later ones. When sufficient terms are included to express this slow movement of y with x, and the residual deviations are random, each of the remaining possible terms reduces the remaining sum of squares by the same amount, within the limits of random errors. Thus, at each stage in fitting equations with more terms, the reduction in residual sum of squares due to one degree of freedom can be compared with the variance estimated from the residual ; if the former is significantly greater than the latter, the last term expresses a real feature of the trend. When the stage is reached that the variances associated with the last one or two terms are not significantly greater than that estimated from the residual, it is presumed that the regression has been adequately expressed and the deviations are random. This presumption is only justified, however, if the polynomial is the form appropriate for describing the regression. This technique of fitting and testing curves should not be followed blindly, and a certain amount of judgment and reference to a diagram may be necessary ; it is possible that the first term or two may account for very little of the variance, but that some of the later ones may be very important ; this would be the case in the curve of Fig. 11.1, where the linear term would be very small but the second one would be important. On the other hand, if a very large number of terms is required, it may be because the polynomial form is not suitable. A regression equation fitted to any data must not only satisfy the statistical tests but it must appear appropriate when plotted on a diagram.

This procedure for testing the significance of polynomial terms is exactly the same as that given in section 10.23 for testing that of terms in a multiple regression equation, except that for the polynomial there is a natural order in which the terms are fitted and tested, and the solution is unique.

Orthogonal Polynomials

11.41. Every time a polynomial equation with an additional term is fitted, equations (11.4a) have to be solved afresh and new values of all the constants be determined. The terms of equation (11.4) are not orthogonal, but the equation may be put into an orthogonal form consisting of a number of terms of successively higher orders in x, each term being multiplied by a constant to be determined from the data. These terms are independent in that they may be determined one at a time, and the addition of the

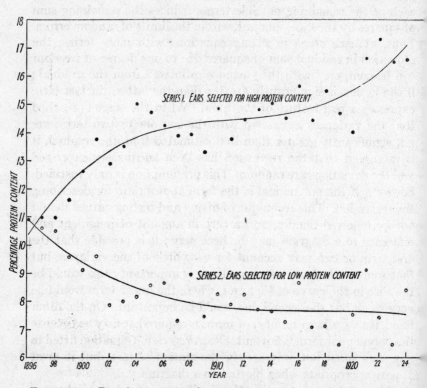

FIG. 11.41. Protein contents of successive annual crops of two series of wheats, the seeds being selected in two ways, with fitted cubic curves [data in Table 9.1].

higher orders does not alter the constants of the lower orders previously determined. This course is easiest when the values of the independent variable are at equal intervals and there is one value of the dependent for each value of the independent variable, as in a time series. Fisher (1925c) describes a convenient system for doing this, and we shall illustrate it by fitting a curve of the third degree to the protein content data of Table 9.1. We shall call the mean protein content (the observed values) y, and the year measured from the middle year 1910 t (i.e. for 1908, $t = -2$), and will fit a curve of the form,

$$Y = a + bt + ct^2 + dt^3 \quad . \quad . \quad . \quad . \quad (11.41)$$

to the 29 values ($N = 29$).*

This Fisher transforms to

$$
\left.
\begin{aligned}
Y &= A + BT_1 + CT_2 + DT_3, \\
\text{where} \quad T_1 &= (t - \bar{t}) = t \text{ (since } \bar{t} = 0), \\
T_2 &= t^2 - \frac{N^2 - 1}{12} = t^2 - 70, \\
\text{and} \quad T_3 &= t^3 - \frac{3N^2 - 7}{20} t = t^3 - 125\cdot8t.
\end{aligned}
\right\} \quad . \quad . \quad (11.41a)
$$

The constants are given by the relations

$$
\left.
\begin{aligned}
A &= \frac{1}{N}Sy = \bar{y}, \\
B &= \frac{12}{N(N^2 - 1)}SyT_1 = \frac{1}{2\,030}Syt, \\
C &= \frac{180}{N(N^2 - 1)(N^2 - 4)}SyT_2 = \frac{1}{113\,274}\{Syt^2 - 70Sy\}, \\
D &= \frac{2\,800}{N(N^2 - 1)(N^2 - 4)(N^2 - 9)}SyT_3 \\
&= \frac{5}{30\,292\,704}\{Syt^3 - 125\cdot8Syt\}.
\end{aligned}
\right\} \quad (11.41b)
$$

The summations Sy, Syt, etc., have to be found from the data, and Fisher gives a convenient method of evaluating them by a series of additions, but for such a small number of observations as we have, it is not very much trouble to obtain the summations directly,

---

* If there is an even number of years, $t = 0$ must still be at the centre, so that the values of t must be $+ 0\cdot5, + 1\cdot5, \ldots - 0\cdot5, - 1\cdot5 \ldots$

particularly if a calculating machine is available. For the protein percentages they are,

$$Sy_1 = 411 \cdot 48 \qquad\qquad Sy_2 = 240 \cdot 78$$
$$Sy_1 t = +342 \cdot 98 \qquad\qquad Sy_2 t = -195 \cdot 36$$
$$Sy_1 t^2 = 28\,408 \cdot 36 \qquad\qquad Sy_2 t^2 = 17\,674 \cdot 16$$
$$Sy_1 t^3 = +49\,329 \cdot 62 \qquad\qquad Sy_2 t^3 = -26\,716 \cdot 68.$$

If $_1 y_1, \; _2 y_1, \; _3 y_1 \ldots \; _{29} y_1$ are the individual readings,

$$Sy_1 t = (_{29}y_1 - _1y_1) \cdot 14 + (_{28}y_1 - _2y_1) \cdot 13 + \ldots + (_{16}y_1 - _{14}y_1) \cdot 1,$$
$$Sy_1 t^2 = (_{29}y_1 + _1y_1) \cdot 14^2 + (_{28}y_1 + _2y_1) \cdot 13^2 + \ldots + (_{16}y_1 + _{14}y_1) \cdot 1^2,$$
$$Sy_1 t^3 = (_{29}y_1 - _1y_1) \cdot 14^3 + (_{28}y_1 - _2y_1) \cdot 13^3 + \ldots + (_{16}y_1 - _{14}y_1) \cdot 1^3,$$
$$\text{etc.} \qquad\qquad\qquad \text{etc.}$$

when the values of t are symmetrically placed about the zero; the labour is diminished if the terms of the brackets are found first, giving two series of fourteen values, one for use when multiplying by the odd powers of t, and the other when multiplying by the even powers.

Substituting the above values in (11.41b) we obtain,

$$A_1 = \frac{411 \cdot 48}{29} = 14 \cdot 188\,97, \qquad A_2 = \frac{240 \cdot 78}{29} = 8 \cdot 302\,76,$$

$$B_1 = \frac{342 \cdot 98}{2\,030} = 0 \cdot 168\,96, \qquad B_2 = \frac{-195 \cdot 36}{2\,030} = -0 \cdot 096\,24,$$

$$C_1 = \frac{-395 \cdot 24}{113\,274} = -0 \cdot 003\,489\,2, \qquad C_2 = \frac{819 \cdot 56}{113\,274} = 0 \cdot 007\,235\,2,$$

$$D_1 = \frac{5 \times 6\,182 \cdot 736}{30\,292\,704} = 0 \cdot 001\,020\,5,$$

$$D_2 = \frac{-5 \times 2\,140 \cdot 392}{30\,292\,704} = -0 \cdot 000\,353\,3.$$

These constants can be substituted in equation (11.41a).

Fisher and Yates (1943) give tables of multipliers such that the terms A, B, C, D, etc., can be obtained by summing the successive products of the values of y and the appropriate multipliers. The use of these multipliers is illustrated below in section 11.55.

It is not necessary to calculate the residual deviations

explicitly, for the successive terms reduce the sums of squares by
the following amounts :

$$NA^2, \quad \frac{N(N^2 - 1)}{12} B^2, \quad \frac{N(N^2 - 1)(N^2 - 4)}{180} C^2,$$

$$\frac{N(N^2 - 1)(N^2 - 4)(N^2 - 9)}{2\,800} D^2, \text{ etc.}$$

The first of these has been encountered before, for it is the ordinary
way of correcting a sum of squares of deviations from some origin
to a sum of squares of deviations from the mean ;

$$NA^2 = N\bar{y}^2 \text{ and } S(y - \bar{y})^2 = Sy^2 - N\bar{y}^2,$$

and the other terms may be regarded as correcting to a moving
mean, the first to a mean which gradually increases (or diminishes)
according to a straight line law, for

$$\frac{N(N^2 - 1)}{12} B^2 = r^2 S(y - \bar{y})^2,$$

and the others to a mean the movements of which become more
complicated as more and higher terms in the regression are used.

TABLE 11.41

ANALYSIS OF VARIANCE

Source of Variation	Degrees of Freedom	Series 1		Series 2	
		Sum of Squares	Variance	Sum of Squares	Variance
First order regression ...	1	57·95	57·95	18·80	18·80
Second order regression ...	1	1·38	1·38	5·93	5·93
Third order regression ...	1	6·31	6·31	0·76	0·76
Residual ...	25	12·34	0·494	12·06	0·482
Total ...	28	77·98	—	37·55	—

We are only concerned with the analysis of sums of squares of
deviations from the means, and these are given in the " total "
row of Table 11.41 for the two series of protein contents, while the
variances of the terms in the regression are given in higher rows.
The variances of the second and third terms are both greater than

the residuals, and we may test their significance in the usual way. We thus find that the first order terms are significant for both series (we arrived at this conclusion in section 9.1 when testing the correlation coefficient), and that the third order terms of the first series and the second order terms of the second are also.

To test whether the cubic regression line as a whole gives a better fit than a straight line we find $F = 3.84/0.494 = 7.8$ and $F = 3.34/0.482 = 6.9$, and on 2 and 25 degrees of freedom these lie above the 0.005 level of significance (Chart E1).

It may be argued that there is no reason why we should stop at the third order term, but Fig. 11.41 shows that the data are quite well followed by the cubic curves, and from Table 11.41 we see that the residual variances for the two series are practically equal, suggesting that they may both be a result of the same random causes. In the next section we shall use these data and assume that cubic equations eliminate sufficiently the slow movements in protein content.

Correlation of Residuals

11.42. If it is desired to estimate the partial correlation coefficient between two variates, x and y say, when both have a non-linear regression on a third, an analysis of co-variance can be performed whether these regressions are represented by sets of array means or by polynomial curves. If polynomial curves are used, a curve of the same degree must be fitted for x and y so that the same degrees of freedom are available for both sets of residuals. The residual deviations from the two curves can be calculated and correlated to give the partial correlation coefficient between x and y with the effect of the third variate eliminated.

When the third variate has equally spaced values and orthogonal polynomial functions are fitted, a short cut can be adopted.

If A_x, B_x, C_x, etc., are the constants for the x series, and A_y, B_y, C_y, etc., those for y, the sums of products of the residuals are obtained by subtracting from Sxy successively the quantities

$$NA_xA_y, \quad \frac{N(N^2 - 1)}{12} B_xB_y, \quad \frac{N(N^2 - 1)(N^2 - 4)}{180} C_xC_y,$$

$$\frac{N(N^2 - 1)(N^2 - 4)(N^2 - 9)}{2\,800} D_xD_y, \text{ etc.} \quad . \quad (11.42)$$

paying due regard to sign. This treatment of products is exactly parallel to the treatment of squares in the previous section.

The results for the protein contents are set out in Table 11.42, which corresponds exactly to Table 11.41.

TABLE 11.42

ANALYSIS OF CO-VARIANCE OF PROTEIN CONTENT

Source of Variation	Degrees of Freedom	Sums of Products
First order regression ...	1	− 33·01
Second order regression ...	1	− 2·86
Third order regression ...	1	− 2·18
Residual	25	+ 3·52
Total	28	− 34·53

Now we are in a position to investigate the question whether any common factor, say weather, affects the variation from year to year in the protein content of the two series of corn in the same way. The crude correlation coefficient as calculated from the totals rows of Tables 11.41 and 11.42 is − 0·638, but this includes the effect of the different selection procedures for the two series, as represented by the regressions on time, and the negative correlation coefficient is probably due largely to those procedures (described in section 9.1). If we eliminate the time effect as a linear factor by applying equation (10.2) we have for the partial correlation coefficient

$$\frac{- \, 0 \cdot 638 + 0 \cdot 862 \times 0 \cdot 708}{\sqrt{(1 - 0 \cdot 862^2)} \sqrt{(1 - 0 \cdot 708^2)}} = -0 \cdot 08,$$

which, on such a small sample, is not statistically significant. We have seen, however, that the regression of protein content on time is well represented by a cubic equation, and the correlation coefficient of the residual deviations is, from Tables 11.41 and 11.42

$$\frac{+ \, 3 \cdot 52}{\sqrt{(12 \cdot 34 \times 12 \cdot 06)}} = +0 \cdot 29.$$

This, although too small to be significant on such a small sample, does suggest the existence of a common factor affecting the annual residual fluctuations of protein content in the same way. (We have treated the first observation in each of the two series as independent, but they are actually the same protein content of a common crop. This does not affect the constants much, nor, in this instance, our conclusions.)

THE ANALYSIS OF TIME SERIES

11.5. The analysis of time series is a large and developing subject.

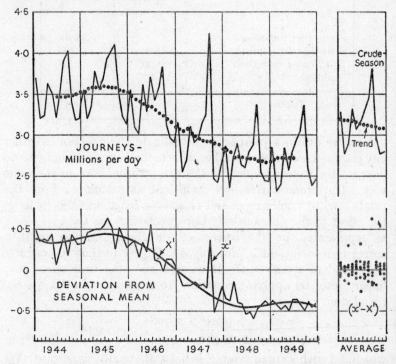

FIG. 11.5. Monthly figures of journeys originating on the British Railways, represented as a time series and analysed into slow movement, seasonal movement, and random deviations [data from Table 11.55].

Here are given only indications of the directions in which developments are taking place and a description of a few of the more elementary methods of analysis. This treatment will suffice for many practical situations.

A time series consists of a number of successive values of some variate associated with successive instants or intervals of time which are usually equally spaced. The protein contents of Table 9.1 are an example. Statistically a series associated with successive points along a length, such as the thickness of a cotton yarn at intervals of, say, one inch, is of the same kind, and its treatment will be included in that for a time series.

When a time series is plotted on a chart there can be discerned one of several types of fluctuation, or two or more of the types superimposed, each type usually being regarded as the effect of a different set of causes and requiring a different form of mathematical or statistical description.

One type is the *slow* or *secular* movement : a gradual change in the level of the chart over the period covered by the series, such as that represented by the curves in Fig. 11.41. The simplest form of slow movement is a *trend*, a more or less continuous rise or fall ; but a curve with one or two maxima will usually be regarded as constituting a slow movement.

A second type is the *periodic* or *cyclical* movement, in which a pattern of variation is repeated at uniform intervals of time. The most common form of this in economic data is the seasonal movement such as that shown by the numbers of passenger journeys in the upper half of Fig. 11.5. The data are monthly averages for the years 1944-9 of the numbers of passenger journeys originating on the British Railways (there was a change in the basis from the end of 1947, but its effect was small and has been neglected). The numbers of days in the months vary, and in order to allow for this the figures are expressed as daily averages, no allowance being made for the day-of-week effect and for the fact that the months did not contain complete weeks. There is a general tendency for the number to fall from 1944 to 1949—a downward trend, but within each year the February average is usually lower than that for January, then there is a rise until April, followed by a fall for May, a rise to a high peak in September, and then a sharp fall to a low value towards the end of the year. This seasonal pattern, presumably due largely to holiday habits (although in 1948 when Easter fell in March the April peak occurred as in the other years when Easter fell in April), is repeated with notable regularity, having regard to the varied events and conditions during those years. The lower chart of Fig. 11.5a shows a periodic variation arising in another field. The chart is a continuous record of thickness taken along a length of cotton yarn. Strictly it is not a time series, but we may regard it as equivalent to one, since discrete readings taken at frequent, regular intervals would form a time series according to our extended definition. There are irregular variations in thickness, and occasional very high momentary readings due to the presence on the yarn of pieces of foreign matter ; but standing out from all this is a well-marked periodic variation with peaks separated by

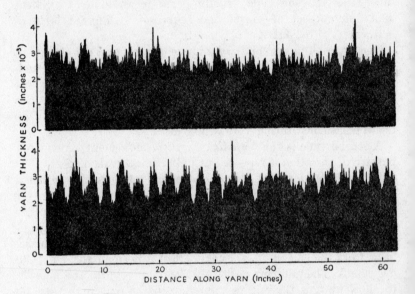

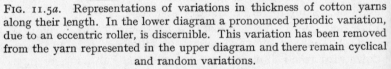

FIG. 11.5a. Representations of variations in thickness of cotton yarns along their length. In the lower diagram a pronounced periodic variation, due to an eccentric roller, is discernible. This variation has been removed from the yarn represented in the upper diagram and there remain cyclical and random variations.

distances corresponding to about three inches of yarn. It becomes lost at about thirty-five inches on the distance scale owing to the disturbing effect of other variations, but shows signs of reappearing at about fifty inches. In a much longer record of this yarn this periodic variation persists strongly ; it is due to an eccentric roller in the spinning system.

The third type of movement is termed *oscillatory* and includes periodic variation as a special case ; it is exemplified in the upper part of Fig. 11.5a. This is a record of a similar yarn to that represented in the lower chart, spun on the same machinery but with the eccentric roller replaced by a true one. This variation is almost wave-like—indeed, between twenty and forty inches from the left there is the appearance of a periodic variation with a wavelength of about four inches of yarn, but the peaks are not uniformly spaced and the wave pattern is neither stable nor persistent. It has long been known that various measures of business activity show this type of variation, and this phenomenon has been the subject of much investigation. Until recently attempts at analysis have been mostly in terms of cyclical movements, and so the phenomenon has been termed the " trade cycle." It is now recognised that the movement, although oscillatory, is not strictly periodic, but the term " trade cycle " will doubtless remain in use for a long time. There is no sharp distinction between a secular and an oscillatory movement ; the two are indistinguishable if the series is so short that there are only two or three maxima and minima.

Most time series also show an element of *random variation*. Purely random results show no pattern in their variation with time ; then the fact that the values are ordered in time may be neglected and the data may be regarded as belonging to a homogeneous frequency distribution which will often be normal. Where there is a secular, periodic or oscillatory movement, there is usually a random variation superimposed.

Sometimes one or two individual readings will deviate so much from the general range covered by the time series that they cannot be regarded as belonging to the system ; they must be treated as exceptions. The two exceptionally high peaks in the lower part of Fig. 11.5a, due to foreign matter on the yarn, are examples.

When two or more types of variation are discovered in a time series, the analysis is made on the assumption that the deviations associated with the various types are arithmetically added, as for the factors in the analysis of variance. This, of course, is a simplifying assumption which does not necessarily correspond to reality, although it may do so closely enough to make the analysis useful as an approximation. The following sections discuss the mathematical and statistical treatment of the types of movement.

Secular Movements

11.51. The polynomial equation forms a convenient and ready

325

means of representing a secular movement that is not too complicated—say one that has not more than three or four maxima and minima. This has been discussed in sections 11.4 and 11.41.

Other forms of equation are occasionally used, such as those involving trigonometrical or exponential functions. Curves expressing the growth of something in time are sometimes exponential, because they express the hypothesis that the rate of increase at any given time is proportional to the value at that time, or to the amount of growth that remains to be completed. The treatment of these forms of equation is beyond the scope of this book.

An easy and much used method of expressing secular movements is by a series of *running averages*. The dots forming a curve going through the crude values of the upper part of Fig. 11.5 are twelve-monthly running averages formed by averaging successively values 1 to 12, 2 to 13, 3 to 14, and so on, the values being numbered by their order in the time sequence. Each running average is plotted at the centre of the time interval to which it belongs. Since each average covers a whole year, the seasonal variations are eliminated from the movement and the effects of the random deviations are much reduced, so that the points show the trend quite smoothly.

Running averages are not only easy to compute but they are also useful for empirical description when the movement is too complicated for description by a polynomial or similar form of equation, but they must be used and interpreted with care. If each average covers too many values, significant variations belonging to the secular movement are smoothed out. Thus, in Fig. 11.5 the monthly seasonal variation has been smoothed out and this is in order because it accords with our analysis. But if we had a time series of seventy-two values with an oscillatory movement containing about five maxima, running averages of twelve values would largely smooth out these fluctuations, possibly in that case to our dismay. On the other hand, if each average covers too few values, random fluctuations are inadequately smoothed out. If running averages are fitted to points following a smooth oscillatory curve, the points for the running averages are always below the curve where it is concave to the time axis and above where it is convex—that is to say, running averages represent a secular movement with a systematic error. On the other hand, if running averages are determined for a purely random series, they follow a more or less smooth curve which is oscillatory in form, even to the point of suggesting periodicity to the inexperienced eye. The analysis of a time series in terms of running averages cannot be tested by the methods of the analysis of variance, because the number of degrees of freedom associated with the averages is unknown and because of the systematic error mentioned above. Compared with all these objections, the fact that running averages cannot extend to the ends of the series is a difficulty of minor importance. Generally, running averages may be regarded as providing a rough but useful empirical description of a slow movement when the number of terms in each average is such that the average spans very little of that movement, and the movement is strong relative to the random fluctuations.

The representation of the movement of Fig. 11.5 by twelve-monthly running averages is equivalent to fitting a straight regression line to each sequence of twelve values and using the regression value at the centre as representing the instantaneous value of the slow movement at that point. More elaborate methods of " smoothing " have been developed that are extensions of this idea, and involve fitting running polynomials to sequences of values, the central value for each polynomial representing one point on the curve for the slow movement. An appropriate smoothing of this kind is free from the systematic error with which a running average represents a slow movement, but it is subject to the other limitations. These methods in effect involve taking running averages in which the values included in each average are given different weights. The running averages dealt with in this section may be described as *simple* or *unweighted* where a distinction must be made. Readers may learn more of these methods by referring to Whittaker and Robinson (1924), Rhodes (1921) and Macaulay (1931).

Periodic Movements

11.52. When a periodic movement is seasonal it is commonly represented by the values for the months (or weeks or quarters) of an average year, usually expressed as deviations from the grand average. The seasonal movement for the numbers of railway passenger journeys is represented to the right of the top half of Fig. 11.5. If there is a slow movement this will affect the apparent seasonal movement slightly, a downward trend like that shown in Fig. 11.5, for example, tending to depress the values for the later months in the season. If a set of running means or a curve is fitted to represent the slow movement, it is an easy refinement to calculate its effect on the seasonal movement, as shown in Fig. 11.5.

The above discussion has been in terms of monthly readings forming a seasonal pattern, but it applies equally wherever there is a periodic variation of known length covering a whole number of readings. If the pattern of variation within a period can be represented approximately by a smooth curve, a trigonometrical function may, if desired, be fitted.

Sometimes variation is known or suspected to be periodic, but the length of the period is unknown; then the length of the period can be determined by *periodogram analysis*. For example, test results similar to those in Fig. 11.5a may be available for a cotton yarn, and it may be impossible to decide by inspection whether the variation is periodic as in the bottom section, or oscillatory as in the top section ; and if it is periodic we may wish to know the length of period in order to say which of several rollers and pinions in the somewhat complicated spinning mechanism is responsible.

Periodogram analysis involves trying successively a number of lengths of period. If the trial length is the time covering u consecutive readings, the data are written down in rows of u, the $(u + 1)$th observation coming under the first, the $(u + 2)$th under the second, and so on. If the total number of observations in the series is not a multiple of u, the last few are temporarily discarded, so that all rows are complete. Then, provided there is no slow movement, the data may be regarded as in the single-factor form for the analysis of variance, and a correlation ratio may be calculated to express the strength of the periodic effect. This may be repeated for a whole series of values of u covering the possible periods, and a curve of the correlation ratio plotted against u is a *periodogram*. It is a detail whether the ordinates of the periodogram are the correlation ratio or its square ; in the classical, and in some ways preferable, form of periodogram a sin-cosine curve is fitted to the u values for each trial period and the amplitude of this is plotted against u. The procedure is elaborated so that the trial periods do not all cover a whole number of observations.

If the time series is made up of a periodic variation plus random deviations, the periodogram will rise to a peak at u equal to the period length, and to minor peaks at u equal to multiples of this length. Thus the period length can be determined. If there are several periods there will be as many peaks provided the series is long enough to resolve the periods. Random variations will make the outline of the periodogram somewhat irregular and will cause spurious peaks, and some work has been done on the testing of significances of peaks. The precision of the information given by a periodogram increases with the length of the series and with the amplitude of the periodic variation compared with the random variations. For further information on the method readers may consult Whittaker and Robinson (1924) and Brunt (1917). Periodogram analysis is exceedingly laborious, but it may be facilitated by an optical method described by Foster (1946).

Periodogram analysis is successful where a pronounced periodic variation is known to exist or where tentative conclusions reached with the aid of a periodogram can be checked by examining a mechanism, or in some such way. But when applied to data that are oscillatory but not strictly periodic, the periodogram has led to misleading conclusions. The study of oscillatory movements is therefore being elaborated along different lines.

Oscillatory Movements

11.53. Periodogram analysis has behind it the tacit assumption that the series is generated by some process analogous to a vibrating pendulum, the position of which, recorded at successive intervals of time much shorter than the period, would give a typical periodic time series. A random element would be superimposed if the position of the pendulum were observed with an appreciable error. Another type of generative process would be a pendulum that was subject to random displacements such as would occur if, before each reading, a pea of sufficient weight were shot at the pendulum. This gives rise to what is termed an *autoregressive series*. In its simplest form this is expressed by the equation

$$_t x = a. _{t-1}x + x' \quad . \quad . \quad . \quad . \quad (11.53)$$

where $_t x$ is the tth observation in the series, $_{t-1}x$ is the previous one, a is a constant and x' is a random deviation. In the general autoregressive series the tth value is related to the p previous values according to the equation

$$_tx = a._{t-1}x + b._{t-2}x + \ldots k._{t-p}x + x' \quad . \quad (11.53a)$$

Each term in an autoregressive series is thus determined by the few previous terms, with a random element superimposed. In general the tth value may be any function of the previous p values, but so far attention has been given only to linear functions. If we start with a random series and construct from it a series of running averages, this second series will be one type of autoregressive series.

Oscillatory series are investigated by calculating serial correlation coefficients. If there are N observations in a series and a correlation coefficient is calculated by regarding the first, second, $\ldots (N - p)$th values as one variate and the $(1 + p)$th, $(2 + p)$th, $\ldots N$th as the corresponding values of the other variate, the result is termed the *serial correlation coefficient of lag p*. The corresponding population value for an infinite series is the corresponding *auto-correlation coefficient.* When for any one series, serial correlation coefficients are systematically calculated for a range of lags, and the coefficient is plotted against the lag, the resulting diagram is termed the *correlogram* of the series. It gives a good deal of information about the series.

If the series is periodic with a period of u, the correlogram rises to peaks all of the same height at $p = u$, $p = 2u$, etc. ; the form of the correlogram is periodic without any damping. Autoregressive series give correlograms showing damped periodicities, the peaks being successively lower for the higher values of p. For an autoregressive series generated by a heavily damped vibratory process and for running averages of random observations the serial correlation coefficient is highest for $p = 1$ and falls rapidly to zero. The correlogram thus tells something of the mathematical form of the generative process underlying the series, and from it estimates can be made of the various constants involved. More research is necessary, however, before the use of the correlogram is fully understood and can be used with confidence. The experimental correlograms for artificially constructed series of limited length do not behave as the theory for the corresponding infinite series suggests they should, and the effects of sampling errors have yet to be fully investigated.

At one time, the analysis of oscillatory movements was performed largely by means of the periodogram, and in fields where exact periodicity did not obtain, the work was reaching a " dead end." The concept of the autoregressive series and the application of the correlogram have opened up new lines of investigation that promise well, although for some time they are more suitable for the specialist than for the general statistician. Perhaps the chief danger to be avoided is the interpretation of all correlograms in terms of periodic or autoregressive series when the generative process may be something other.

For a fuller exposition of this subject and for comprehensive references to the literature, readers should see Kendall's (1946a and 1946b) books.

Random Variation

11.54. In the analysis of a complex series the random fluctuations are usually expressed as the deviations of the actual values from the values obtained by fitting equations representing the various movements. These deviations may, of course, be due to the unsuitability of the equations chosen to represent the movements or to wrongness of the assumption that they are independent and merely additive in their effects. The seasonal pattern, for example, could be different during a period of upward trend from what it was during a period of downward trend, and this change would give deviations that might be confused with the random variation. It is a good thing to plot the data so that any marked departure from randomness in the deviations can show itself. We have already decided, for example, that the deviations of the points from the lines in Fig. 11.41 are not noticeably systematic. If more stringent tests are required, the deviations can first be formed into a frequency distribution in order to see whether the variation is homogeneous and to identify and separate highly exceptional values ; and then some test for randomness of the order of the deviations can be imposed.

There are, as stated in section 2.13, many tests for randomness of order. If the first serial correlation coefficient does not differ significantly from zero there is not likely to be system in the order, but, if desired, greater stringency can be achieved by testing also the coefficient of lag 2. There is no readily available exact test of significance for these coefficients, particularly if the deviations are from values given by some fitted equation, but for a rough test on a long series the standard error of the first two serial correlations can be taken as equalling $1/\sqrt{(N-1)}$ where N is the number of terms in the series.

Another test involves transforming the series of values into a series of $+$ and $-$ signs, the $+$ or $-$ sign being written according as each value is followed immediately by a higher or lower value. Then a test is made of whether there is a greater tendency for the signs of the same kind to occur in runs than would be expected in a random sequence. This test is easy to apply if access is had to charts and tables given by Olmstead (1946).

Example

11.55. It is a good statistical exercise to analyse completely the data of Fig. 11.5 of the numbers of railway journeys, and this we shall now do in sufficient detail to enable readers to repeat the work.

We shall refer to the raw data as x; the figures are in Table 11.55. The first step is to represent the seasonal variation for an average year; the means for the twelve months are as follows and are plotted in Fig. 11.5 as the " crude season " :

$$3\cdot28, \ 2\cdot79, \ 2\cdot91, \ 3\cdot31, \ 3\cdot08, \ 3\cdot16,$$
$$3\cdot30, \ 3\cdot45, \ 3\cdot82, \ 2\cdot95, \ 2\cdot78, \ 2\cdot80.$$

There is, however, a general downward trend in x which has an effect on the above figures although it does not belong to the seasonal pattern proper, and for which a correction has to be made. For this purpose the approximate representation of the trend given by the twelve-monthly running means is sufficient. The first running mean is $3\cdot48$ and is associated with the interval between June and July 1944; as an approximation the six previous running means have been arbitrarily put equal to $3\cdot48$ (there is very little trend during the first half of 1944). Likewise the last running mean is $2\cdot72$, associated with June-July 1949, and the six subsequent means have been arbitrarily put equal to $2\cdot72$. For each year there are then thirteen running means, the first being for December of the previous year-January of the current year and the last being for December of the current

TABLE 11.55. PASSENGER JOURNEYS ON BRITISH RAILWAYS
[Millions per day (x), Deviations from Corrected Seasonal Means (x') and
Fitted Values to x' (X')]

Year and Month	x	x'	X'	Year and Month	x	x'	X'
1944				**1947**			
Jan. ...	3·70	+0·48	+0·39	Jan. ...	3·15	−0·07	−0·02
Feb. ...	3·21	+0·37	+0·37	Feb. ...	2·55	−0·19	−0·06
March	3·25	+0·38	+0·35	March	2·70	−0·17	−0·10
April ...	3·64	+0·36	+0·34	April ...	3·10	−0·18	−0·13
May ...	3·50	+0·44	+0·34	May ...	2·91	−0·15	−0·17
June ...	3·22	+0·07	+0·34	June ...	2·97	−0·18	−0·20
July ...	3·55	+0·24	+0·34	July ...	3·14	−0·17	−0·24
Aug. ...	3·90	+0·43	+0·35	Aug. ...	3·25	−0·22	−0·27
Sept. ...	4·03	+0·18	+0·36	Sept. ...	4·22	(−0·36)*	−0·30
Oct. ...	3·42	+0·43	+0·37	Oct. ...	2·48	−0·51	−0·33
Nov. ...	3·19	+0·36	+0·38	Nov. ...	2·44	−0·39	−0·35
Dec. ...	3·21	+0·35	+0·40	Dec. ...	2·66	−0·20	−0·38
1945				**1948**			
Jan. ...	3·55	+0·33	+0·41	Jan. ...	2·87	−0·35	−0·40
Feb. ...	3·20	+0·46	+0·42	Feb. ...	2·37	−0·37	−0·41
March	3·35	+0·48	+0·43	March	2·73	−0·14	−0·43
April ...	3·78	+0·50	+0·43	April ...	2·89	−0·39	−0·44
May ...	3·56	+0·50	+0·44	May ...	2·65	−0·41	−0·45
June ...	3·69	+0·54	+0·44	June ...	2·61	−0·54	−0·45
July ...	3·94	+0·63	+0·44	July ...	2·80	−0·51	−0·45
Aug. ...	4·00	+0·53	+0·44	Aug. ...	2·88	−0·59	−0·45
Sept. ...	4·11	+0·26	+0·43	Sept. ...	3·37	−0·48	−0·45
Oct. ...	3·51	+0·52	+0·42	Oct. ...	2·56	−0·43	−0·45
Nov. ...	3·24	+0·41	+0·41	Nov. ...	2·45	−0·38	−0·44
Dec. ...	3·14	+0·28	+0·39	Dec. ...	2·44	−0·42	−0·43
1946				**1949**			
Jan. ...	3·55	+0·33	+0·37	Jan. ...	2·85	−0·37	−0·42
Feb. ...	3·10	+0·36	+0·35	Feb. ...	2·31	−0·43	−0·42
March	3·03	+0·16	+0·33	March	2·40	−0·47	−0·41
April ...	3·62	+0·34	+0·30	April ...	2·85	−0·43	−0·40
May ...	3·29	+0·23	+0·27	May ...	2·57	−0·49	−0·39
June ...	3·70	+0·55	+0·24	June ...	2·79	−0·36	−0·39
July ...	3·43	+0·12	+0·21	July ...	2·95	−0·36	−0·39
Aug. ...	3·58	+0·11	+0·17	Aug. ...	3·07	−0·40	−0·40
Sept. ...	3·84	−0·01	+0·14	Sept. ...	3·37	−0·48	−0·40
Oct. ...	3·13	+0·14	+0·10	Oct. ...	2·60	−0·39	−0·42
Nov. ...	2·96	+0·13	+0·06	Nov. ...	2·38	−0·45	−0·45
Dec. ...	2·92	+0·06	+0·02	Dec. ...	2·46	−0·40	−0·47

* The actual value of x' is + 0·37. This is rejected as exceptional and − 0·36
is substituted for the purpose of computing X'.

year-January of the subsequent year. When these are summed for the six years the thirteen totals come to

$$19{\cdot}17, \ 19{\cdot}14, \ 19{\cdot}07, \ 19{\cdot}01, \ 18{\cdot}95, \ 18{\cdot}89, \ 18{\cdot}82,$$
$$18{\cdot}75, \ 18{\cdot}68, \ 18{\cdot}60, \ 18{\cdot}54, \ 18{\cdot}46, \ 18{\cdot}41.$$

The means between consecutive pairs are then taken as expressing the monthly values so that the mean for January is $(19{\cdot}17 + 19{\cdot}14)/24$. The twelve monthly means representing the effect of the trend on an average year are thus :

$$3{\cdot}19, \ 3{\cdot}18, \ 3{\cdot}17, \ 3{\cdot}16, \ 3{\cdot}15, \ 3{\cdot}14,$$
$$3{\cdot}13, \ 3{\cdot}12, \ 3{\cdot}11, \ 3{\cdot}10, \ 3{\cdot}08, \ 3{\cdot}07.$$

These values are plotted in Fig. 11.5.

A reasonable representation of this trend as monthly deviations from the annual mean, to two decimal places, is :

$$+ 0{\cdot}06, \ + 0{\cdot}05, \ + 0{\cdot}04, \ + 0{\cdot}03, \ + 0{\cdot}02, \ + 0{\cdot}01,$$
$$-0{\cdot}01, \ -0{\cdot}02, \ -0{\cdot}03, \ -0{\cdot}04, \ -0{\cdot}05, \ -0{\cdot}06.$$

When these are subtracted from the crude monthly means, the corrected seasonal effect is represented by the following means :

$$3{\cdot}22, \ 2{\cdot}74, \ 2{\cdot}87, \ 3{\cdot}28, \ 3{\cdot}06, \ 3{\cdot}15,$$
$$3{\cdot}31, \ 3{\cdot}47, \ 3{\cdot}85, \ 2{\cdot}99, \ 2{\cdot}83, \ 2{\cdot}86.$$

From each value of x is subtracted the corresponding monthly value to give the deviations x' of Table 11.55, representing the slow movements plus the random deviations. These are plotted in the lower part of Fig. 11.5.

Next we attempt to represent the slow movement so that the random fluctuations can be isolated. This could be done by using running means of, say, seven values of x'; there is no need to confine the number to twelve, since the seasonal variation has been eliminated, and an odd number makes it easy to centre each mean on a monthly value. However, inspection of Fig. 11.5 suggests that a polynomial equation should fit the values of x', and accordingly one has been determined.

Inspection of Fig. 11.5 also shows that although there are several fairly large deviations from the general movement, that for September 1947 is much larger than any other. Accordingly, as an act of judgment, this value has been regarded as exceptional and not belonging to the random deviations for the rest of the series ; and in calculating the equation it has been rejected. For convenience in computation another value has been substituted ; it is not necessary to choose this with elaborate care, and the mean of the preceding and succeeding values of x' has been used.

It is laborious and unnecessary to fit a polynomial equation to 72 values, so the number has been reduced to 36 by combining the values of x' in consecutive pairs, giving the sums $+ 0.85$, $+ 0.74$, $+ 0.51$, etc., which we shall term y ; and as a first step a polynomial equation has been fitted to these. This can be conveniently done by using the tables of multipliers for obtaining the orthogonal terms of a fifth order equation, given by Fisher and Yates in their Statistical Tables (1943). An extract of the table for a series of 36, with their original nomenclature,* is reproduced in Table 11.55a by permission of the authors and their publishers, Messrs. Oliver & Boyd Ltd.

TABLE 11.55a

No. in Series	ξ_1'	ξ_2'	ξ_3'	ξ_4'	ξ_5'
1	-35	$+595$	$-6\,545$	$+5\,236$	$-162\,316$
⋮	⋮	⋮	⋮	⋮	⋮
18	-1	-323	$+323$	$+2\,584$	$-12\,920$
19	$+1$	-323	-323	$+2\,584$	$+12\,920$
⋮	⋮	⋮	⋮	⋮	⋮
36	$+35$	$+595$	$+6\,545$	$+5\,236$	$+162\,316$
	λ_1 2	λ_2 3	λ_3 10/3	λ_4 7/24	λ_5 21/20
	$S(\xi_1'^2)$ 15 540	$S(\xi_2'^2)$ 3 011 652	$S(\xi_3'^2)$ 307 618 740	$S(\xi_4'^2)$ 191 407 216	$S(\xi_5'^2)$ 199 046 103 984

The values of ξ' are given in Fisher's and Yates's tables for only the second 18 terms. Term 36 is numerically the same as term 1, term 35 as term 2, and so on ; the corresponding terms in the two halves are of the same sign for ξ_2' and ξ_4' and of opposite sign for ξ_1', ξ_3' and ξ_5'. From these multipliers, the values of y, and the terms given at the foot of Table 11.55a, are computed :

$$B' = \frac{S(y\xi_1')}{S(\xi_1'^2)}, \qquad C' = \frac{S(y\xi_2')}{S(\xi_2'^2)}, \dots \quad F' = \frac{S(y\xi_5')}{S(\xi_5'^2)}.$$

* The symbols ξ and λ here have no connection with the meanings given to them hitherto in this book, and ξ in particular is in no way equivalent to x.

The quantities B, C, etc., of section 11.41 are given by the relations

$$B = B'/\lambda_1, \quad C = C'/\lambda_2, \text{ etc.,}$$

the λ's being those given in Table 11.55a. These ratios are introduced so that the tabulated values of ξ_1', etc., can be whole numbers. However, it is not necessary for our purpose to use the λ's, for the polynomial value is

$$Y = A + B'\xi_1' + C'\xi_2' + \ldots F'\xi_5',$$

where A is the mean, and the sum of squares associated with each term for the analysis of variance is :

$$B'S(y\xi_1'), \ C'S(y\xi_2'), \text{ etc.}$$

For computing the sums of products it is convenient to adopt the procedure of section 11.41, reducing the 36 terms to 18 by using $(_1y + _{36}y)$, $(_2y + _{35}y)$, etc., with the multipliers ξ_2' and ξ_4', and $(_1y - _{36}y)$, $(_2y - _{35}y)$, etc., with the multipliers for ξ_1', ξ_3' and ξ_5'. The results are :

$$
\begin{aligned}
S(y\xi_1') &= & -504\text{·}66, & \quad B' &= -0\text{·}032\ 475, \\
S(y\xi_2') &= & -263\text{·}76, & \quad C' &= -0\text{·}000\ 087\ 580, \\
S(y\xi_3') &= & +25\ 062\text{·}68, & \quad D' &= +0\text{·}000\ 081\ 473, \\
S(y\xi_4') &= & -340\text{·}90, & \quad E' &= -0\text{·}000\ 001\ 781\ 0, \\
S(y\xi_5') &= & -291\ 199\text{·}94, & \quad F' &= -0\text{·}000\ 001\ 463\ 0.
\end{aligned}
$$

In Table 11.55b we analyse the variance of y in order to decide whether five terms are necessary.

The total sum of squares of deviations from the mean is 19·53, and this has been attributed to 30 degrees of freedom because, in effect, the 36 values have been measured as deviations from six bi-monthly means by the elimination of the seasonal effect. The effect of rejecting the one exceptional value is probably slight, but there is some doubt about the exact number of degrees of freedom. However, no reasonable adjustment of the degrees of freedom will alter the clear conclusion that the first, third and fifth order terms are significant, and that the second and fourth are not—although we shall use them in calculating Y. Table 11.55b does not show that the five terms are enough, but it would be very laborious to go further, and if a fifth order equation does not fit a series of 36 values, the polynomial form is probably unsuitable. We shall therefore proceed with the fifth order equation.

The values of Y are readily computed from the values of A, B', C', etc., and the terms ξ_1', ξ_2', etc. The first five values are :

$$+ 0\cdot760, + 0\cdot687, + 0\cdot672, + 0\cdot688, + 0\cdot729.$$

The division of each of these into two parts to give the 72 values of X', the fitted monthly values, has been done in the following way. The differences between the first and second, and the second and third of the above values of Y are 0·073 and 0·015 ;

TABLE 11.55*b*

ANALYSIS OF VARIANCE y

Source of Variation	Degrees of Freedom	Variance
First order ...	I	16·39
Second order ...	I	0·02
Third order ...	I	2·04
Fourth order ...	I	0·000 6
Fifth order ...	I	0·43
Residual	25(?)	0·026(?)
Total ...	30(?)	—

the average of these, viz. 0·044, is taken as the rate of change of Y per double unit of time at the value of 0·687, and one-quarter of this, viz. 0·011, as the rate of change of X' per single unit of time. From this and the knowledge that the two values of X' add up to 0·687 it is easy to see that they are 0·349 and 0·338. In this way, all values of X' except the four at the ends have been computed to three decimal places, and the results to two places are in Table 11.55 ; they are plotted as the smooth curve in Fig. 11.5. The end values were computed by extrapolating with the same slope as that obtaining near the ends.

The fitted curve in Fig. 11.5 goes well through the actual values of x' ; it does not differ much from the slow movement represented by the running means in the upper part of the diagram. The curl in the curve at the beginning of 1944 and in 1949 should not be taken seriously. A polynomial of the fifth order is necessary to represent the very little change during 1944 and 1945 and during 1948 and 1949, together with the rapid fall during 1946 and 1947 ; and such a polynomial cannot do this without curling at the ends.

The deviations of x' from the curve do not appear to be quite random. Thus there is a sequence of seven positive deviations between February and August 1945 and of six between December 1947 and May 1948 ; there are also several shorter sequences of negative deviations. It is unlikely that purely random deviations would give so many and such long sequences in a series of 72 values. The series has been reduced to two series of 44 and 27 terms respectively by omitting the value of $(x' - X')$ for September 1947, and the first two serial correlation coefficients have been calculated. The two series were made into circuits by joining the first reading in each to the last, so that there were 71 pairs of values for each correlation coefficient. The two coefficients are $+$ 0·01 and $-$ 0·03 and are negligibly small ; so the sequences of positive and negative deviations have a negligibly small effect on the variation $(x' - X')$.

The values of $(x' - X')$ are plotted for the twelve months of an average year in the bottom right-hand corner of Fig. 11.5. The variation differs for the months, but not seriously (its significance could be tested by the method of section 5.5 if desired), except for the month of September, which contains the exceptional value.

Thus, the fitted values of X' represent the slow movements well, although probably not perfectly ; but the systematic deviations of x' are negligible in extent compared with the random deviations, and for the purpose of making approximate predictions $(x' - X')$ may be regarded as substantially a random variate.

The frequency distribution of $x' - X'$ is in Table 11.55c ; the one exceptional value is very apparent. This value has affected all the September values of x' (and to a very much lesser extent, X'), so that for calculating the standard deviation of $(x' - X')$ it will be well to omit the September values. The sum of squares of the 66 deviations of $(x' - X')$ from their mean is 0·581 2. The degrees of freedom cannot be stated with certainty, but it will be reasonable to take them as $66 - 11 - 6 = 49$ (11 being allowed for the 11 monthly means from which x' is measured, and six for the additional constants of the fitted polynomial equation). The variance is thus 0·011 86 and the standard deviation is 0·109 millions of passengers per day. It is against these that the significance of the corrected seasonal variations can be tested. Thus, the standard error of the difference between two monthly means (there are six years) is 0·109 $\times \sqrt{2}/\sqrt{6} = 0.063$; the difference between November and December is $2 \cdot 86 - 2 \cdot 83 =$ $0 \cdot 03$ and that between May and June is $3 \cdot 15 - 3 \cdot 06 = 0 \cdot 09$; these are not significant. All the other differences between consecutive monthly means in the corrected seasonal pattern are greater than twice the standard error, and thus probably signify true seasonal changes.

We see from Table 11.55 that by rough extrapolation the value of X' for January 1950 is $- 0 \cdot 49$, the corrected seasonal value is

TABLE 11.55c

$x' - X'$ Central Value	Frequency
$- 0 \cdot 25$	1
$- 0 \cdot 20$	2
$- 0 \cdot 15$	5
$- 0 \cdot 10$	7
$- 0 \cdot 05$	12
0	12
$0 \cdot 05$	22
$0 \cdot 10$	7
$0 \cdot 15$	—
$0 \cdot 20$	1
$0 \cdot 25$	1
$0 \cdot 30$	1
$\vdots$	$\vdots$
$0 \cdot 65$	1
Total	72

$3 \cdot 22$, so that the " predicted " value for January 1950 is $2 \cdot 73$, with a standard error of something greater than $0 \cdot 109$ (allowing for the fact that X' is subject to a sampling error). Only if the actual value comes well outside the limits $2 \cdot 73 \pm 2 \times 0 \cdot 109$, i.e. well outside the limits $2 \cdot 51 - 2 \cdot 95$, would it be taken as suggesting that some new conditions had set in or some exceptional event had happened (the actual value, noted after the above calculations were made, is $2 \cdot 86$). It is not safe, of course, to carry this kind of extrapolation very far.

Discussion

11.56. All statistical analysis requires to be done with judgment and in the light of knowledge of the field of investigation additional to that given by the data, but this is specially true of the analysis of time series. The subject has not developed so far as to give a body of standard methods that can be uncritically applied in a wide variety of situations : indeed most time series are not the result of experiments but concern naturally occurring phenomena, and the mathematical models used in the analysis are often too simple to fit the real world closely.

As an aid to judgment it is always a good thing to plot the data graphically and to train the eye to detect the forms of variation present and to assist in deciding whether the chosen form of representation is adequate.

A time series may be analysed in order to arrive at an empirical description or to provide a basis for short-period predictions. Commonly monthly and quarterly figures of economic quantities are corrected for the seasonal effect so that changes in trend can be more easily discerned. For example, the British railway authorities, anxiously looking for an improvement in the trend of passenger traffic after the end of 1949, might correct each monthly average for the seasonal effect as measured in the previous section as it becomes available, and compare the corrected result with the value given by an extrapolation of the slow movement, any deviation being assessed for significance against the random deviations. This procedure differs only slightly from that adopted at the end of the previous section. The process is, of course, subject to the dangers associated with any extrapolation, and caution must be exercised in making interpretations.

Much analysis of time series, particularly series of economic data, has apparently been done with the hope of learning something of the causes underlying the variations, and much of it has served only to increase knowledge and experience of the mathematical methods involved. There is little profit and some danger in investigating causes by applying to actual situations mathematical models chosen arbitrarily or from only superficial knowledge. Progress is only likely where the statistical analysis is guided by good qualitative knowledge of the causal system underlying the phenomena studied, and is required only to test hypotheses suggested by that knowledge or to provide estimates of parameters in equations describing those hypotheses.

CHAPTER XII

PROBLEMS OF PRACTICAL APPLICATION

In the foregoing chapters we have taken the numerical data as given : as satisfying various assumptions and as already in a form suitable for some standard type of statistical analysis. In this chapter we deal largely with the more practical problems of how to obtain the data in this state. There is a good deal in these problems that is special to the field of inquiry and cannot be dealt with here, but there are also a number of general questions which we consider.

Choice of Variate : Transformations

12.1. Any measured phenomenon can be expressed in a very large number of ways. For example, we may measure electrical resistivity or conductivity, density or specific volume ; and we may use as measures a variety of mathematical functions of these —logarithms, powers, and so on. Which is the best measure to use for statistical analysis ? From the point of view of the general theory of measurement, if x is a satisfactory measure, any function of x,

$$u = f(x)$$

is also a satisfactory measure provided $f(x)$ satisfies certain conditions, the condition most necessary to stress being that over the range of variation there shall be only one value of u for each value of x and vice versa ($u = x^2$ would not be a satisfactory function if there were positive and negative values of x). If the function is linear, u and x are exactly equivalent for the purposes of statistical analysis, and such a transformation is purely a matter of computing convenience. Sometimes, however, it is desirable to make other transformations of the raw data before the statistical analysis is attempted. General reasons are given in the following paragraphs.

In the analysis of variance all the effects are expressed by adding deviations to the various means, as for example in separating out the treatment and loom effects in Tables 7.2 and 7.2a. There is a suspicion, however, that the treatment effect is greater on the looms with the higher warp breakage rates ; for example, breakage rates for treatments (i) and (iv), yarn X are respectively 2·4 and 1·4 on loom 7 and 8·8 and 2·6 on loom 9. This would show as an interaction were it possible to separate the interaction variance from the error in the residual. Were the effect of any change of treatment on the average proportional to the warp breakage rate before the change, the use of the logarithm of the warp breakage rate would destroy the interaction between treatments and looms and an analysis in terms of the logarithms of the warp breakage rates would be statistically simpler and easier to interpret—although whether the interpretation in technical terms would be as easy or easier is another matter.

Most statistical analysis is based on the assumption of normality, and when x is far from normal a suitable transformation will sometimes give a substantially normal distribution for u. Seldom, if ever, is a transformation made for this purpose when the number of observations is small, for the form of the distribution is then difficult to determine, and the various tests of significance are not much affected by quite large departures from normality. But when the number of observations is large and the form of the distribution is determinable, a transformation to give normality is sometimes made. The normal distribution is very common, and one feels intuitively that a quantity distributed normally is more fundamental and satisfying ; moreover, it is an undoubted statistical convenience that the mean and standard deviation are sufficient to describe the distribution.

A transformation is sometimes made in order to turn a non-linear regression between two variates into a linear regression. For example, in biological assay the efficacy of, say, an insecticide, at various concentrations or in various doses, is observed as the proportion of experimental insects that survive the dosage. For statistical analysis, the dosage, in physical terms such as grams per litre, is transformed to the logarithm dosage, and the proportion of survivors to the *probit*. In arriving at the probit the resistance to the insecticide is imagined to be a quantity that, for different insects, is distributed normally, and the probit is the value on this normal scale that would give the observed proportion of survivors. Conventionally the probit scale is chosen to have a mean of 5·0 and a standard deviation of unity, so that the probit corresponding to 75 per cent. of survivors is 5·674 (see Table 2.52) and that corresponding to 16 per cent. is 4·0. The mean is made equal to 5·0, so that practically all probit values are positive. The regression of the probit value on logarithm dosage is usually linear, but the analysis is complicated by the fact that the error with which the probit is determined is not constant throughout the range.

There is no well-developed systematic way of arriving at transformations for these three purposes. Technical knowledge may suggest a suitable transformation, a general knowledge of the graphical forms of mathematical functions is a help, but there is usually a substantial element of " trial and error " in the process. Usually, a transformation will have little effect if the range of variation of the variate is small compared with the deviation of its average from the origin, for over small ranges $u = f(x)$ does not usually depart far from the straight line law, and a substantially linear transformation merely changes the scale.

A fourth purpose in making transformations, for which systems have been somewhat more highly developed, is to make residual variances homogeneous for the analysis of variance and related methods. For example, it is shown in section 2.4 that warp breaks in weaving successive lengths of cloth can be distributed according to the Poisson law, and when this is so the variance is proportional to the mean. A considerable investigation has shown that although the Poisson law does not always describe variations in warp breaks exactly, the variance usually tends to increase with the mean, almost in proportion. Hence, the error variance for the treatments and looms in Table 7.2 giving high breakage rates is greater than that for the treatments and looms giving low breakage rates ; and the full analysis of variance is invalidated. The conclusion from Table 7.2a that there are real effects is not falsified, for had the data been compatible with the hypothesis that there were no real differences between looms, treatments and periods, the error variance would have been homogeneous. But because of the heterogeneity of the residual variance, we cannot be sure that the loom and treatment effects are both real. For example, the loom effect might be real and the apparent treatment effect be due to the heterogeneity of variance. If the transformation $u = \sqrt{}$(warp breakage rate) is used, the variance of u is substantially homogeneous. The " yarn breakages " referred to in the example at the end of section 5.5 are in fact breakage rates so transformed.

The square root transformation may be derived in the following way. By applying the argument of section 4.15 we find that the error variance V_u in terms of the error variance V_x is given by the equation

$$V_u = \left(\frac{du}{dx}\right)^2 V_x.$$

If V_x is proportional to x, as it is when the sampling distribution of x follows the Poisson law or is proportional to such a quantity, and we wish V_u to be constant, we have

$$du \propto \frac{dx}{\sqrt{x}}$$

and on integration this gives

$$\mu \propto \sqrt{x}.$$

Since the choice of any particular constant of proportionality merely alters the scale of u, we may replace the $\propto$ by an $=$ sign. This derivation merely suggests a suitable transformation; the constancy of V_u for different values of u requires to be demonstrated. This has been done by Bartlett (1947). If x is a count distributed according to the Poisson law, and the transformation $u = \sqrt{(x + \frac{1}{2})}$ is used, the $\frac{1}{2}$ being analogous to Yates's correction for continuity (see section 4.31), V_u approaches 0·25 for large values of x and is 0·214 for $x = 2·0$; for values of x smaller than this V_u becomes much smaller.

If x is a ratio whose sampling distribution is described by the binomial distribution,

$$V_x \propto x(1 - x),$$

and the above procedure leads to the transformation

$$u = \sin^{-1} \sqrt{x}.$$

Tables for facilitating the use of this are given by Fisher and Yates (1943). Experimenters have found a number of other transformations useful for equalising the error variance in various circumstances.

If a transformed variate u having convenient statistical properties can be substituted for x in the technical arguments from the results and in their applications, there is everything to be said for making the transformation. But otherwise the situation can become obscure. Suppose, for example, as suggested in the second paragraph of this section, that there is an interaction between treatments and looms when the measure is warp breakage rate and that the interaction disappears for the logarithm of the warp breakage rate. It requires some clear thinking to decide what this signifies technically ; and the situation becomes somewhat obscure when, as so often happens, the effects are not overwhelmingly significant, and it is remembered that a verdict "no significant interaction" is not equivalent to "no inter-action." If the technical interpretation has to be in terms of the untransformed variate x, and after the statistical analysis has been performed on u, means and so on have to be converted back to x, statistical difficulties arise and the waters deepen. Readers are advised not to make transformations on statistical grounds alone unless they are good swimmers and have experience of the currents.

A good survey of the subject of transformations and a bibliography of papers are given by Bartlett (1947).

Differences and Ratios

12.11. The problem of choice of variate arises when it is required to express one quantity relative to another. In Table 5.2 the effect of the electrical current on the growth of seedlings is expressed as the *difference* between the treated and untreated seedlings. In the analysis of time series in sections 11.5 and 11.55 we have expressed the components as deviations, whereas economists usually express the seasonal and other values as *ratios* of the corresponding secular values. Often the question arises : shall we take differences, or ratios, or some other function ?

If the differences are small compared with the basic values and the ratios are near to 1·0 (say between 0·8 and 1·2), it does not usually matter much which measure is chosen. If the two sets of results are available for some constant conditions so that the variations are random, guidance can be obtained by plotting them on a scatter diagram. For example, in Table XXXIII of my *Technological Applications of Statistics* are given figures of the resistance to air flow of forty handfuls of cotton, together with corresponding control values ; these are plotted in Fig. 12.11. The points are scattered about a straight line parallel to the *resistance=control* line and the scatter about the line is substantially the same for the small as for the large values ; the difference is the appropriate measure. Had the points been scattered about a straight line with another slope, the degree of scatter being uniform, a linear regression equation would have been a good expression of the relationship, and the analysis of co-variance would have been a useful tool to use. Had the points been scattered about a line of

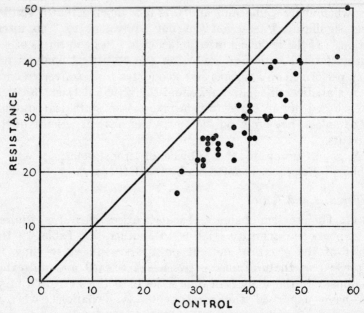

Fig. 12.11. Resistance to air-flow of experimental and corresponding control handfuls of cotton fibre.

any slope going through the origin, the degree of scatter increasing in proportion to the distance from the origin, the ratio would have been the appropriate measure, or alternatively, the difference between the logarithms of the values. Other relationships require other, probably more complicated, measures.

For most practical purposes, visual inspection of a diagram like Fig. 12.11 is sufficient, but the chosen relationship can usually be tested statistically if desired. Mostly, investigators are prepared to assume the appropriateness of some measure without examining the data, using general knowledge of the kind of measure that is likely to be appropriate. Sometimes examination of the data is complicated. Thus, had the data of Fig. 12.11 been for, say, two or three sets of conditions, the points would have been scattered about two or three lines, but they would be separable and the form of scatter about them recognisable. With many sets of conditions and, say, two or three points per set, or with a time series, some different method of examining the data may have to be devised, or the choice of measure may have to be made on *a priori* grounds.

SAMPLING

12.2. The theory of inference from samples given in earlier chapters assumes the existence of a sample satisfying the conditions of randomness described in section 2.13. In the following sections we shall deal with first the practical problem of obtaining a random sample, and then with the more complex samples that often arise.

Simple Random Sampling

12.21. Before attempting to draw a sample it is necessary to be clear about the population that is to be sampled : whether it is all the people of a country or only a section ; whether the fields of a country or a county ; whether one delivery of a manufacturer's products or the whole of his manufactures for an extended period. It is obvious that the sample can be representative of the population only if all parts of the population have a chance of being included.

The population must be divided into individuals, the selection of which form the *sample units*, whose standard deviation and number enter into the formulæ for the standard errors. These may be the natural units of the material, such as boys or girls, or natural complexes such as families ; or they may be more artificial sub-divisions of a population, as when a land area is divided into regions for sampling, or a bale of cotton fibres is, in imagination, divided into tufts for sampling purposes. A sampling unit consisting of a complex of natural units is sometimes termed a cluster. Sometimes the material is continuous, but it must be sampled in units as when a number of small " increments " or " specimens " of a powder or molten steel or a liquid factory effluent are taken. The population is not necessarily divided into the units in fact, but the sample must be, and each unit must yield a separate result so that the error variance on standard error can be estimated.

Every unit in the population must have an equal and independent chance of being included in the sample, and as a consequence there must be no bias. This is achieved by paying attention to the definition of the sampling units and the method of selection.

When the units are things indistinguishable from each other in size, shape, density, colour or feel, and are well mixed, there is little difficulty in drawing a random sample ; physically they are like the balls in an urn. This situation is comparatively rare, although it obtains substantially in the sampling of some manufactured articles. When the units are distinguishable to the senses or are distributed in space or time according to some pattern, it is virtually impossible to make a random selection without the aid of some special randomising procedure. He is a rare human being who can behave randomly.

The most common procedure is to have the individuals in the population arranged in some order or pattern termed the *frame*, and to make a random selection of positions in the frame. This can conveniently be done with the aid of random numbers. Thus, the adults in a certain area may be listed in a voters' register, and each individual may be drawn by selecting at random, first a section of the register, then a page in the section, and finally a name from the page. For a simple sample and procedure, each section and page would require to have the same number of names. Likewise, growing wheat plants may be sampled by selecting at random rows in the plot, then sections of the rows, and finally individual plants from the sections. A sample of anything varying continuously in time can be taken in the same way. Suppose, for example, twenty-four readings of the voltage of the public electrical supply are required in order to estimate the mean voltage for one day. A particular hour may be chosen by selecting at random one of the numbers 1-24, then a particular minute in that hour by choosing one of the numbers 1-60, and finally a particular second in that minute ; this can be repeated independently twenty-four times, and the readings be taken at the twenty-four seconds thus chosen—it would not be worth while attempting to localise a reading more closely than to one second. Strictly these times of the readings should not be identified by an electrical clock worked from the same mains.

The characteristic of this sampling method is that the random selection secures a random sample whatever the pattern of variation in the frame of the population. If the pattern is weak or non-existent so that the variation is substantially random as in the middle section of Fig. 2.13, the selection may be according to any pattern. For example, a 1 per cent. sample of people is sometimes taken by selecting every hundredth name from a list in alphabetical order. But there is danger in adopting this procedure, for there may be an unsuspected pattern in the frame. Patterned selections from a patterned frame produce *systematic* samples, which have their place in sampling methods, but they should not be treated as simple random samples.

The single value which each sample unit yields may be obtained in a number of ways. The whole unit may be measured or tested as when it is a simple natural unit such as a man, or only a part. The part may be a sub-sample taken either at random or systematically. If the units are bins of manufactured articles, each bin may be characterised by the mean value for, say, ten articles taken at random. If the units are rolls of wire, each may be characterised by the result of measuring a piece taken from the outside end, although a correction may be necessary for bias (see next section). A 100-yard length of fabric, as a sample unit, may be characterised by the mean of measurements made on, say, four specimens systematically disposed across the width and along the length so as to include representative portions of warp and weft. In obtaining the readings of electrical voltage mentioned above, we may take as a sample unit twenty-four readings, spaced at intervals of exactly one hour and starting at a randomly chosen second in the first hour of the day. If two such sets of twenty-four readings are taken each day, starting at independently chosen seconds, perhaps the 73rd and the 2 963rd on one day, the 785th and the 1 797th on another, and so on, each pair of means constitutes two independent estimates of the daily mean, and the sampling variance can be estimated by pooling the results for many days, each day contributing one degree of freedom. Each set of twenty-four readings is a sample unit and the sample for each day contains two units.

Indeed, in routine testing and investigation generally, where the same kinds of determinations are being made on many successive batches of the same kinds of materials, it is a good plan to adopt a well-standardised sampling and testing procedure (the sampling can often be systematic with advantage), to make duplicate determinations for each batch, and from many pairs of readings to obtain a pooled estimate of the composite standard error due to sampling variations and testing errors. For such an estimate to be valid it is only necessary, (a) that the duplicates are quite independent and repeat the procedure *ab initio*, and (b) that the error variance is homogeneous. The only kind of error that this procedure does not take account of is bias. An example of the procedure is in section 5.1.

Treatment of Bias

12.22. The statistical meaning of bias is dealt with in section 2.13. In practice it usually arises because of the size of the individuals, because of their position, or because of " non-response " ; these three types will be dealt with in turn.

Most methods of selecting the natural units of a material that vary in size are sensitive to size. Thus, if cotton fibres are selected singly there is a tendency to take too many long ones ; and in selecting lumps of coal it is difficult to avoid taking too many large, or small, or " average " ones according as the selector tries to avoid bias by exercising personal judgment. If the population can be divided into units distributed in a frame, the method of the preceding section can be adopted and all is well ; but often this cannot be done—it is a superhuman task to specify a frame for the cotton fibres in a bale. One common procedure is to take as sample units aggregates that are large in linear dimensions compared with the natural units, so that there is substantially no bias for size. Thus, cotton fibres may be selected in sample units consisting of tufts, and small coal in shovelfuls.

When this is done the selected material may be too bulky for test and there arises the problem of reducing it without introducing bias. For cotton fibres this is done by dividing each tuft into halves and discarding one chosen, say, by a toss of a coin, further halving the reduced tufts, and proceeding in this way until the bulk is suitably reduced. If there are originally sixty-four tufts, there are sixty-four reduced tufts, and these form the sample units. As a matter of convenience these are in a certain laboratory combined to form two lots each of thirty-two tufts, so that for each cotton there are only two sample units per sample.

Bulk samples of coal are reduced by crushing the lumps and this, like any other bulk of particles or powder, can be reduced by successive halvings or quarterings.

Bias due to position can arise when the natural units are arranged according to a pattern, and some parts of the frame are more accessible than others. It is impracticable to take cotton from the middle of a bale in the warehouse, or sand from the bottom of a truck in a railway siding, or wire from the middle of a long roll. In such instances the only course is to make a preliminary study of the pattern of variation so that a correction can subsequently be made for bias.

Bias due to non-response occurs characteristically in social surveys. A sample of, say, houses has been planned on paper, but field-workers fail to obtain the information from some of them and the features that cause the missing houses to be missed may cause the remaining houses to be a biased sample of the whole. Missing data can occur in all types of investigation and neglect of them can lead to bias, which is not removed by the substitution of a second choice.

In some social surveys, houses that do not yield information on a first visit by a field-worker are visited a second and, if necessary, perhaps a third time. Then the results for houses giving information on the first, second, and third visits are analysed separately and, with a little extrapolation to cover the houses that resist even three visits, a reasonably reliable estimate of the effect of the non-response on the results is made.

Complex Random Samples

12.23. A random sample is complex when the sample units are clusters of the natural units of the population, and the whole is thought of in terms of the natural units.

Consider, for example, the data of Table 6.2 as representing a random sample of ovaries from an infinite population of shrubs. If we incorrectly regard the 1 000 ovaries as being independent and apply the simple theory, the standard deviation is estimated from the " totals " column of Table 6.2 and the standard error is estimated as

$$\pm \sqrt{\left(\frac{5\cdot385}{1\ 000}\right)} = \pm\ 0\cdot073\ 4.$$

This estimate is incorrect, because the ovaries are not independent;

each group of 100 comes from the same shrub. However, the ten shrubs are independent sample units and form a small random sample, and the standard error of the grand mean may be estimated from the shrub means. From Table 6.2a we calculate that the variance between shrub means after allowing for weighting is 2·614 92, and the standard error based on nine degrees of freedom is

$$\pm \sqrt{\left(\frac{2 \cdot 614\ 92}{10}\right)} = \pm\ 0 \cdot 511\ 4.$$

This estimate is correct, although subject to the limitations of a small sample, and is about seven times the incorrect estimate.

It may be seen how the difference arises by considering the fact that the standard error of the mean is made up of two parts, one due to the substantive variance between shrubs, σ_s^2, and the other due to the variance within a shrub, σ_r^2. If there are m shrubs and n ovaries per shrub, the first source of variation is represented by only m individuals, the second is represented by mn, and therefore the

$$standard\ error\ of\ mean = \sqrt{\left(\frac{\sigma_s^2}{m} + \frac{\sigma_r^2}{mn}\right)}. \quad . \quad (12.23)$$

and from equation (6.2a) we see that the best estimate of this is $\sqrt{(v_s/mn)}$. The simple theory assumes that both sources of variation are sampled independently mn times, and would require the ovaries to be taken one at a time from the population of shrubs, with either each ovary from a separate shrub, or with chance deciding whether some shrubs are represented more than once. Then we would have

$$standard\ error\ of\ mean = \sqrt{\left(\frac{\sigma_s^2 + \sigma_r^2}{mn}\right)}. \quad . \quad (12.23a)$$

If the estimates of σ_s^2 and σ_r^2 given in section 6.2 are substituted in (12.23a) the result differs only slightly from the first estimate of the standard error given in this section.

A sample like that of Table 6.2 is termed a *two-stage* sample, the first stage being the selection of the shrubs and the second the selection of the ovaries from the shrubs. There can be a long hierarchy of stages, e.g. shrubs, branches and ovaries, giving rise to *multi-stage* sampling. The standard error of the grand mean can easily be obtained from the means for the largest aggregates in the hierarchy, by treating these as sample units.

Economy in Two-Stage Sampling

12.24. It is useful to know the variability of the natural units within the units of the various stages of a multi-stage sample for the purpose of deciding the most economical distribution of observations. We shall deal here with the simpler case of two-stage sampling.

If we use the notation of the previous section and let the total number of observations, mn, be N, the standard error of the mean given by equation (12.23) reduces to

$$\sqrt{\left(\frac{n\sigma_s{}^2 + \sigma_r{}^2}{N}\right)}.$$

For a given number, N, this is least when n equals unity. That is to say, unless there are technical difficulties it is best to have as many sample units as there are individuals, selecting one independently from each unit.

Sometimes, however, it costs more to increase the number of units than to increase the number of observations within a unit, and then a different distribution is preferable. For example, Smith and Prentice (1929), in obtaining soil samples for counts of cysts, took a number of " borings " of soil and made several counts on each boring ; the boring took time, which had to be added to the time required to make the counts.

The cost may be measured in time or money. Generally let there be m sample units and n observations per unit, and let the cost of making an observation on an already selected sample unit be unity and the cost of selecting a sample unit be k. Then the total cost of the sample is

$$T = m(n + k) \quad . \quad . \quad . \quad . \quad (12.24)$$

and the sampling variance of the mean (the square of the standard error) is, by equation (12.23),

$$V = \frac{\sigma_s{}^2 + \sigma_r{}^2/n}{m} . \quad . \quad . \quad . \quad (12.24a)$$

The product of these two equations,

$$TV = (n + k)\,(\sigma_s{}^2 + \sigma_r{}^2/n), \quad . \quad . \quad (12.24b)$$

contains only constants of the population and the one variable n. In order to find the value of n that gives the minimum sampling variance for a given cost, we regard T as a constant and solve

z   353

$T(\partial V/\partial n) = (\partial T V/\partial n) = 0$ for n. In order to find the value of n that gives the minimum cost for a given sampling variance we regard V as a constant and solve $V(\partial T/\partial n) = (\partial T V/\partial n) = 0$. The result is the same whichever we do, and leads to the expression

$$n^2 = k\,\frac{\sigma_r^{\,2}}{\sigma_s^{\,2}}. \qquad . \quad . \quad . \quad . \quad . \quad (12.24c)$$

For the cyst counts on soil borings Smith and Prentice estimated σ_s and σ_r to be respectively 40·5 and 23·1 per cent. of the mean, and if we assume that it costs five times as much to make a boring as to take a count, we find from equation (12.24c) that $n = $ 1·3. Under such circumstances it is better to increase the number of borings than to make more than two counts on each one.

The foregoing is a simple example of the way in which principles of economy can be taken into account in designing sampling schemes.

Sampling from Limited Field

12.25. All sampling theory has so far been based on the assumption that the population is infinite. When the population is large compared with the sample, say more than ten times as large, the theory applies closely enough for all practical purposes ; and when the sampling is so done (say with the aid of random numbers) that the same individual in the population has a chance of being included at every draw and can appear in the sample more than once, the theory applies exactly. Readers are reminded that the mathematical meaning of the assumption is that the composition of the population remains unchanged as sampling proceeds. Thus, in sampling from the voters' register by the technique mentioned in section 12.21, the assumption applies even though there are, say, only thirty sections of the register and the final sample contains 1 000 individuals.

When, however, the sample is an appreciable fraction, say f, of the population, and each individual is removed from the population as it is drawn from the sample so that it can appear in the sample only once, the only adjustment that is necessary is to multiply the sampling variance for the mean, calculated according to the foregoing formulæ, by $(1 - f)$, and the standard error by $\sqrt{(1 - f)}$. It is satisfying to note that when $f = 1$ the standard error becomes zero.

For example, equation (12.23) gives the standard error with which the sample mean represents the mean for an infinite population of shrubs. If the m shrubs are a fraction f of a small plantation of shrubs, the standard error with which the sample mean represents the plantation mean becomes

$$\sqrt{\left(\frac{\sigma_s^2(\mathrm{I}-f)}{m}+\frac{\sigma_r^2}{mn}\right)}. \qquad . \quad . \quad . \quad (12.25)$$

If the substantive variances in this expression have to be estimated from the sample and the population of shrubs is infinite $(f \to 0)$, σ_s^2 is given by equations (6.2a); if there are only m shrubs so that $f = \mathrm{I}$, this value must be multiplied by $(m - \mathrm{I})/m$ because σ_s^2 is determined and not estimated. If f is some value between o and I, a multiplier something less than $(m - \mathrm{I})/m$ must presumably be employed—its value I do not know.

When the sample is complex and represents one stage of the population completely, a new possibility arises. We may illustrate this by further reference to the ovaries and shrubs of Table 6.2, and suppose that the ten shrubs are the complete population of shrubs. There are now two standard methods of sampling.

In the first, the method of unrestricted random sampling, ovaries are taken at random without any regard being paid to the shrub from which they come. This might be done by numbering the shrubs with the ten digits o to 9, selecting I ooo digits from a set of random numbers, and for each selected digit taking an ovary from the corresponding shrub. Then the number of ovaries from each shrub will not be the same, and shrub variations will contribute to the sampling errors. The " totals " column of Table 6.2 represents this population of indiscriminately mixed ovaries and the variance estimated from this leads to the standard error of the mean which has already been estimated as $\pm$ 0·073 4. The equation for this standard error is equation (12.23a), with the substantive variance σ_s^2 estimated according to equations (6.2a) and multiplied by $(m - \mathrm{I})/m$.

The second method of *stratified sampling* consists in dividing the population into a number of parts or strata, and taking a random sub-sample of individuals from each part, the number in each sub-sample not being left to chance but being usually proportional to the number of individuals in each part of the population. In our example the shrubs are the strata, and if we assume each shrub to contain substantially the same number of ovaries, Table 6.2 as it stands presents the results of a stratified sample. The shrub variations do not contribute to the sampling error, which is due entirely to the within-shrub variations and for a sample of N is $\sqrt{(\sigma_r^2/N)}$. This is obtained by putting $f = 1$ in equation (12.25). For our sample this comes to $\sqrt{(3.057/1\ 000)} = 0.055\ 3$. The relative efficiencies of the two methods may be expressed as 100 times the ratio of the two sampling variances, and for our example it is $100 \times 0.073\ 4^2/0.055\ 3^2 = 176$. In this example the random method requires 176 individuals to give the same precision as that given by 100 selected by the method of stratified sampling. Generally, the relative efficiency of the two methods is

$$100(\sigma_r^2 + \sigma_s^2)/\sigma_r^2 \text{ per cent.}$$

The art of designing a scheme for sampling in strata consists in arranging the strata so as to make σ_s^2 as large and σ_r^2 as small as possible. Technical knowledge helps in this, as do investigations of the pattern of variation by the analysis of variance. The analysis of variance also provides the data on which the advantage of the method can be estimated. At the worst, when $\sigma_s^2 = 0$, sampling in strata is no better than random sampling, but it is never worse. It should be noted that unless there are at least two randomly selected individuals from each stratum, σ_r^2 and hence the standard error of the sample cannot be estimated.

Very similar analytical methods to those just described can be used to investigate the relative advantage of a systematic and random sample such as those described above for observing electrical voltages. We may take the $24 \times 3\ 600$ seconds of a day as units and arrange the voltage readings in the two-factor basic form, analysing the variance into parts associated with : between hours of the day (23 degrees), between seconds of the hour (3 599 degrees) and a residual (82 777 degrees). In practice, the 3 600 seconds of each hour would be sampled by taking, say, sixty readings at intervals of one minute. Let the three substantive variances be σ_s^2, σ_t^2 and σ_r^2 respectively. Then if forty-eight readings are taken at random, the sampling variance is $(\sigma_s^2 + \sigma_t^2 + \sigma_r^2)/48$. If the systematic procedure described in section 12.21 is adopted, the hour-to-hour variation makes no contribution, there are only two representatives of the second-to-second variation within the hour, and there are forty-eight of the random variation, so that the sampling variation of the combined forty-eight readings is $(\sigma_t{}^2/2 + \sigma_r{}^2/48)$. The systematic procedure is unlikely to give greater precision than the other, but it is likely to be much more convenient administratively, and more economical on that account.

12.26. The foregoing sections give only an introduction to the subject of sampling, and deal with some of the simpler basic situations. In particular fields, especially in social and agricultural surveys, more complicated sample designs are used. We have assumed the sample units to be equal in size and statistical weight : that is not always so. We have assumed variances to be homogeneous : the more elaborate theory takes account of heterogeneity. We have dealt only with the estimation of the mean from samples : the same principles apply to the estimation of other statistical measures, although the theory of calculation has not been far advanced. Finally, the study of the costs of different types of sample has been considerably advanced in some fields. Readers who wish to study the subject further should refer to the books by Deming (1950) and Yates (1949). A good deal of the discussion of these sections is repeated with industrial examples in my book, Tippett (1950).

THE PRINCIPLES OF EXPERIMENTAL ARRANGEMENT

12.3. Statistics is a relatively new subject, the methods described in this book having been developed largely during the present century. Until about 1920 most experimentalists did their work without giving a thought to statistics. Then biologists and agriculturists, working with inherently variable material and under conditions in which precise experimental control was impossible, began to turn to statistics for help in making sense of the results. Gradually it became realised that statisticians have their limitations. They cannot make sense of results presented in any form whatever : the results must be in a form amenable to statistical analysis, and preferably should be in one of the standard forms for which the analytical procedure has been worked out. It was found, too, that some forms gave greater precision to the experimental comparisons than others, according to the circumstances. Thus the design of experiments came to be a function of the statistician, and it has developed into a considerable subject.

From the point of view of statistical theory it is closely parallel to the subject of sampling.

The conditions that are experimentally varied for the investigation are termed generally the experimental *treatments*. The field of investigation varies in an uncontrolled way—the plots of ground in an agricultural experiment vary in natural fertility, looms vary in their effects on warp breakage rates in weaving (see Tables 7.2 and 7.2a), and so on. Some of these variations can be made to affect all treatments equally, others cannot and must be treated as random variations. The arrangement of the experiment so that the uneliminated variations can be treated as random, i.e. the randomisation of the treatments, is an absolute necessity for making valid inferences ; the arrangement so as to eliminate the effects of some variations is a matter of expediency and economy.

Random Arrangement

12.31. Consider the arrangement of the four treatments for the weaving experiment of Table 7.2, and for simplicity suppose that there are four weaving units for each treatment and four looms (numbers 7, 8, 9 and 10) and one yarn. One loom can accommodate one unit at a time, and it is obviously convenient to have the looms working simultaneously for four periods. The framework for the experiment becomes like the upper part of Table 7.2 (with the body of the table left blank).

According to the simple random arrangement, the sixteen units (four for each treatment) would be distributed at random in this table ; the results would be in the single-factor basic form and the analysis would be into treatments (3 degrees) and error (12 degrees). Any loom and period differences would affect the comparisons between the treatments, but would do so in a random way, and the inference from the analysis of variance as to the significance of the treatments effect would be valid. If we regard the eight looms and periods of Table 7.2 as random samples of periods and looms in general, we may estimate the substantive variances from Table 7.43 ; the estimates are :

$$\text{periods} : (1 \cdot 725 - 0 \cdot 712)/4 = 0 \cdot 253,$$
$$\text{looms} : \quad (6 \cdot 127 - 0 \cdot 712)/4 = 1 \cdot 354, \text{ and}$$
$$\text{residual} : \qquad\qquad\qquad = 0 \cdot 712.$$

The period variance in Table 7.42 is not statistically significant, but for the purposes of this example we shall treat it as though it were. There would be no harm in doing this in practice, for the approximateness of the estimates would need to be borne in mind whatever the significances. The error variance for the random arrangement would be approximately $0.253 + 1.354 + 0.712 = 2.319$.

Randomised Blocks

12.32. Almost anyone with technical knowledge of weaving would expect the looms to differ in their tendency to cause warp breaks and would expect more precise comparisons if they could be made between four treatments woven on the same loom. This suggests dividing the sixteen weaving units into blocks of four, each block containing one of each treatment and being woven on one loom. In order to satisfy the essential principle of randomisation, it is necessary for the order in which the treatments are woven on each loom to be a random order. Such is an arrangement in *randomised blocks*. The data are in the two-factor basic form, the components of variance being treatments (3 degrees), looms (3 degrees) and error (9 degrees). The period and residual effects contribute to the error variance, which is thus approximately $0.253 + 0.712 = 0.965$. The reduction in error variance from 2.319 represents a considerable gain in precision from the adoption of the randomised block arrangement, the relative percentage efficiency being $231.9/0.965 = 240$. Against this must be set the fact that in an actual experiment the degrees of freedom on which the error variance is estimated are reduced from twelve to nine, and this has an effect on the test of significance.

Alternatively, the four blocks can be arranged to eliminate the period effect, but the error variance is then greater. It should be noted that for the randomised block arrangement there may be any number of treatments, but the number of replicates per treatment must equal the number of blocks.

A special case occurs when there are two treatments. Table 5.3 gives the results of an experiment in which the treatments are a " control " and the injection of insulin. The two sets of animals are different, so the arrangement is random and animal variations add to the error with which the difference due to treatments is estimated. For Table 5.2, on the other hand, the " treatments " (treated with electrical current and untreated) are performed on parallel pairs of boxes of seedlings, each pair thus forming a block. Variations between pairs add nothing to the errors with which the difference due to treatments is estimated, and the variations between the differences of Table 5.2 show only the within-pair variation.

For the case of two treatments the situation can be described in terms of the correlation coefficient. Let x_1' and x_2' be the two sets of results for the two treatments, measured as deviations from their respective means, and so arranged that each value of x_1' can be associated with one value of x_2'. Then on summing over all pairs we have

$$S(x_1' - x_2')^2 = S(x_1'^2) + S(x_2'^2) - 2S(x_1' x_2').$$

If the correlation coefficient between the members of the pairs is ρ, we have from equation (8.3)

$$S(x_1' x_2') = \rho\sqrt{(Sx_1'^2 \, Sx_2'^2)}.$$

On substituting this in the above equation, and taking means for an infinite population of pairs, we have

$$\sigma_{1-2}{}^2 = \sigma_1{}^2 + \sigma_2{}^2 - 2\rho\sigma_1 \sigma_2,$$

where σ_{1-2}, σ_1 and σ_2 are the standard deviations respectively of $(x_1' - x_2')$, x_1' and x_2'. If the pairs are independent, i.e. if the association in pairs is arbitrary and purely formal, $\rho = 0$ and the above equation leads straightforwardly to the ordinary formula for the standard error of the difference between the means of two independent samples. If ρ is positive, the standard error of the difference is reduced ; if ρ is negative, the standard error of the difference is increased.

Latin Square

12.33. Now let us return to the weaving experiment. The loom and period effects can both be eliminated from the experimental comparisons by adopting the Latin square arrangement exemplified in Table 7.2, analysed as shown in Table 7.2a. The error variance is now reduced to approximately 0·712 and the residual degrees of freedom in a 4×4 layout to 6. In this instance, the Latin square arrangement is probably not superior to the arrangement in randomised blocks with the loom effect eliminated, especially in view of the sometimes inconvenient limitation that for the Latin square the number of replicates per treatment must equal the number of treatments.

Randomisation, within the limits imposed by the arrangement, is as important as ever : for example, an arrangement with each treatment along a diagonal of the table might easily coincide with a pattern in the uncontrolled variation, and so invalidate the inference from the test of significance. If an experiment is done only occasionally, it is convenient to have one ticket for each treatment marked with the treatment number. The tickets are shuffled and drawn, and allocated to the places in the first column in the order in which they are drawn. This is repeated for the second and subsequent columns, except that each treatment as it is drawn is put into the highest vacant permissible position, having in mind the restriction that no treatment may occur twice in the same row. This procedure will usually allocate some of the treatments in later columns in forbidden positions, and some adjustment will then be necessary. This can usually be done without difficulty, and no special rules are in practice necessary to prevent departures from randomness. For example, in forming a particular 6×6 square the first four draws gave

$$
\begin{array}{cccc}
4 & 3 & 1 & 2 \\
5 & 2 & 4 & 1 \\
1 & 4 & 6 & 5 \\
6 & 1 & 5 & 4 \\
2 & 5 & 3 & 6 \\
3 & 6 & 2 & (3)
\end{array}
$$

The numbers in the last column were drawn in the order 2 4 1 5 6 3, but according to the rules of procedure they were entered in the order shown, the highest vacant permissible position for the 4, for example, being the fourth from the top. The 3 is in a forbidden position and may be exchanged with the 1, 5 or 4 ; let us exchange it with the nearest—the 4. Then, with the fifth draw the procedure gave

$$
\begin{array}{ccccc}
4 & 3 & 1 & 2 & 5 \\
5 & 2 & 4 & 1 & 3 \\
1 & 4 & 6 & 5 & 2 \\
6 & 1 & 5 & 3 & 4 \\
2 & 5 & 3 & 6 & 1 \\
3 & 6 & 2 & 4 & (6)
\end{array}
$$

The 6 in the last row may be exchanged with the 5 only, and then the square may be completed without further draws. The randomisation of a Latin square is equivalent to choosing one at random from all the possible Latin squares of the given size, and it is advisable to adopt this procedure when doing many experiments. Fisher and Yates (1943) give tables for facilitating this procedure.

The Græco-Latin square arrangement is not much used in experimentation.

12.34. The foregoing are the three simplest standard experimental arrangements, and owe their simplicity to the fact that the means measuring the various effects are orthogonal so that the effects are easily separable. They serve for a wide variety of circumstances, but have their limitations. When there are many treatments, very large randomised blocks or Latin squares are necessary, and these often lead to an unduly large error variance. In an agricultural field trial arranged in randomised blocks, for example, the smallness of the error variance depends on the relative uniformity of the plots within each block ; and the variation usually increases as the area covered by the block increases. In such circumstances the treatments can be divided into groups and a " control " run with each; or better, one of the incomplete forms mentioned in section 7.51 can be adopted.

There are many practical considerations that decide which of the many established forms of experimental arrangement should be adopted. The pattern of variation in the experimental material is one, and general technical knowledge and experience as well as statistical studies provide guidance. It will be noted that in this section we have obtained information from the results of an actual experiment ; it is not always necessary to do special exploratory trials. The development of sequential sampling (see section 3.5) encourages the hope that in time systematic procedures will be developed for doing experiments in stages, so that the arrangement at each stage is based on information gained at previous stages and the experiment can cease when sufficient precision is attained.

Important technical considerations that determine an arrangement are the extent to which the experimental material can be subdivided (there is, for example, an optimum size of field plot), and the practicability of switching the treatments about. In agricultural field trials one result only can be obtained each growing season, and the available trial ground has to be carefully set out to give the maximum of information each year. In many industrial investigations, experiments can follow each other in rapid succession, each can give guidance for later experiments, and it is advisable to work in a more " hand to mouth " manner. In some fields it is possible to handle many treatments at once, in others only a few. Some experimenters have a good knowledge and experience of the most elaborate statistical procedures and can consult specialists : these can advisedly use the most elaborate and efficient arrangements. Other experimenters not in this position will rightly sacrifice efficiency (in the narrow statistical sense) for simplicity ; it is important that the responsible experimenter should understand his results and that he should not take too much on faith. Administrative difficulties, the capability of field workers, and the vulnerability of the experiments to accidents are other considerations to be taken into account.

Attention is again called to the fundamental assumption of the additivity of effects and the homogeneity of the error variances that underly the analysis of variance, and hence affect the practical applicability of the associated arrangements.

The classical work on the subject of experimental design is by Fisher (1936a), and readers will find another, fairly general, treatment and a good bibliography by Cochran and Cox (1950). A shorter treatment for agriculturists is by Wishart (1940), and one for industrialists by Brownlee (1946). I have given some further examples taken from industry in my *Technological Applications of Statistics* (1950).

ABBREVIATED METHODS

12.4. Several "short-cut " statistical methods have been proposed from time to time ; some of them, such as the use of the mean range to estimate the standard deviation, have already been mentioned in this book. Mostly these methods are less efficient than the standard methods they purport to replace, in the sense that for a given number of observations they estimate the population value of some statistical measure with less precision and have less power to discriminate between hypotheses in tests of significance. This is not a serious objection when more observations are easily obtainable, and it ceases to be an objection if the abbreviated method requires data that are much easier and less costly to obtain than the standard method. A more serious objection often is that for occasional use time may be lost in looking up the abbreviated method, and it may be necessary to look up charts or tables that are available only in some journal inconveniently placed on a library shelf a few buildings away. Nevertheless situations tend to recur in which particular abbreviated methods are advantageous, and these methods come to be commonly used. Doubtless as time goes on other methods that now appear only in original papers in the journals will find their place in common practice. Accordingly, mention is here made of a few of the methods.

It is sometimes so much easier to " gauge " manufactured articles, i.e. to determine the fraction larger or smaller than certain limits of size, than to measure them, that it is more economical in effect to estimate the mean and standard deviation of the population from the proportionate frequencies between and beyond, say, two limits. The theory of this method of statistical control has been worked out by Stevens (1948).

The mean range is now well established for estimating the standard deviation of manufactured articles in routine production, as may be seen by reference to any book on industrial quality control. Lord (1947) has developed a modified form of the t test of significance in which the range is used in place of the standard deviation, and Link (1950) has proposed an equivalent to the F test based on the range.

Swed and Eisenhart (1943) have calculated tables for a short-cut substitute for the t test which only involves counting sequences of results belonging to the same series when all the results for the two series are placed in order of magnitude.

Olmstead's (1946) test for association in time series, already referred to in section 11.54, involves counting " runs up " and " runs down," i.e. sequences of consecutive results that are in order of increasing or decreasing magnitude. These tests both involve determining whether a sequence of equally likely alternatives departs from a random order. They are *non-parametric* tests in that they do not involve making estimates of any parameters of the frequency distribution of the population ; and they involve no assumptions as to the form of that distribution.

The estimation and the test of correlation from data in ranks has been dealt with in section 9.9. This method has been used as a short cut even when values of the variates are available ; see, for example, the paper by Wilcoxon. Olmstead and Tukey (1947) have proposed another extremely quick method of testing data for association. Good approximations to regression lines can be readily obtained by dividing the total range of variation of x into three broad sub-ranges, finding the means of x and y for the individuals in the extreme sub-ranges, and joining the two points so obtained ; see, for example, Bartlett (1949).

Readers interested in abbreviated methods may also refer to Mosteller (1946).

REFERENCES

ANSCOMBE, F. J. (1949). Tables of sequential inspection schemes to control fraction defective. *Jour. Roy. Stat. Soc.*, Series A, **112**, 180.

ASPIN, ALICE A. (1949). Tables for use in comparisons whose accuracy involves two variances, separately estimated. *Biometrika*, **36**, 290.

BARNARD, G. A. (1946). Sequential tests in industrial statistics. *Supp. Jour. Roy. Stat. Soc.*, **8**, 1.

BARNARD, M. M. (1935). The secular variations of skull characters in four series of Egyptian skulls. *Annals of Eugenics*, **6**, 352.

BARTLETT, M. S. (1937). Properties of sufficiency and statistical tests. *Proc. Roy. Soc.*, A, **160**, 268.

— (1947). The use of transformations. *Biometrics*, **3**, 39.

— (1949). Fitting a straight line when both variables are subject to error. *Biometrics*, **5**, 207.

BATESON, W. (1913). Mendel's Principles of Heredity. Cambridge University Press. 345.

BINNS, H. (1934). Psychological investigations of the influence of the various methods of manufacturing worsted yarns. *Jour. Text. Inst.*, **25**, T89.

BROSS, I. (1950). Fiducial intervals for variance components. *Biometrics*, **6**, 136.

BROWN, G. W. (1947). Discriminant functions. *Annals Math. Stats.*, **18**, 514.

BROWNLEE, K. A. (1946). Industrial Experimentation. (4th edition, 1949.) H.M. Stationery Office, London, and Chemical Publishing Co., Brooklyn.

BRUNT, D. (1917). The Combination of Observations. (2nd edition, 1931.) Cambridge University Press.

COCHRAN, W. G. (1936). Statistical analysis of field counts of diseased plants. *Supp. Jour. Roy. Stat. Soc.*, **3**, 49.

— (1942). The χ^2 correction for continuity. *Iowa State College Jour. of Sci.*, **16**, 421.

—, and COX, GERTRUDE M. (1950). Experimental Designs. Wiley, New York, and Chapman & Hall, London.

COLLINS, G. N., FLINT, L. H., and McLANE, J. W. (1929). Electric stimulation of plant growth. *Jour. Agri. Research*, **38**, 585.

COLUMBIA UNIVERSITY STATISTICAL RESEARCH GROUP (1948). Sampling Inspection. McGraw-Hill, New York and London.

CO-OPERATIVE STUDY (1923). On the nest and eggs of the Common Tern. *Biometrika*, **15**, 294.

CORKILL, B. (1930). The influence of insulin on the distribution of glycogen in normal animals. *Biochem. Jour.*, **24**, 779.

DANIELS, H. E. (1939). The estimation of components of variance. *Supp. Jour. Roy. Stat. Soc.*, **6**, 186.

REFERENCES

DARBISHIRE, A. D. (1904). On the result of crossing Japanese Waltzing with Albino mice. *Biometrika*, **3**, 1.

DAVID, F. N. (1938). Tables of the Ordinates and Probability Integral of the Distribution of the Correlation Coefficient in Small Samples. Biometrika Office, London.

DAVIES, O. L. (1947), Editor. Statistical Methods in Research and Production. (2nd edition, 1949.) Pub. for Imperial Chemical Industries Ltd. by Oliver & Boyd, London and Edinburgh.

DEMING, W. E. (1950). Some Theory of Sampling. Wiley, New York, and Chapman & Hall, London.

DODGE, H. F., and ROMIG, H. G. (1944). Sampling Inspection Tables. Wiley, New York, and Chapman & Hall, London.

DUDDING, B. P., and JENNETT, W. J. (1942). Quality Control Charts. British Standards Institution.

EDEN, T., and FISHER, R. A. (1927). The experimental determination of the value of top dressings with cereals. *Jour. Agri. Sci.*, **17**, 548.

EISENHART, C. (1939). The interpretation of certain regression methods and their use in biological and industrial research. *Annals Math. Stats.*, **10**, 162.

EZEKIEL, M. (1930). Methods of Correlation Analysis. (2nd edition, 1941.) Wiley, New York, and Chapman & Hall, London.

FINNEY, D. J. (1947a). Probit Analysis. Cambridge University Press.

— (1947b). The principles of biological assay. *Supp. Jour. Roy. Stat. Soc.*, **9**, 46.

FISHER, R. A. (1915). Frequency distribution of the values of the correlation coefficient in samples from an indefinitely large population. *Biometrika*, **10**, 507.

— (1921). On the " probable error " of a coefficient of correlation deduced from a small sample. *Metron*, **1**, No. 4.

— (1922a). On the mathematical foundations of statistics. *Phil. Trans. Roy. Soc.*, A, **222**, 309.

— (1922b). On the interpretation of χ^2 from contingency tables, and the calculation of P. *Jour. Roy. Stat. Soc.*, **85**, 87.

— (1924a). On a distribution yielding the error functions of several well-known statistics. *Proc. of the International Math. Congress, Toronto*, 805.

— (1924b). The distribution of the partial correlation coefficient. *Metron*, **3**, No. 3.

— (1925a). Theory of statistical estimation. *Proc. Camb. Phil. Soc.*, **22**, 700.

— (1925b). Applications of " Student's " distribution. *Metron*, **5**, No. 3.

— (1925c). Statistical Methods for Research Workers. (11th edition, 1950.) Oliver & Boyd, London and Edinburgh.

— (1928a). Triplet children in Great Britain and Ireland. *Proc. Roy. Soc.*, B, **102**, 286.

— (1928b). The general sampling distribution of the multiple correlation coefficient. *Proc. Roy. Soc.*, A, **121**, 654.

FISHER, R. A. (1930a). The moments of the distribution for normal samples of measures of departure from normality. *Proc. Roy. Soc.*, A, **130**, 16.

— (1930b). Inverse probability. *Proc. Camb. Phil. Soc.*, **26**, 528.

— (1935). The logic of inductive inference. *Jour. Roy. Stat. Soc.*, **98**, 39.

— (1936). The use of multiple measurements in taxonomic problems. *Annals of Eugenics*, **7**, 179.

— (1936a). The Design of Experiments. (6th edition, 1951.) Oliver and Boyd, London and Edinburgh.

— (1938). The statistical utilisation of multiple measurements. *Annals of Eugenics*, **8**, 376.

— (1940). The precision of discriminant functions. *Annals of Eugenics*, **10**, 422.

— (1941). The asymptotic approach to Behren's integral, with further tables for the *d* test of significance. *Annals of Eugenics*, **11**, 141.

— (1948). Combining independent tests of significance. *The American Statistician*, Volume **2**. October, p. 30. Washington, D.C.

—, and HOBLYN, T. N. (1928). Maximum- and minimum-correlation tables in comparative climatology. *Geografiska Annaler*, **3**, 267.

—, THORNTON, H. G., and MACKENZIE, W. A. (1922). The accuracy of the plating method of estimating the density of bacterial populations. *Annals of Appl. Biology*, **9**, 325.

—, and YATES, F. (1943). Statistical Tables for Biological, Agricultural and Medical Research. (3rd edition, 1948.) Oliver & Boyd, London and Edinburgh.

FOSTER, G. A. R. (1946). Some instruments for the analysis of time series and their applications to textile research. *Supp. Jour. Roy. Stat. Soc.*, **8**, 42.

FRY, T. C. (1928). Probability and its Engineering Uses. Macmillan, New York.

GLANVILLE, W. H., and REID, D. A. G. (1934). Mortar tests as a guide to the strength of concrete. *Structural Engineer*, **12**, 242.

GOULD, C. E., and HAMPTON, W. M. (1936). Statistical methods applied to the manufacture of spectacle glasses. *Supp. Jour. Roy. Stat. Soc.*, **3**, 137.

GOULDEN, C. H. (1939). Methods of Statistical Analysis. Wiley, New York.

HARMON, G. E. (1926). On the degree of relationship between head measurements and reaction time to sight and sound. *Biometrika*, **18**, 207.

HARRIS, J. A. (1910). On the selective elimination occurring during the development of the fruits of *Staphylea*. *Biometrika*, **7**, 452.

HARTLEY, H. O., and PEARSON, E. S. (1950). Table of the probability integral of the *t*-distribution. *Biometrika*, **37**, 168.

— — (1950a). Tables of the χ^2 integral and of the cumulative Poisson distribution. *Biometrika*, **37**, 313.

IRWIN, J. O. (1931). Mathematical theorems involved in the analysis of variance. *Jour. Roy. Stat. Soc.*, **94**, 284.

JEFFREYS, H. (1939). Theory of Probability. (2nd edition, 1948.) Clarendon Press, Oxford.

A2

369

REFERENCES

JONES, H. G. (1910) (data for a note by K. P.). On the value of the teachers' opinion of the general intelligence of school children. *Biometrika*, **7**, 542.

KENDALL, M. G. (1943). The Advanced Theory of Statistics, Vol. I. (4th edition, 1948.) Griffin, London.

— (1946a). The Advanced Theory of Statistics, Vol. II. (3rd edition, 1951.) Griffin, London.

— (1946b). Contributions to the Study of Oscillatory Time Series. Cambridge University Press.

— (1948). Rank Correlation Methods. Griffin, London.

—, and BABINGTON-SMITH, B. (1939). Random sampling numbers (2nd series.) *Tracts for Computers*, No. **24**. Cambridge University Press.

KOSHAL, R. S., and TURNER, A. J. (1930). Studies in the sampling of cotton for the determination of fibre-properties. *Jour. Text. Inst.*, **21**, T325.

LATTER, O. H. (1902). The egg of *Cuculus canorus*. *Biometrika*, **1**, 164.

LINK, R. F. (1950). The sampling distribution of the ratio of two ranges from independent samples. *Annals Math. Stats.*, **21**, 112.

LORD, E. (1947). The use of range in place of standard deviation in the *t* test. *Biometrika*, **34**, 41.

MACAULAY, F. R. (1931). The Smoothing of Time Series. Nat. Bur. of Econ. Research, New York.

MAHALANOBIS, P. C. (1932). Auxiliary tables for Fisher's *z*-test in analysis of variance. *Indian Jour. Agri. Sci.*, **2**, 679.

MERRINGTON, MAXINE, and THOMPSON, CATHERINE M. (1943). Tables of percentage points of the inverted beta (*F*) distribution. *Biometrika*, **33**, 73.

MINER, J. (1922). Tables of $\sqrt{(1 - r^2)}$ and $1 - r^2$ for Use in Partial Correlation and Trigonometry. John S. Hopkins Press, Baltimore.

MOLINA, E. C. (1943). Poisson's Exponential Binomial Limit. Van Nostrand, New York.

MORANT, G. (1921). On random occurrences in space and time when followed by a closed interval. *Biometrika*, **13**, 309.

MORTON, W. E. (1926). The importance of hair weight per centimetre as a measurable character of cotton and some indications of its practical utility. *Jour. Text. Inst.*, **17**, T537.

MOSTELLER, F. (1946). On some useful " inefficient " statistics. *Annals Math. Stats.*, **17**, 377.

MUMFORD, A. A., and YOUNG, M. (1923). The interrelationships of the physical measurements and the vital capacity. *Biometrika*, **15**, 109.

NATIONAL BUREAU OF STANDARDS (1949). Tables of the Binomial Probability Distribution. Superintendent of Documents, Washington, D.C.

NEWBOLD, E. M. (1926). A contribution to the study of the human factor in the causation of accidents. *Industrial Fatigue Research Board*, Report No. 34.

— (1927). Practical applications of the statistics of repeated events, particularly of industrial accidents. *Jour. Roy. Stat. Soc.*, **90**, 533.

NEYMAN, J. (1934). On the two different aspects of the representative method : the method of stratified sampling and the method of purposive selection. *Jour. Roy. Stat. Soc.*, **97**, 558.

— (1939). On a new class of " contagious " distributions applicable in entomology and bacteriology. *Annals Math. Stats.*, **10**, 35.

— (1942). Basic ideas and some recent results of the theory of testing statistical hypotheses. *Jour. Roy. Stat. Soc.*, **105**, 292.

—, and PEARSON, E. S. (1931). On the problem of k samples. *Bull. de l'Acad. Polonaise des Sci. et des Let.*, Série A, 460.

OLMSTEAD, P. S. (1946). Distribution of sample arrangements for runs up and down. *Annals. Math. Stats.*, **17**, 24.

—, and TUKEY, J. W. (1947). A corner test for association. *Annals Math. Stats.*, **18**, 495.

ORENSTEEN, M. M. (1920). Correlation of cephalic measurements in Egyptian born natives. *Biometrika*, **13**, 17.

PARKES, A. A., and DRUMMOND, J. C. (1925). The effect of vitamin B deficiency on reproduction. *Proc. Roy. Soc.*, B, **98**, 147.

PAULL, A. E. (1950). A preliminary test for pooling mean squares in the analysis of variance. *Annals Math. Stats.*, **21**, 539.

PEARL, R. (1907). Variation and Differentiation in *Ceratophyllum*. Carnegie Institution of Washington.

PEARSE, G. E. (1928). On corrections for the moment-coefficients of frequency distributions. *Biometrika*, **20**A, 314.

PEARSON, E. S. (1926). A further note on the distribution of range in samples taken from a normal population. *Biometrika*, **18**, 173.

— (1930). A further development of tests of normality. *Biometrika*, **22**, 239.

— (1932). The percentage limits for the distribution of range in samples from a normal population. *Biometrika*, **24**, 404.

— (1938). The probability integral transformation for testing goodness of fit and combining independent tests of significance. *Biometrika*, **30**, 134.

— (1942). The probability integral of the range in samples of n observations from a normal population. *Biometrika*, **32**, 301.

PEARSON, K. (1895). Skew variation in homogeneous material. *Phil. Trans. Roy. Soc.*, A, **186**, 343.

— (1900). On the criterion that a given system of deviations from the probable in the case of a correlated system of variables is such that it can be reasonably supposed to have arisen from random sampling. *Phil. Mag.*, Series V, **50**, 157.

— (1905). On the general theory of skew correlation and non-linear regression. *Drapers' Company Research Memoirs*, **2**.

— (1910). On a new method of determining correlation. *Biometrika*, **7**, 248.

— (1914) (Editor). Tables for Statisticians and Biometricians. Part I (3rd edition, 1931). Cambridge University Press. (See footnote to p.17.)

— (1920a). The fundamental problem of practical statistics. *Biometrika*, **13**, 1.

REFERENCES

PEARSON, K. (1920b). On the probable errors of frequency constants. *Biometrika*, **13**, 113.

—, and LEE, A. (1903). On the laws of inheritance in man. *Biometrika*, **2**, 357.

PRZYBOROWSKI, J., and WILEŃSKI, H. (1935). Statistical principles of routine work in testing clover seed for dodder. *Biometrika*, **27**, 273.

RHODES, E. C. (1921). Smoothing. *Tracts for Computers*, **6**. Cambridge University Press.

SMITH, A. M., and PRENTICE, E. G. (1929). Investigation on *Heterodera schachtii* in Lancashire and Cheshire. *Annals Applied Biology*, **16**, 324.

SNOW, E. C. (1911). On the determination of the chief correlations between collaterals in the case of a simple Mendelian population mating at random. *Proc. Roy. Soc.*, B, **83**, 37.

STEVENS, W. L. (1948). Control by gauging. *Jour. Roy. Stat. Soc.*, Series B, **10**, 54.

" STUDENT " (1907). On the error of counting with a hæmacytometer. *Biometrika*, **5**, 351.

— (1908). The probable error of a mean. *Biometrika*, **6**, 1.

— (1925). New tables for testing the significance of observations. *Metron*, **5**, No. 3, 18.

SWED, FRIEDA S., and EISENHART, C. (1943). Tables for testing randomness of grouping in a sequence of alternatives. *Annals Math. Stats.*, **14**, 66.

THOMPSON, CATHERINE M., and MERRINGTON, MAXINE (1946). Tables for testing the homogeneity of a set of estimated variances. *Biometrika*, **33**, 296.

TIPPETT, L. H. C. (1927). Random sampling numbers. *Tracts for Computers*, **15**. Cambridge University Press.

— (1934). Statistical methods in textile research ; uses of the binomial and Poisson distributions. *Shirley Inst. Mem.*, **13**. 35, or *Jour. Text. Inst.*, 1935, **26**, T13.

— (1950). Technological Applications of Statistics. Wiley, New York, and Williams & Norgate, London.

TOWER, W. L. (1902). Variation in the ray-flowers of *Chrysanthemum leucanthemum*. *Biometrika*, **1**, 309.

TSCHEPOURKOWSKY, E. (1905). Contributions to the study of interracial correlation. *Biometrika*, **4**, 286.

UNDERWOOD, C. (1935). The relationship between some properties of cotton hairs and the spinning quality of the cottons. *Shirley Inst. Mem.*, **14**, 1, or *Jour. Text. Inst.*, **26**, T309.

WALD, A. (1947). Sequential Analysis. Wiley, New York, and Chapman and Hall, London.

WARREN, E. (1909). Some statistical observations on Termites. *Biometrika*, **6**, 329.

WELCH, B. L. (1938). The significance of the difference between two means when the population variances are unequal. *Biometrika*, **29**, 350.

WELCH, B. L. (1947). The generalisation of Student's problem when several different population variances are involved. *Biometrika*, **34**, 28.

WELDON, W. F. R. (1901). Change in organic correlation of *Ficaria ranunculoides* during the flowering season. *Biometrika*, **1**, 125.

WHELDALE, M. (1907). The inheritance of flower colour in *Antirrhinum majus*. *Proc. Roy. Soc.*, B, **79**, 288.

WHITTAKER, E. T., and ROBINSON, G. (1924). The Calculus of Observations. Blackie, London.

WILCOXON, F. (undated). Some rapid approximate statistical procedures. American Cyanamid Company, New York.

WINTER, F. L. (1929). The mean and variability as affected by continuous selection for composition in corn. *Jour. Agri. Research*, **39**, 451.

WISHART, J. (1940). Field Trials ; their layout and statistical analysis. Imperial Bureau of Plant Breeding, Cambridge.

— (1950). Field Trials II : The analysis of covariance. Commonwealth Bureau of Plant Breeding and Genetics, Cambridge.

WOLD, H. (1949). Random Normal Deviates. *Tracts for Computers*, No. **25**. Cambridge University Press.

YATES, F. (1933). The analysis of replicated experiments when the field results are incomplete. *Empire Jour. Exp. Agri.*, **1**, 129.

— (1934). Contingency tables involving small numbers and the χ^2 test. *Supp. Jour. Roy. Stat. Soc.*, **1**, 217.

— (1936a). Incomplete Latin squares. *Jour. Agri. Sci.*, **26**, 301.

— (1936b). A new method of arranging variety trials involving a large number of experiments. *Jour. Agri. Sci.*, **26**, 424.

— (1936c). Incomplete randomised blocks. *Annals of Eugenics*, **7**, 121.

— (1937a). A further note on the arrangement of variety trials : quasi-Latin squares. *Annals of Eugenics*, **7**, 319.

— (1937b). The Design and Analysis of Factorial Experiments. Imperial Bureau of Soil Science, Harpenden.

— (1939). The recovery of inter-block information in variety trials arranged in three-dimensional lattices. *Annals of Eugenics*, **9**, 136.

— (1940). Lattice squares. *Jour. Agri. Sci.*, **30**, 672.

— (1949). Sampling Methods of Censuses and Surveys. Griffin, London.

—, and HALE, R. W. (1939). The analysis of Latin squares when two or more rows, columns, or treatments are missing. *Supp. Jour. Roy. Stat. Soc.*, **6**, 67.

YULE, G. U. (1927). An Introduction to the Theory of Statistics, 7th edition. (14th edition with M. G. KENDALL, 1950.) Griffin, London.

ZINN, J. (1923). Correlations between various characters of wheat and flour as determined from published data, etc. *Jour. Agri. Research*, **23**, 529.

INDEX

INDEX

INDEX

SIGNIFICANCE TABLES AND CHARTS

SIGNIFICANCE TABLES AND CHARTS

TABLE A

MEAN AND STANDARD DEVIATION OF
RANGE FOR SAMPLES FROM NORMAL
POPULATION WITH UNIT STANDARD
DEVIATION

Sample Size	Mean Range	Standard Deviation of Range
2	1·128	0·852
3	1·693	0·888
4	2·059	0·880
5	2·326	0·864
6	2·534	0·848
7	2·704	0·833
8	2·847	0·820
9	2·970	0·808
10	3·078	0·797
20	3·735	0·729
50	4·498	0·652
100	5·015	0·605

Taken, by permission, from a table by E. S. Pearson (1932), *Biometrika*, *24*, p. 416.

TABLE B

EXPONENTIAL DISTRIBUTION. VALUES OF $e^{-u/\bar{u}}$ FOR VARIOUS VALUES OF $u/\bar{u}$

$u/\bar{u}$	·00	·01	·02	·03	·04	·05	·06	·07	·08	·09
0·0	1·00 0	·990 0	·980 2	·970 4	·960 8	·951 2	·941 8	·932 4	·923 1	·913 9
0·1	·904 8	·895 8	·886 9	·878 1	·869 4	·860 7	·852 1	·843 7	·835 3	·827 0
0·2	·818 7	·810 6	·802 5	·794 5	·786 6	·778 8	·771 1	·763 4	·755 8	·748 3
0·3	·740 8	·733 4	·726 1	·718 9	·711 8	·704 7	·697 7	·690 7	·683 9	·677 1
0·4	·670 3	·663 7	·657 0	·650 5	·644 0	·637 6	·631 3	·625 0	·618 8	·612 6
0·5	·606 5	·600 5	·594 5	·588 6	·582 7	·576 9	·571 2	·565 5	·559 9	·554 3
0·6	·548 8	·543 4	·537 9	·532 6	·527 3	·522 0	·516 9	·511 7	·506 6	·501 6
0·7	·496 6	·491 6	·486 8	·481 9	·477 1	·472 4	·467 7	·463 0	·458 4	·453 8
0·8	·449 3	·444 9	·440 4	·436 0	·431 7	·427 4	·423 2	·419 0	·414 8	·410 7
0·9	·406 6	·402 5	·398 5	·394 6	·390 6	·386 7	·382 9	·379 1	·375 3	·371 6

$u/\bar{u}$	·0	·1	·2	·3	·4	·5	·6	·7	·8	·9
1·0	·367 9	·332 9	·301 2	·272 5	·246 6	·223 1	·201 9	·182 7	·165 3	·149 6
2·0	·135 3	·122 5	·110 8	·100 3	·090 7	·082 1	·074 3	·067 2	·060 8	·055 0
3·0	·049 8	·045 0	·040 8	·036 9	·033 4	·030 2	·027 3	·024 7	·022 4	·020 2
4·0	·018 3	·016 6	·015 0	·013 6	·012 3	·011 1	·010 1	·009 1	·008 2	·007 4
5·0	·006 7	·006 1	·005 5	·005 0	·004 5	·004 1	·003 7	·003 3	·003 0	·002 7
6·0	·002 5	·002 2	·002 0	·001 8	·001 7	·001 5	·001 4	·001 2	·001 1	·001 0

Taken, by permission, from *Standard Four-Figure Mathematical Tables* by L. M. Milne-Thomson and L. J. Comrie (Macmillan, London).

TABLE C

NORMAL DISTRIBUTION

$2(1-A_w)$	·00	·01	·02	·03	·04	·05	·06	·07	·08	·09
0·00	∞	2·575 8	2·326 3	2·170 1	2·053 7	1·960 0	1·880 8	1·811 9	1·750 7	1·695 4
0·10	1·644 9	1·598 2	1·554 8	1·514 1	1·475 8	1·439 5	1·405 1	1·372 2	1·340 8	1·310 6
0·20	1·281 6	1·253 6	1·226 5	1·200 4	1·175 0	1·150 3	1·126 4	1·103 1	1·080 3	1·058 1
0·30	1·036 4	1·015 2	0·994 5	0·974 1	0·954 2	0·934 6	0·915 4	0·896 5	0·877 9	0·859 6
0·40	0·841 6	0·823 9	0·806 4	0·789 2	0·772 2	0·755 4	0·738 8	0·722 5	0·706 3	0·690 3
0·50	0·674 5	0·658 8	0·643 3	0·628 0	0·612 8	0·597 8	0·582 8	0·568 1	0·553 4	0·538 8
0·60	0·524 4	0·510 1	0·495 9	0·481 7	0·467 7	0·453 8	0·439 9	0·426 1	0·412 5	0·398 9
0·70	0·385 3	0·371 9	0·358 5	0·345 1	0·331 9	0·318 6	0·305 5	0·292 4	0·279 3	0·266 3
0·80	0·253 3	0·240 4	0·227 5	0·214 7	0·201 9	0·189 1	0·176 4	0·163 7	0·151 0	0·138 3
0·90	0·125 7	0·113 0	0·100 4	0·087 8	0·075 3	0·062 7	0·050 2	0·037 6	0·025 1	0·012 5
1·00	0	—	—	—	—	—	—	—	—	—

This table is arranged like an ordinary logarithm table, with values of the variate, w, in the body, and in the first column and row the corresponding values of the sum of the two " tails " beyond the limits $+$ and $-$ w, i.e. $2(1 - Aw)$ (see section 2.51).

This table is taken by consent from *Statistical Methods for Research Workers*, by Professor R. A. Fisher, published by Oliver & Boyd, Edinburgh, and attention is drawn to the larger collection in *Statistical Tables*, by Professor R. A. Fisher and F. Yates, published by Oliver & Boyd, Edinburgh.

TABLE D

VALUES OF χ^2 ON THE 0·05 AND 0·01 LEVELS OF SIGNIFICANCE FOR g DEGREES OF FREEDOM

g	$\chi^2_{0\cdot05}$	$\chi^2_{0\cdot01}$	g	$\chi^2_{0\cdot05}$	$\chi^2_{0\cdot01}$	g	$\chi^2_{0\cdot05}$	$\chi^2_{0\cdot01}$
1	3·841	6·635	11	19·675	24·725	21	32·671	38·932
2	5·991	9·210	12	21·026	26·217	22	33·924	40·289
3	7·815	11·341	13	22·362	27·688	23	35·172	41·638
4	9·488	13·277	14	23·685	29·141	24	36·415	42·980
5	11·070	15·086	15	24·996	30·578	25	37·652	44·314
6	12·592	16·812	16	26·296	32·000	26	38·885	45·642
7	14·067	18·475	17	27·587	33·409	27	40·113	46·963
8	15·507	20·090	18	28·869	34·805	28	41·337	48·278
9	16·919	21·666	19	30·144	36·191	29	42·557	49·588
10	18·307	23·209	20	31·410	37·566	30	43·773	50·892

TABLE E

VALUES OF t ON THE 0·05 AND 0·01 LEVELS OF SIGNIFICANCE FOR v DEGREES OF FREEDOM

v	$t_{0\cdot05}$	$t_{0\cdot01}$	v	$t_{0\cdot05}$	$t_{0\cdot01}$
1	12·706	63·657	11	2·201	3·106
2	4·303	9·925	12	2·179	3·055
3	3·182	5·841	13	2·160	3·012
4	2·776	4·604	14	2·145	2·977
5	2·571	4·032	15	2·131	2·947
6	2·447	3·707	16	2·120	2·921
7	2·365	3·499	17	2·110	2·898
8	2·306	3·355	18	2·101	2·878
9	2·262	3·250	19	2·093	2·861
10	2·228	3·169	20	2·086	2·845
			25	2·060	2·787
			30	2·042	2·750
			∞	1·960	2·576

These tables are taken by consent from *Statistical Methods for Research Workers*, by Professor R. A. Fisher, published by Oliver & Boyd, Edinburgh, and attention is drawn to the larger collection in *Statistical Tables*, by Professor R. A. Fisher and F. Yates, published by Oliver & Boyd, Edinburgh.

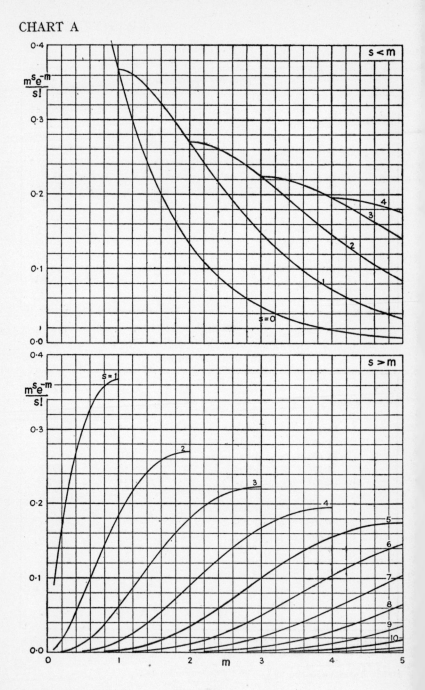

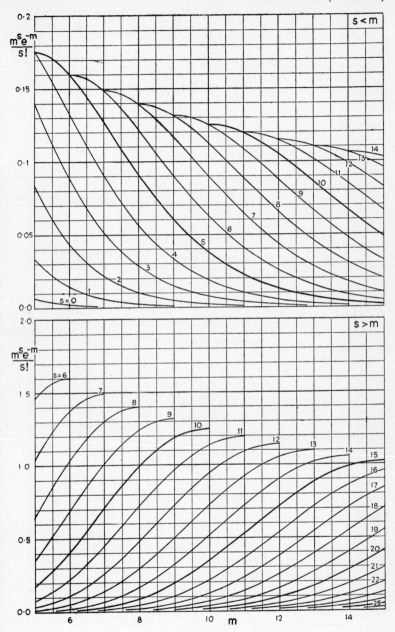

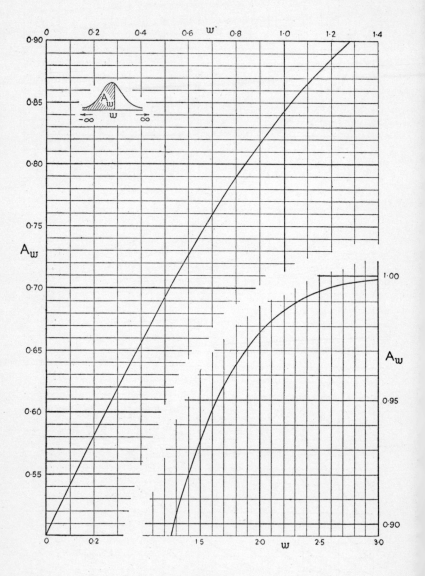

CHART C

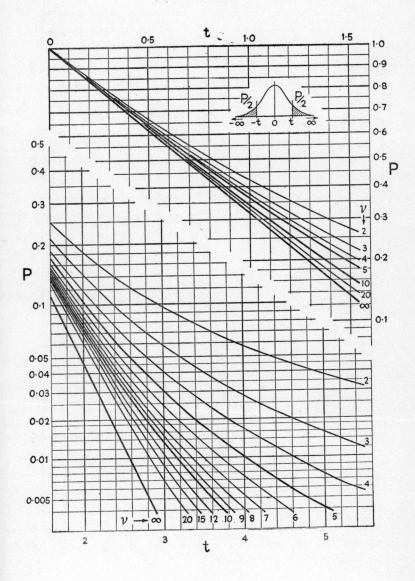

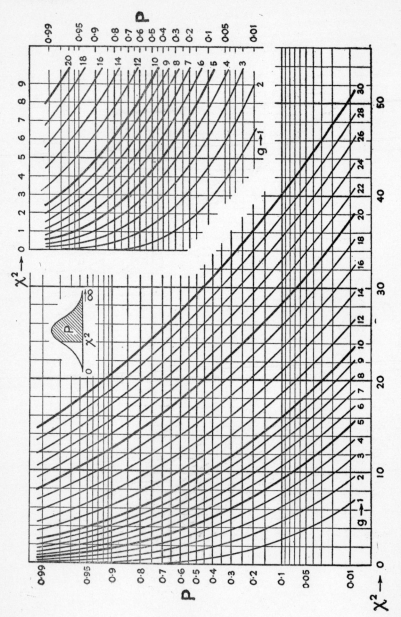

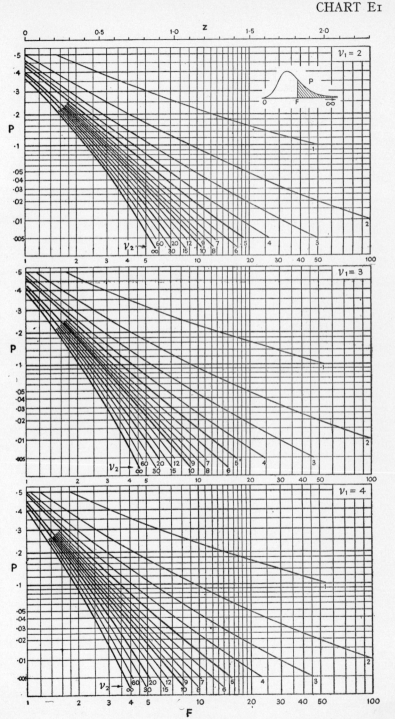

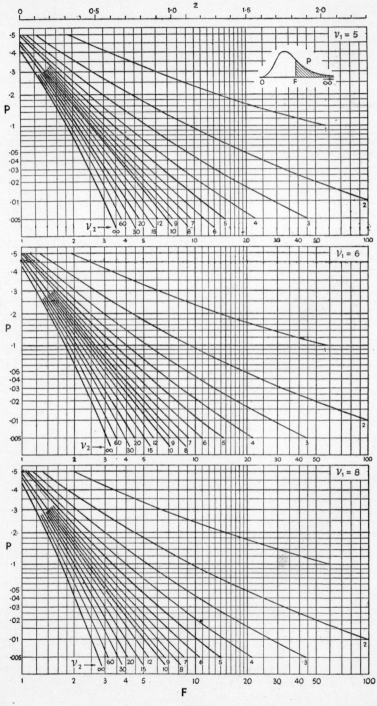

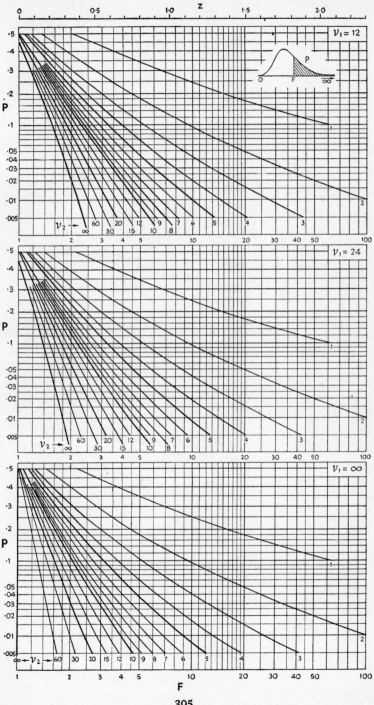